ORGANIZATIONAL BEHAVIOUR

D1635769

Acknowledgements

The authors would like to acknowledge the contribution of Gregory and Sophie Huczynski in the preparation and presentation of the learning activities contained in the workbook and manual.

ORGANIZATIONAL BEHAVIOUR

An Introductory Text

THIRD EDITION, 1997

STUDENT WORKBOOK

David Buchanan

Leicester Business School, De Montfort University

Andrzej Huczynski

University of Glasgow Business School

Prentice Hall

London   New York   Toronto   Sydney   Tokyo   Singapore
Madrid   Mexico City   Munich   Paris

First published 1994 as *Student Workbook: second edition* by
Prentice Hall Europe
This edition published 1997 by
Prentice Hall
A Pearson Education company
Edinburgh Gate
Harlow, Essex
CM20 2JE England

© Prentice Hall Europe 1997

All rights reserved. No part of this publication may be reproduced, stored in a retrieval system, or transmitted, in any form, or by any means, electronic, mechanical, photocopying, recording or otherwise, without prior permission, in writing from the publisher.

ISBN 0-13-861162-9

Typeset in 10/12pt Times and Optima
by Hart McLeod, Cambridge

Printed and bound in Great Britain by
Redwood Books, Trowbridge, Wiltshire

3   4   5   01   00   99

pp. 216–17 A.C. Bluedorn, 'The Thompson interdependence demonstration', *Journal of Management Education*, 17 (4), pp. 505–9, copyright © 1993 by Sage Publications, Inc. Reprinted by Permission of Sage Publications, Inc.

pp. 76–9, 243–5, 271–4 From *Organizational Behavior: Experience and Cases*, 4e by D. Marcic Copyright © 1989. By permission of South-Western College Publishing, a division of International Thomson publishing Inc., Cincinnati, Ohio 45227.

pp. 323–4 From *Organizational Behavior*, 6e by D. Hellriegel, J.W. Slocum and R.W. Woodman Copyright © 1992. By permission of South-Western College Publishing, a division of International Thomson Publishing Inc., Cincinnati, Ohio 45227.

pp. 330–3 From *Organizational Theory: Cases and Applications* by R.L. Daft and M.P. Sharfman Copyright © 1995. By permission of South-Western College Publishing, a division of International Thomson Publishing Inc., Cincinnati, Ohio 45227.

Every effort has been made to locate all copyright holders for all items reproduced in this text but in the event of there being any query or omission please contact the publisher.

Contents

The ORBIT series

We hope that you enjoy using this book, and that it lives up to your expectations. However, we would welcome your suggestions on how it could be improved. We would like to invite you to send us criticisms, suggestions, ideas and general comments about this book, or indeed about any of the four books in the ORBIT series: core text, readings, student workbook, instructor's manual. We would like to learn about features which you liked, as well as features which you think could be changed, dropped or improved. Your advice will be used to improve these books, and all suggestions will be fully acknowledged. The simplest way to do this is through email, and here are our addresses. We look forward to hearing from you.

David Buchanan d.buchanan@dmu.ac.uk
for chapters 1–6, 16–17, 19–20 and 23

Andrzej Huczynski a.a.huczynski@mgt.gla.ac.uk
for chapters 7–15, 18, 21–22

Student's briefing

This *Student Workbook* is designed to complement the book, *Organizational Behaviour: An Introductory Text*, Prentice Hall, 1997 (third edition). We will refer to that text as *ORBIT3* for short. The purpose of this *Workbook* is to provide you with a comprehensive, integrated learning resource that will enable you to work through the subject matter of organizational behaviour in an interesting and challenging way. Several of the materials in this Workbook are designed to complement or replace more conventional lecture room techniques, and offer your organizational behaviour instructor a flexible and easy-to-use set of teaching materials. You should not attempt to read this *Workbook* like a conventional text. Your instructor will tell you when you are expected to have your copy available, and how he or she would like you to use it. If you do not have your copy with you as requested by your instructor for scheduled sessions, you will not be able to make best use of these materials, as they have not been designed solely for independent study.

We have designed the materials with four fundamental principles in view.

1. Complementarity

These materials are designed to complement (and not replace) both *ORBIT3* and the other materials that your instructor will use. Different instructors approach the subject of organizational behaviour in different ways, as you would expect, and have their own emphases and preferences. Your instructor may use some of the materials in this *Workbook* and not others, and he or she may use some of these materials in a manner different from that offered here. A number of factors can affect the sequence in which material is covered, and it is not necessary to follow the sequence in the textbook. We recommend, therefore, that you remove pages and sections from this *Workbook* and punch them into your own ring binder for your particular course. In this way you can build up a systematic set of materials that relates specifically to your organizational behaviour course, and use this for revision.

2. Awareness

These materials seek to demonstrate that organizational behaviour can be observed and studied in many different settings, and not just in factories and offices. Together with the textbook, *ORBIT3*, we hope to raise your awareness of the factors which influence human behaviour in all kinds of organizations. So examples are drawn from banks, pizza restaurants, schools, street gangs, shops and a range of industrial organizations. The sources of these materials are similarly wide and unconventional.

3. Stimulation

The materials are designed to stimulate interest and debate. One criticism of existing (mainly American) workbooks is that they tend to be dull, as well as ethnocentric. We would like you, even if you never study our subject further, to remember organizational behaviour as stimulating and interesting. Many such workbooks deter student and instructor with conventional content and layout. We have in contrast tried to bring together material that we enjoy using, which our students find enjoyable, and which we hope will encourage you to study the subject further.

4. Ease of use

The materials are easy to use. All the exercises in this *Student Workbook* have been selected for maximum impact, to generate maximum classroom debate and learning. Moreover, the exercises are designed to be flexible, to fit different teaching time frames and the needs and preferences of different instructors. We have suggested ways in which each of the exercises in the *Workbook* can be used; the same materials can, however, be put to different uses according to how your instructor wants to deliver his or her own course.

Workbook structure

The *Student Workbook* is divided into twenty-three sections, each relating to the corresponding chapter in *ORBIT3*. Each section contains four teaching activity types. These vary in length, but cover a wide range of interesting, provocative and varied activities suitable for undergraduate and postgraduate *ORBIT3* users. The four teaching activity types are:

1. Large group activities (LGAs)

The distinguishing features of these activities are *student participation* (even in a large group), and *no preparation*. They typically focus on the introduction of key concepts and theories.

These are teaching activities which can be used with very large student groups (say, 60 to 300 students) in sessions of sixty to ninety minutes. The main constraints of this setting include the limited scope for physical student movement and syndicate work, and for student–instructor dialogue. Materials used in this context have to be short enough to run 'cold', without advance preparation. These activities can typically take from ten to twenty minutes. Large syndicate groups may be impractical, but students can discuss issues in 'buzz groups' made up of pairs and threes. So ten minutes of small group discussion can be followed by ten minutes of instructor's debriefing. The remainder of a teaching session in this mode may be devoted to a short lecture, perhaps combined with a video presentation. Such exercises can of course also be used in small group sessions if required.

2. Small group activities (SGAs)

The distinguishing feature of these activities is *small group discussion*. They are likely to focus on the operationalization of concepts or the application of theories in practical organizational settings.

These are teaching activities designed for small seminar, workshop or tutorial groups, and for larger classes where syndicate or 'break out' rooms are available. Syndicate group size may vary from four to fifteen students, and the exercise and debriefing together are likely to occupy from sixty to ninety minutes altogether.

3. Prepared tasks (PREPs)

The distinguishing feature of these activities is that they require advance student preparation. They are likely to require data collection and depth of analysis, and the output may be some form of student preparation.

These are therefore activities that students carry out between scheduled lecture and tutorial sessions. You may be required to prepare a case, collect some data, analyse a problem situation and bring these materials with you to a session as specified by your instructor.

4. Reviews (REVs)

Reviews are designed to provide students with opportunities for continuing feedback to allow you to assess your understanding and progress through the course material. They are not intended to be used as part of a formal assessment system. We have used a variety of approaches, including case studies, multiple choice questions, sentence completion, matching pairs, crosswords, true–false choice and short (one- or two-sentence) answer tests. Each section includes such review material, but this varies from section to section to maintain student interest.

In this *Student Workbook*, the LGAs, SGAs, and PREPs each follow broadly the same sequence:

Objectives
Introduction
Procedure
The exercise, case or other material
Supplementary materials as appropriate
Notes (special features, sources, etc.)

The 'correct answers' to exercise questions are omitted for three reasons. First, in many organizational settings, there are no correct answers, there is no best way. This is a feature of the subject which is reinforced in some of the early exercises in this *Workbook*. Second, as already indicated, your instructor may decide to use these materials in a manner different from that in which the authors would use them, depending on different needs and preferences. So look to your instructor for an appropriate debriefing. Third, we don't want you to be able to cheat and look up the 'correct answers' before carrying out the work.

In the REVs, the sequence is similar and includes:

Objectives
Procedure
The review materials

Once again, your instructor will provide you with an answer guide in each case; you may on occasion be required to grade or mark you own work, or that of a colleague.

Chapter 1

Introduction to organizational behaviour

1.1 LGA: Self-test

Objectives

- To explore the ways in which we as individuals construct explanations of human behaviour in organizations.
- To explore individual differences in our understanding of and assumptions about human behaviour in organizations.
- To explore the limits of 'common sense' explanations of human behaviour in organizations.

Introduction

We are all experts in the subject of human behaviour – or at least we like to think we are. There must be some truth in this belief, given the rich base of personal and social experiences from which each of us can draw. However, this thinking leads to the claim that psychology, social psychology and sociology – the core subjects that underpin the study of organizational behaviour – are merely common sense wrapped in obscure jargon. Students with scientific, mathematical and engineering backgrounds are particularly likely to hold such a dismissive view. It is therefore useful at the beginning of a course of study in organizational behaviour to confront this issue, and not to avoid it. The underlying aim of this exercise is to ensure that, whatever students' backgrounds, and whatever view individual students hold or develop with respect to the study of organizational behaviour, their view is a considered one, based on evidence and argument, and not on unthinking prejudice.

Procedure

Step 1 Complete this step on your own, without discussion with colleagues. On the following page is a list of 20 statements. Your task is to indicate whether each statement is either true or false by writing a T or an F at the side. In some cases you will naturally want to answer, 'it depends'. However, you are asked here to take a stand and indicate whether you feel that, in your view, on the whole, in most circumstances, for most practical purposes, the statement is true or false. If you are still not happy with this you may put a circle round your response to indicate this.

Step 2 Compare your responses with at least two people sitting round about you. Identify responses where you have clearly disagreed, choose up to three disagreements that you find interesting, share your thinking, and establish why you have disagreed. If time allows, share your reasoning on items where you were particularly unhappy about making a clear commitment.

Step 3 Instructor interrupts the discussion in Step 2 when appropriate, and takes about five examples from around the group, concentrating on disagreements with respect to the truth of these statements, and in particular identifying the reasons for such disagreements. It should become clear by this stage that there are a number of specific causes or sources of such disagreements.

Step 4 Debrief.

Self-test

Read each of the following statements carefully and determine, in the light of your experience, whether it is True or False, and write a T or an F beside each statement accordingly.

1. Men are naturally better when it comes to decisive managerial decision making, compared with women.

2. People who are satisfied in their work are more productive than those who are not.

3. Resistance to new technology increases with age.

4. Alcohol in small amounts is a stimulant.

5. You can 'read' a person's emotional state by watching their facial expressions closely.

6. The more challenging the goals you face, the more you are likely to accomplish.

7. Selection interviews, handled correctly, are effective ways to assess candidates' suitability for a job.

8. When asked to rank features of their work in order of personal importance, the vast majority of people put pay at the top of their list.

9. Punishment is an effective way of eliminating undesirable behaviour.

10. When you have to remain working for several hours, it is better to take a small number of long rest periods than a larger number of short breaks.

11. When people can share their thinking in groups, they can come up with more original ideas than individuals working on their own.

12. Most people, if they are being honest with themselves, can tell you what their motives are.

13. People have a natural resistance to organizational change and managers always have to overcome this first.

14. Conflict in an organization is disruptive and should be avoided at all costs.

15. Some people are born leaders, and this is evident in their behaviour.

16. A reliable personality test is a good predictor of job performance.

17. People learn new tasks better when they are only told about their successes and their mistakes are overlooked.

18. It is not possible for individual managers to change their style because this reflects an innate aspect of their personalities.

19. Organizations always become ineffective when people do not have clear job descriptions that set out their responsibilities and define their place in the organization structure.

20. Extroverts invariably make better salespersons.

Note

This exercise is based on and influenced by a similar exercise, with an interesting accompanying article: 'Social psychology as common sense', by Adrian Furnham, *Bulletin of the British Psychological Society*, 1983, vol. 36, pp. 105–9.

1.2 SGA: Incident analysis

Objectives

- To illustrate the nature and benefits of a systematic 'micro-analysis' of management behaviour in an organization.
- To give students an opportunity to experience the role of management consultant or adviser, giving practical advice on the basis of systematic analysis.
- To consider the extent to which an individual manager's style or approach can and should change.

Introduction

We each have our own preferred ways of dealing with the world and with other people. In an organizational context, this is often reflected in an individual's 'management style'. Given the differences in management style between individuals, two fundamental questions arise. First, is it possible to distinguish more effective and less effective styles? Second, can individual managers change their styles in practice, or do inherited and immutable personality traits prevent this? In this exercise, students are invited to consider a short report of a conversation between a superior and his subordinate, to consider what the superior is trying to achieve in this incident, and to offer practical advice as you feel appropriate to the manager concerned. The incident report is based on a real (of course disguised) conversation.

Procedure

Step 1   Complete this step on your own, without discussion with colleagues. Read the following Incident Report which gives a verbatim account of a short conversation between a Project Leader, Jan van Beek, and one of the Project Managers who report to him, Peter Vermaat.

Step 2   In syndicate groups of three to five participants, complete the Incident Analysis sheet which follows the Incident Report. Here you are invited to consider, first, what the superior van Beek was trying to achieve. You are then asked to consider what his objective(s) in this meeting should have been. These two issues should be dealt with separately and in sequence. The two issues should not become confused. Appoint a spokesperson for your syndicate.

Step 3   Share your syndicate responses to the Incident Analysis with the other groups. Agree on what the objective or objectives should have been.

Step 4   Returning to syndicate groups, consider the Incident Replay question concerning the advice you would like to offer to van Beek given that you are now agreed on what he is trying to achieve. Put a summary of this advice on an overhead foil, on a flipchart sheet, or on a whiteboard, depending on what is available. Remember to nominate a spokesperson.

Step 5   Then share your advice with the whole class in a plenary session. When there is broad collective agreement on the advice to feed back, consider the following questions:

1.   How easy, or how difficult, is it for someone to follow the kind of advice that you are giving?

2. To what extent can van Beek argue that you are trying to change his personality?

3. To what extent can van Beek argue that his subordinates will see him acting inconsistently if he follows your advice – and that this will damage his reputation?

4. On the basis of your analysis and advice, how would you now respond to the question – can a manager change his or her style?

5. Debrief.

Incident report

Jan van Beek is a Project Leader in the research and development division of a plastics manufacturing company. Reporting to him are four Project Managers who co-ordinate the work of specialist staff whose project allocations change two or three times each year depending on client demand. At the planning and review meeting this morning, the Division Head was concerned about progress on one of Jan's major projects. He was clearly angry, and Jan was taken by surprise. It was not unusual for deadlines on large projects to 'slip', and nobody had complained about this project before. When Jan got back to his office, he telephoned his young Project Manager, Peter Vermaat, to tell him to come to his office as soon as possible to discuss the matter:

PETER: (Arrives at Jan's door looking glum and upset. Jan waves him into the room and he stands in front of Jan's desk.) Good morning, Mr van Beek. I believe you wanted to talk to me?

JAN: (Sitting at his desk.) Yes, Peter, your electrofusion project. Well I'm not surprised you look miserable, like your progress account on this one, eh! Well, what the hell's gone wrong here?

PETER: Gone wrong? I'm not sure that …

JAN: (Waving the papers from the planning and review meeting.) Look at the evidence. Three major deadlines missed in three months. Are your people working a three day week now? (Laughs.) Things are going to pick up this month then?

PETER: Ah well, you remember that four months ago after the appraisal interviews you asked us to draw up action plans for individual staff development. You see, that has started to change the way in which we decide project allocations, and the problem since then that we've been trying to find a way around is that we seem to have been developing ....

JAN: (Interrupting impatiently.) I don't want you to bring me problems, Peter. I want you to bring me solutions. (The telephone rings. Jan answers it. Peter stands for five minutes while Jan deals with a casual request for information from another project leader.) Where were we? That's it then. I want that project back on schedule. I want you to get on top of this and fix it, fast.

PETER: So, it's fast action you want?

JAN: Of course, Peter. I want you to sort this problem out immediately. That's what you're paid for, isn't it? And you're not going to fix it standing there pulling faces at me, are you? (Peter turns around and slams Jan's door shut as he leaves.)

Incident analysis

From this report, what would your say were the objectives of the superior, Jan van Beek?

1. _____

2. _____

3. _____

From a professional management point of view, what do you think the objectives of the superior, Jan van Beek, should have been?

To _____

Incident replay

Imagine that Jan van Beek has been given an opportunity to 'replay' this incident, and that you have an opportunity to give him some advice on how to achieve his management objective.

Be as detailed and specific as you feel you have to be, about what he should do and say differently this time to achieve his objective. What advice are you going to give him? Prepare a syndicate report summarizing and justifying your advice.

1.3 PREP: Resolving the dilemma

Objectives

- To collect specific practical examples of a key introductory concept – the organizational dilemma.
- To consider whether and how such organizational problems can be resolved.
- To offer an opportunity to relate a textbook concept directly to personal experiences.

Introduction

Chapter 1 of *ORBIT3* introduces the concept of the 'organizational dilemma' on page 12. This concept concerns the potential inconsistency and conflict between the goals of individuals and the purposes of organizations. We would like to invite students to consider this dilemma and its implications in more depth. That chapter argued that organizations, as social arrangements, are not given but can be changed. Management behaviour is similarly not constrained by personal or organizational factors but is also open to change. Does this mean that we do not need to accept the organizational dilemma – that we can challenge and effectively resolve such inconsistencies and conflicts? You are invited to carry out the following analysis, in preparation for a tutorial, or as a piece of written course work.

Procedure

Step 1 Consider the example of an organization dilemma that is provided for you in the table overleaf.

Step 2 Identify two additional and specific examples of the 'organizational dilemma' of your own, and write a description of each. These could be based on current or past personal experience. They could rely on accounts from relatives or friends. They could be based on media reports. Try asking a relative or friend (somebody not directly involved with your course of study) about this topic if you can; you could be surprised by the answers and illustrations you collect. Your write-up for this step should be around 1,000 words long (at only 350 words an illustration, this is not going to be difficult).

Step 3 Then, recommend for each of the three instances (one supplied, two of your own), the organizational changes or changes to management behaviour that would be required to resolve the problems described. Assess the advantages and disadvantages of each proposal.

The resolution may be obvious; on the other hand you may need to exercise some creative or lateral thinking here. Note that there is not necessarily 'one best way' to resolve these issues, and that several different approaches may all be effective in some respects. Your write-up for this step should again be around 1,000 words long.

Step 4 Write a short concluding assessment on the practicality of dealing with such organizational dilemmas; can it be done, and if so is it worth the cost, time and effort?

Step 5 Prepare a five minute oral summary presentation of your illustrations, recommendations, and assessment.

Your instructor may announce:

- whether or not the analysis is to be submitted for assessment, and if so when;

- whether and in what context students will present their analysis and assessment to colleagues;

- the criteria on which the analysis may be assessed and, where applicable, the criteria on which the presentation will be assessed too.

Organization	Collective goals	Human goals	'Organizational dilemma', i.e. conflict
1.			
2.			
3.			

1.4 REV: Sentence completion

Objective

- To encourage students to pay attention to detail in their reading.

Introduction

This test is based on Chapter 1, Introduction to *ORBIT3*. If you have read and remembered this chapter, this test will present few difficulties. However, if you have not absorbed it, there may be little point in proceeding with this review.

Some students may be able to guess some of the correct responses, but most of these require a close reading of the material first. If somebody wants to claim that this is a test of memory and not of understanding – then they are correct. We simply wish to reinforce the point that attention to detail is one desirable learning discipline. Ask students to score the answers of someone else in the class, out of 20, by reading them the correct responses. Or, have them find all the correct answers for themselves in the text.

Procedure

Complete the following eighteen sentences with words chosen from the following list:

control	corporate
organization	organizers
retention	organizational dilemma
diagnostic reading	social psychology
David Weir	archaeology
behaviourists	Robert Hughes
multi-disciplinary	standards
psychic prisons	performance
social	globalization
age	human potential
flexibility	flexible
political systems	sex discrimination
anorexic	symphony orchestras
autonomous	sociology
multi-disciplinary	trading conditions
recruitment	controlled
organizational factors	Fritz Roethlisberger
collective	inter-disciplinary
Derek Pugh	social
humanists	tired crew members
efficiency	convergence

You get one point for each correctly completed sentence, irrespective of the number of blank words.

There are more items on the list than blanks in the following sentences; some are simply not relevant. Where you feel that you have two or more options for completing a sentence, choose the one that you think is best; the other choices could be wrong, but they could just be less appropriate.

1. A single European labour market can make the _____ and _____ of staff difficult for countries and companies which do not offer standard conditions of work.

2. The increasing vociferocity of minority groups in society demanding a hearing was noted by _____ _____ .

3. According to a *Time* magazine analysis, _____ _____ were to blame for the Exxon Valdez tanker disaster.

4. Peoples' expectations of how organizations and their members should function have been shaped by the development of the 'lean and mean' organization, demographics, and _____ .

5. The first head of organizational behaviour at the Harvard Business School was _____ _____ .

6. According to *The Economist*, the stress caused by the reducing employee numbers, work intensification, and the creation of the 'high performance' workplace is creating the _____ organization.

7. Jack Wood argued that since organizational behaviour draws upon different social science disciplines, yet remains an incoherent field, it should be described as _____ .

8. One form of discrimination at work which is not yet the subject of legal control is _____ .

9. Organizations are distinguished from other social arrangements because of their emphasis on _____ and _____ .

10. The study of organizational behaviour draws on, for example, _____ and _____ , among other subjects.

11. Senior managers within a company who decide on objectives may often re-label these as _____ mission or _____ strategy.

12. Organizations can be defined as _____ arrangements for achieving _____ performance in pursuit of _____ goals.

13. Organizational control means comparing actual outcomes with _____ .

14. The American management writer, Peter Drucker, argues that modern organizations can be compared with _____ _____ .

15. The management writer, Gareth Morgan, invites us to 'critically evaluate' organizations with the help of eight metaphors, which include organizations as _____ _____ , and as _____ _____ .

16. The problem of reconciling organizational and individual goals is called the _____ _____ .

17. Organizational design trades off _____ against _____ _____ development.

Chapter 2
Natural and social science

2.1 Large group activity: Memo
2.2 Small group activity: Morale at Mouldswich
2.3 Prepared task: Is this any good?
2.4 Review: Crossword

2.1 LGA: Memo

Objectives

- To highlight some of the ways that social science differs from natural science.
- To identify key aspects of research design and research methods.
- To explore the implications of these on how research in organizations is conducted and the results used.

Procedure

Below is a short memo by a recently appointed graduate management trainee, reporting progress and some results of their investigation into company morale. Read the memo and, working with the person next to you:

Identify the problems that you see in the way the study was conducted and the validity of the results obtained.

Note the number of the paragraph in which the problem is described. Not all the paragraphs necessarily contain a problem.

Memo

To: Managing Director
From: Management trainee
Re: Company morale

Because of poor productivity and high absenteeism, you asked me to investigate the state of morale within the company, and this memo updates you on my progress.

As an engineering company with 1000 employees, it was impossible for me to talk to everyone. I therefore began by talking to the administrative staff, accountants, designers

---

and marketing department people. By the end of the week, I realised that some believed that morale related to getting good pay, others that it was about job satisfaction, and still others considered it to relate to good working conditions. Despite these differences, all agreed that morale was good, and I was about to write a report to that effect.

On the train home however, I bumped into one of the shopfloor employees, and told him about the high level of morale within the company. He was surprised about this as people in the workshop appeared to be down-in-the-mouth, and had held a meeting to discuss some disquieting rumours about a possible take-over. Whatever the details of this, it seemed clear than morale was lower on the shopfloor than on the management floor, and that I would have to investigate further.

The self-administered questionnaire was of my own design and was circulated to all shopfloor employees. It requested some personal details (age, time with the company, marital status, etc.), and asked them to assess the level of morale on a 5 point scale (1= very high; 5 = very low). In addition, they were also given a list of measures, and asked to tick which, if introduced by the management, would increase morale. The measures listed included flexible working hours, quality circles, briefing groups, team working, job rotation, and some others. The results were most interesting. The majority of those surveyed saw quality circles and briefing groups as the greatest morale boosters. My train companion was surprised by this, not least because he did not know what either of them were, and felt that his colleagues didn't know either. I said that, in my view, he was underestimating his colleagues' level of awareness.

It took me a week to analyse all the data from the shopfloor survey. The workshop staff's average score was 3.8, although there were wide variations. Workers with under 2 years of service and more than 15 years recorded morale to be highest. Those with about 10 years reported it to be lowest. The reasons for this distribution are unclear.

I had just finished summarising the survey results when the shop steward arrived in my open plan cubicle. He said that he had come to discuss, to use his own words, 'the impending company redundancies and short time working'. I said I knew nothing of this, and there had been no management announcement. He extracted a copy of my questionnaire from his pocket, pointed at flexible working hours and job rotation, and said that if management wasn't going to introduce these, why had it included them in the questionnaire. Apparently, his members had understood these to mean that half of them would be made redundant, and would take turns doing the reduced number of jobs: one week on, one week off.

I was in the middle of clarifying this misunderstanding with him, and explaining the true nature of these modern management techniques, when the personnel manager phoned me. Apparently, both I and my questionnaire were featuring extensively in the exit-interviews that she was conducting with the growing number of departing workshop staff. It appeared that my morale questionnaire had been interpreted as asking for volunteers for redundancies.

From my study I can report that company morale is unfortunately low amongst the majority of employees, and is falling. It seems to be the cause of the accelerating turnover rate amongst our skilled shopfloor plant. The drop in morale seems to be caused by a fear of redundancy which itself was triggered by the rumoured take-over. The Korean electronics plant in the town must have a higher level of morale since our workers are joining.

I therefore recommend that management immediately issue a statement which denies that a take-over is imminent; that it is not seeking voluntary redundancies; and that it is not planning to introduce job rotation or flexible working hours. I am confident that these actions will stabilise morale. I have heard that our sister plant at Mouldswich is also experiencing a morale problem, and the Product Manager there has established a research group to investigate the problem in greater depth. We might wish to consider a similar strategy for the medium term.

2.2 SGA: Morale at Mouldswich

Objectives

- To explore the practical application of the research designs and methods introduced in Chapter 2 of *ORBIT3*, with respect to an organizational setting.
- To consider the strengths and limitations of different research approaches.
- To establish criteria on which research work can be assessed.

Introduction

The organizational researcher has a range of available approaches and tools with which to answer research questions. Chapter 2 of *ORBIT3* distinguishes between research design – the broad strategy; and research methods – specific ways of collecting data. These designs and methods can be applied in a wide variety of combinations. The designs and methods used very often depend less on theoretical considerations and more on the practical realities of the organizational setting in which they are applied. The line between organizational research for academic purposes and consultancy for purely managerial purposes is often blurred, as the goals and approaches can typically overlap. We invite students in the following exercise to design a research approach that will generate academic information about current trends in manufacturing work organization, and which will also help the company to address specific problems that it is experiencing with the introduction of these work organization changes.

Procedure

Step 1   First read the Morale at Mouldswich briefing that follows this section, on your own and without discussion with colleagues. As you do this, make preliminary notes on how you think you would begin to approach this task. The aim at this stage is not to produce a complete answer but to begin the decision-making process.

Step 2   Move into syndicate groups with three to five members. Decide as a group how you propose to tackle this research brief. Remember to nominate a spokesperson, and prepare a five-minute presentation that will explain and justify your recommendations.

Step 3   Present your summary to the class as a whole, concentrating on the four primary questions in the briefing. Allow five minutes for each presentation, and five to ten minutes for questions. Invite the 'listening' groups to assess critically the presentations from the other groups, to probe aspects which are not clear, and to challenge ideas with which they disagree. This can become boring and repetitive with a large number of syndicate groups (more than five or six). The alternative is for the first presenting group to deal with question one, the second group to deal with question two, and so on.

Step 4   Optional: if you have time. Present your responses to the three secondary questions stated in the briefing. As in Step 3, to avoid repetition over a large number of syndicate groups, have those syndicates that have still to present concentrate on the secondary questions. Note how different groups may have tackled these issues.

Step 5   In open discussion identify the criteria on which you now feel it appropriate to assess a piece of research work published in an academic journal. Record the points on a board or flipchart, (you could nominate someone to do this for you). Individual students should keep a set of their own notes from this discussion; these may come in useful for a later exercise.

Step 6   Debrief.

Morale at Mouldswich

Your organizational research group has been approached by a Product Manager from a local engineering company which manufactures high precision, high value-added titanium fabrications (which sell for around £1,000 each). He has been introducing some Japanese-inspired manufacturing methods, such as just-in-time scheduling, and giving the operators on the shop floor more discretion to determine their own work allocation. However, things don't seem to have been going as planned. Teamwork on the shop floor has not developed effectively, and although the first line supervisors were supposed to adopt a new 'facilitating' role, in contrast with their traditional 'policing' function, this does not seem to be happening. The new system does appear to be working quite well in many respects, and some very significant savings have been made. On the other hand, morale is low, and communications between management and the shop floor have become strained. The Product Manager would like to enlist your help to find out what is going on, what is going wrong, and to establish what might be done to improve the situation. He thought that some kind of attitude or opinion survey might be helpful, but these have not been welcomed in the company in the past (they've been conducted by company personnel), and he is looking to you for suggestions, ideas and professional advice.

The Mouldswich factory is one of several that the company operates around the country. The Mouldswich site is home to a number of the company's businesses. The Product Manager who has approached you is responsible for just one of the businesses at Mouldswich – the 'A Module' business. This business was chosen as the pilot for the implementation and testing of the changes to manufacturing work organization. In this respect, it is even more important that the changes are implemented smoothly, because the intention is to spread the changes first to other businesses on the Mouldswich site, and then to the company's other locations. The A Module business has an annual turnover of around £15 million, and employs 69 skilled and semi-skilled workers who each belong to one of seven skill groups; welders, resistance welders, millers, finishers, process operators, machinists and inspectors. These workers are deployed over three shifts. There are in addition three Shift Supervisors who report to a Superintendent who in turn reports to the Product Manager.

That is all the briefing you're going to get. The Product Manager is not sure what the problem is – he wants you to find that out for him – so you have to design your approach on this basis. In determining your approach, you are required to deal with the following four primary questions:

1.   What are the aims of your research project?

2.   What research design(s) and what research method(s) do you recommend, and why?

3.   How will the research be implemented and phased? Or put more crudely, how long is this going to take?

4.   Be realistic about this: what are the strengths and limitations of the approach you are recommending?

Depending on the time allowed at this part of your course, and on your instructor's aims, consider the implications of the following issues:

5. Your Product Manager is in a hurry. He has to prepare a report for senior managers and wants to incorporate your findings. He has to do this by the end of next week. How does this affect your plans – if at all?

6. Your Product Manager is now not in a hurry, but other company managers are interested in your findings which could be of value to other sites. They have offered to finance a larger-scale study of the company's changes to manufacturing work organization. How does this development affect your plans – if at all?

7. The local Shop Stewards Convenor has taken your proposals to a union meeting – and they have been rejected. The Shop Stewards don't want their members passing information to outsiders, and they have instructed their members not to cooperate with the research team. How does this development affect your plans – if at all?

Notes

This exercise is based on an actual piece of published research: Buchanan, D. and Preston, D., 1992, 'Life in the cell: supervision and teamwork in a "manufacturing systems engineering" environment', *Human Resource Management Journal*, vol. 2, no. 4, pp. 55–76.

The research design and methods are outlined in an appendix to the article, on pages 73–4. This is *not* the correct answer that syndicate groups should have generated. This approach was conditioned by circumstances prevailing in the organization concerned at the time of the study, and by the resources available to the researchers at that time.

2.3 PREP: Is this any good?

Objectives

- To develop critical skills in evaluating published research output.
- To establish the criteria on which published research work can be assessed.

Introduction

If your group has worked through the previous exercise, Morale at Mouldswich, you will have already discussed the criteria on which a piece of published research can be assessed. If you have, then recover your notes from that discussion. If you do not have those notes, then you will need to spend some time now deciding what criteria are important in this respect. You are invited here to decide on your own criteria, using terms with which you feel comfortable, and under headings that you feel are important. You are also invited here to be critical. Just because it is published in an expensive journal by somebody with a prestigious title from a reputable institution does not mean that one has to accept every word of it without question. On the contrary, it is through rigorous criticism that our understanding, and our research activity, develops.

You must have an assigned article on which to base this exercise. The Instructor may indicate and supply an article. Students may choose one for themselves. The assigned article must report empirical research, in any aspect of personnel or human resource management, industrial relations or organizational behaviour. The article on which the previous exercise, Morale at Mouldswich, is based would be suitable. There are advantages in all members of the class each carrying out an independent assessment of the same article. The comparison of notes afterwards should prove interesting and instructive. However, this depends on the Instructor's aims and there are advantages in using a number of different assigned articles for this exercise. Selecting an appropriate article in the first place could be part of the task. You should not use an article that offers only a literature review, reports a theoretical development, or is a 'position statement' of some kind (such as a paper seeking to outline a new research agenda).

Procedure

Step 1 You are about to read and to assess critically a published account of a piece of organizational behaviour research. Is it any good? What criteria are you going to apply in order to reach a conclusion? Your first step is to decide what criteria you wish to apply. If you have already done this, remind yourself what they are. If not, spend some time thinking through this issue, and decide what criteria you are going to use.

Step 2 List your criteria down the left margin of a sheet of A4 paper. Six or eight criteria should be enough, but take these figures as a guide. It's up to you. You are going to make comments against each of these criteria on the remainder of the page.

Step 3 Work through the assigned article making notes as you feel appropriate against each of your listed criteria. Note aspects of the publication that you find satisfactory and interesting as well as those you find unsatisfactory and wish to criticize.

Step 4   Write an evaluation report on the assigned article, using your listed criteria as sub-headings to organize the report. You may find that you have to add new headings, and perhaps drop some of those with which you began. Introduce your report with a brief summary of the content of the assigned article. End your report with your considered conclusions about the article: was it any good?

Step 5   The report should be around the length indicated by your Instructor. It may be submitted for grading, as part of your overall course or term assessment. You may also be required to present your report in class, perhaps to a tutorial group.

2.4 REV: Crossword

Objective

- To assess student familiarity with the language and concepts of Chapter 2 of *ORBIT3*.

Introduction

If you have read this chapter and understood it, you will find this exercise straightforward. This is a simplified crossword with only eight clues – seven across and one down. You have to locate the one down answer for yourself.

Procedure

Complete the seven across clues, then find the answer to the single down clue.

Across:

1. what's the meaning of this behaviour?

2. studying people is no different in this view

3. explores self-interpretations

4. the type of validity that makes findings applicable elsewhere

5. the independent really did affect the dependent – that type of validity

6. not unless it's observable!

7. just one step beyond description

Down:

? there are moral constraints on the pursuit of this goal

1																
2																
3																
4																
5																
6																
7																

PART I

THE INDIVIDUAL IN THE ORGANIZATION

Communication and perception

3.1 LGA: Character assassination

Objectives

- To examine how we perceive other people.
- To identify factors influencing our judgement of other people's character.
- To identify factors that affect how other people might judge us.

Introduction

The way in which we perceive other people influences how we relate to them, how we deal with them, how we respond to them. Person perception thus plays a vital role in our social lives in influencing patterns of friendship. Person perception also plays a vital role in organizations, affecting such processes as staff selection and interdepartmental co-operation. Chapter 3 of *ORBIT3* on communication and perception, explains the basic principles of the psychology of perception. It is often useful to relate material like this to one's own personal psychology. This exercise encourages an examination of the specific factors affecting one individual's judgement of the character of another. The way in which we as individuals perceive other people is only one side of the issue; it is also interesting and valuable to know how others make judgements about us.

One approach to the description of character useful for this exercise concerns identifying personality *traits*. The English language is rich in words that describe such traits; aggressive, warm, hostile, friendly, trustworthy, dishonest, introvert, outgoing, punctual, tough, unethical, and so on.

We would like you to carry out this exercise with *care* and with *precision*: care with respect to your observation, and precision with respect to your inferences.

Procedure

Step 1   Divide into pairs. Select close neighbours, not necessarily pairs sitting next to each other, and preferably split into 'stranger' pairs rather than 'friendship' pairs.

Step 2   Look closely at your chosen partner, at every aspect of their appearance that you can see (this will depend on your seating arrangements; the more you can see the better). Without entering into any further conversation, what judgements or inferences can you make about their character? Use this space to record your judgements.

Observation: **Character inference:**

Step 3   Take about five minutes each to explain your observations and inferences to your partner. You may find it helpful, if it is possible, to change seats to bring you together for this step. Do this without comment or challenge from each recipient, other than questions designed to clarify and to explain the observations and inferences that have been made.

Step 4   Each member of the pair takes about another five minutes to give feedback to their observer on how they would rate the accuracy of the inferences.

Step 5   Each member of the pair then identifies one aspect of their appearance that they might consider changing as a result of this exercise, and explains why. This is shared with the other member of the pair.

Step 6   The Instructor asks for comments on two issues. First, how accurate or inaccurate were the judgements? Second, are there any examples of 'behaviour change' triggered by this exercise?

3.2 SGA: Impression management checklist

Objectives

- To make you aware of some of the ways in which you relate to other people.
- To help you to evaluate whether and how you could improve your interpersonal effectiveness through appropriate behaviour change.
- To consider the practicalities and ethics of changing one's behaviour to suit different people and different social settings.

Introduction

We each have our own preferences with respect to the ways in which we deal with and relate to others. You could say that we each have our own 'comfort zone' which includes ways of behaving and interacting that we enjoy, and excludes ways of behaving and interacting that we dislike. Our individual comfort zones in this respect may be expected to overlap; there will also be differences. This is relevant to the subject of perception because the ways in which we behave affect how others perceive and respond to us – and vice versa. What can we do to make our interactions with others more effective, to make mutual perceptions of each other more accurate? These are the questions addressed by the following exercise.

Procedure

Step 1 Think about the ways in which you interact with other people across the range of social settings (work, leisure, domestic, romantic) in which you might find yourself. Below there are 18 short statements. We would like to ask you simply to give a 'yes' or 'no' response to each statement, depending on whether or not you think the statement applies to you. Write a Y or an N alongside each statement number.

You will, naturally, feel that you want to answer, 'sometimes' or 'it depends' in response to some of these statements. However, with this checklist, you do not have the option of sitting on the fence. In each case decide where your personal preferences, strengths and priorities lie and answer with a clear 'yes' or 'no' accordingly.

This is not a test with right or wrong answers. It is designed as a basis for personal reflection and group discussion.

Step 2 Compare your answers with those of one or two colleagues sitting around you. Note one or two items where you have responded differently. Briefly compare your thoughts and feelings about your different responses to those particular items.

Step 3 Score your responses, out of 18, using the scoring key provided. Compare your score with those of one or two colleagues sitting around you.

Step 4 Instructor debriefing.

Step 5 In syndicate groups of four discuss the four Analysis questions provided. Nominate a spokesperson and prepare a short feedback report.

Step 6 Syndicate groups report back, the first group dealing with analysis question 1, the second dealing with question 2, and so on. Each group's report can be used to trigger a discussion of each set of issues in turn, drawing also on the other groups' different responses.

Impression management checklist

1. I have difficulty imitating the behaviour of other people.

2. When I attend social occasions, like parties, I try to say and do things just because others there will like that.

3. I can only argue for ideas in which I really believe.

4. I can make an 'on the spot' speech to an audience even on a topic on which I have very little information.

5. I often put on a show to impress or to entertain others.

6. I would probably make a good actor or actress.

7. I am rarely the centre of attention when I am with a group of other people.

8. I often act like a different person, in different situations and with different people.

9. I am not particularly good at making other people like me.

10. I am not always the person that I appear to be.

11. I do not change my views or the way I do things in order to please someone or win their favour.

12. I have considered being an entertainer.

13. I have never been good at acting, or at games like charades that involve improvisation.

14. I find it difficult to change my behaviour to suit other people.

15. At parties I let other people keep the jokes and stories going.

16. I often feel awkward with other people and do not present myself as positively as I should.

17. I can look someone in the eye and tell a lie with a straight face, if I have a good reason.

18. I can deceive people by being friendly with them, when I actually dislike them.

Analysis questions

Regardless of your individual responses, consider and be prepared to report on the following issues:

1. Can we learn impression management skills, or is this something with which we are either born or not?

2. Is it immoral or unethical to adjust one's behaviour in order to manipulate the feelings and behaviours of others?

3. Regardless of your own impression management abilities, in what ways would it benefit you to be *more aware of how other people use these skills*? Give examples.

4. In what ways would it benefit you to *improve your own impression management skills* – or to enhance your awareness of how you use them? Give examples.

Scoring

You get either one point or zero for each statement, depending on your response. Simply add up the number of points you got, giving you a score out of 18.

Statement	Score		Your score
	Yes	No	
1.	0	1	_____
2.	1	0	_____
3.	0	1	_____
4.	1	0	_____
5.	1	0	_____
6.	1	0	_____
7.	0	1	_____
8.	1	0	_____
9.	0	1	_____
10.	1	0	_____
11.	0	1	_____
12.	1	0	_____
13.	0	1	_____
14.	0	1	_____
15.	0	1	_____
16.	0	1	_____
17.	1	0	_____
18.	1	0	_____
		your total:	_____

Notes

This exercise is based on the work of Mark Snyder, *Public Appearances and Private Realities: The Psychology of Self-Monitoring*, W.H.Freeman, New York, 1987.

3.3 PREP: Waiting for the interview

Objectives

- To examine how perception is influenced by knowledge and past experience.
- To demonstrate how our individual and unique perceptual worlds are shaped by these factors.

Introduction

You are about to go for a job interview, but you will be kept waiting in the interviewer's office for a time beforehand. During that time, you can observe clues about your interviewer and perhaps about the company. What clues do you consider to be significant and revealing? Can you identify your own personal experiences that affect how you observe and judge in this kind of setting? How does that past experience colour your perception today? These are the issues addressed in this exercise.

Procedure

This exercise is to be completed outside class time, but a report will be required. This report may be written or presented, depending on the aims of your Instructor.

Step 1   Read *The manager's room description* on the next page, to get a feel for the setting in which you find yourself.

Step 2   Complete the analysis sheet that follows in the following sequence.

First, record in the data column (1), those observations that you find significant and revealing about the kind of person who occupies this room.

Second, in the perception column (3), note the inferences that you make, or the conclusions that you reach about the room's occupant from your data.

Third, in the experiences column (2), record past incidents or events, recent or distant, that you think influence your observation, and the inference you draw from it. These may include experiences at school or work; watching films or television; reading and listening to the radio.

Step 3   Summarize your inferences and perceptions by writing a short profile of the interviewer beginning, 'This person ...'

Step 4   In syndicate groups, discuss the following questions, or those identified by your instructor.

1. Taking turns, identify the data that you thought was significant, and the inference that you drew from it. Note the differences, and consider what that tells you about the nature of people's perceptual sets? What has influenced yours?

2. Identify any inconsistencies, either between your inferences, or between the data and your inferences. Suggest the reasons for these.

3. To what extent did the inferences that you make about the person colour later ones? What does this tell us about the perception process?

1 Observation	2 Knowledge	3 Inference
Raw data	Experiences that underpin your observation	Resulting perception
- Pink carpet! - Motorbike clothes. - Picture of woman → a man. - Comm. books. → interest in being a good manager	- Film, Mad Max (biker clothes).	- A bloke - Exhuberant. - Well endowed + very smart. (all mod-cons). - Up to date on todays issues.

4. Look for examples of (i) the same data producing different inferences, and (ii) the same data producing the same inferences. Ascertain the possible reasons for the differences or similarities in perceptions.

5. Make a list of the types of experiences that group members used to make their inferences about the room occupant.

6. In the light of your group's discussion, has your impression of the room's occupant now changed? In what way does it differ from the short profile that you wrote in step 3?

7. Some psychologists argue that we have to 'see to know', while others believe we have to 'know to see'. Explain the difference between these two perspectives, illustrating them with examples from the activity.

8. Explain how the analysis that you have just completed can be used to illustrate the concepts of selective attention, perceptual set, perceptual organization, perceptual world and stereotyping.

Step 5   Present your findings, according to your instructor's directions.

The manager's room description

You are now in the Acme Holdings company offices for your job interview. It sounds like your ideal position, personal assistant to the managing director. You would be working for the managing director who has asked to interview you. You have reached the office on time and are met by the managing director's secretary who apologises and tells you there will be some delay. The managing director has been called to an important meeting which will take up to fifteen minutes. The secretary tells you that you are welcome to wait in the managing director's private office, and shows you in.

You go into the private office. You know that you will be alone here for fifteen minutes. You look around the room, naturally curious about the person with whom you may be working.

The shallow pile carpet is a warm pink, with no pattern. You choose one of six high-backed chairs, comfortably upholstered in a darker fabric that matches the carpet and curtains, and with polished wooden arms. In the centre of the ring of chairs is a low glass-topped coffee table. On the table there is a large white ashtray, advertising a well known national brand of beer. There is no sign of cigarettes, but the ashtray holds two books of matches, one from a hotel in Geneva and the other from a local restaurant. On the wall behind you is a large photograph of a vintage motor car, accompanied by its driver in leather helmet, goggles, scarf and long leather coat; you can't make out the driver's face. The window ledge holds four plants arranged equal distances apart; two look like small exotic ferns and the others are a begonia and a geranium in flower.

On the other side of the room sits a large wooden executive desk, with a black leather chair. A framed copy of the company's mission statement hangs on the wall behind the desk, and below that sits a closed black leather briefcase with brass combination locks. The plain grey waste paper basket by the wall beside the desk is full of papers.

You can see most of the objects on the desk from where you are sitting. At the front of the desk sits a pen-stand with a letter opener. To the side is an expensive programmable calculator and a desk lamp. In front of the lamp sits a metal photograph frame holding two pictures. One is of an attractive woman in her thirties with a young boy around eight years old. The other photograph is of a retriever dog in a field to the side of some farm buildings. In front of the frame is a stack of file folders. Immediately in front of the chair, on the desk, is a small pile of papers and a Parker pen with the company's logo stamped on the barrel.

On the other side of the desk is a delicate china mug. In front of it lies what looks like a leather-covered address book or perhaps a diary, and a pad of yellow paper. Beside the pad there is a pile of unopened mail with envelopes of differing sizes. On top of the mail and behind are some half-folded newspapers: *The Guardian*, *The Independent*, and *The Financial Times*. You note that there is no telephone on the desk.

Behind the desk and to one side is a small glass-fronted display case with three shelves. There are some books lined up on top of the case: *In Search of Excellence*, *The Oxford Dictionary of New Words*, *Dealing with Difficult People*, *You Are What You Eat*, and *Shattering the Glass Ceiling: The Woman Manager*. Also on top of the case sits a small bronze statue, of a man sitting with his legs crossed in a Yoga position, but abstract. There is a cheese plant climbing up and out from the far side of the display case. Inside the case, behind the glass, you see some company computing systems manuals and on the bottom shelf books and pamphlets on employment law, some of which deal with race and sex discrimination issues.

The window is on the far wall, and you get up to go over and look out. There is a three-seater settee under the window, covered in the same fabric as the armchairs with two matching scatter cushions sitting in the corners. From the window you can easily see people shopping and children playing in the nearby park. You turn to another table beside the settee. Several magazines sit in front of a burgundy ceramic lamp with a beige shade. There are two recent copies of *The Economist*, and a copy each of *Asia Today*, *Vanity Fair* and *Fortune*.

As you head back to your chair, you notice that the papers on the desk in front of the chair are your application papers and curriculum vitae. Your first name, obviously indicating your sex, has been boldly circled with the Parker pen. As the Managing Director may return at any moment, you go back and sit in your chair to wait.

Note

This exercise was inspired by and draws on 'Sherlock: an inference activity', in *A Handbook of Structured Experiences for Human Relations Training*, by J.W. Pfeiffer and J.E. Jones, University Associates Press, San Diego, 1994.

3.4 REV: Multiple choice test

Objective

• To assess your knowledge of the concepts and ideas in Chapter 3 of *ORBIT3*.

Introduction

This test concerns the psychology of perception. If you have read and understood the contents of Chapter 3, you should find this test straightforward.

Procedure

This is a conventional multiple choice objective test with fifteen questions. It takes about fifteen minutes to complete. *Ring the letter* of the answer which in each case you think is most appropriate.

HINT: Each question has only *one* correct answer. If you have difficulty choosing an answer because the alternatives provided seem similar, remember that you are also asked for the *best* answer.

Multiple choice test: the psychology of perception

1. People's behaviour is related to what goes on in the world around them. Which statement best summarizes this relationship?

   (a) Human behaviour is determined by environmental influences.   A
   (b) Human behaviour is influenced by environmental stimuli.   B
   (c) Human behaviour is a response to environmental information.   C

2. Which of these statements best defines the concept of 'perception'?

   (a) A mental event that filters out redundant environmental information.   A
   (b) The individual's decisions about the relative importance of various
       environmental stimuli.   B
   (c) A mental process that selects and organizes environmental stimuli in   C
       meaningful patterns.

3. Only one of these statements is correct: which one?

   (a) Environmental stimuli which are not perceived cannot directly
       influence behaviour.   A
   (b) Environmental stimuli which are perceived will directly influence
       behaviour.   B
   (c) Environmental stimuli which are misinterpreted cannot directly
       influence behaviour.   C

4. Which of the following statements best defines the concept of perceptual set?

   (a) The way in which an individual systematically misperceives some environmental stimuli.   A
   (b) The fixed pattern of an individual's perception that is established through time.   B
   (c) The individual's readiness to respond to some stimuli rather than others.   C

5. Only one of these statements is true: which one?

   (a) The individual's perceptual set is acquired through experience over a long period of time.   A
   (b) The individual's perceptual set can be affected by instructions and by the context in which perception takes place.   B
   (c) The individual's perceptual set is innate and can only be influenced with difficulty.   C

6. The manner in which a person chooses to word and express a message to another is referred to as:

   (a) Non-verbal   A
   (b) Coding   B
   (c) Perception   C

7. When making judgements about a person, we often categorize them on the basis of one outstanding characteristic, such as hair length, skin colour, occupation, and so on. What is the term given to this phenomenon?

   (a) The halo effect   A
   (b) Selective attention   B
   (c) Stereotyping   C

8. When making evaluations of a person, we often use only one trait (either a good or a bad one) as the basis for judgements of all the person's other traits. What is the term given to this phenomenon?

   (a) The halo effect   A
   (b) Perceptual organization   B
   (c) Stereotyping   C

9. Only one of these statements is correct: which one?

   (a) Actions and objects possess meanings that are perceived differently by different people.   A
   (b) Different people attach different meanings to otherwise identical actions and objects.   B
   (c) Actions and objects cannot be given 'meanings'.   C

10. Only one of these statements is correct: which one?

    (a) The meaning associated with an action or object depends on
        its relationship with other actions and objects in the perceptual field. A
    (b) The meaning associated with an action or object depends on the
        motives and personality of the perceiver. B
    (c) Meanings cannot be associated with actions and objects. C

11. Environmental stimuli that are below a given level of intensity (like a
    very quiet musical note) are normally ignored. What is the term given to
    this level?

    (a) Perceptual filter A
    (b) Perceptual screen B
    (c) Perceptual threshold C

12. Some stimuli actually stop being sensed if they are familiar and unimportant.
    Examples might be the sound of a clock, or the pressure of the shoes around
    your feet. What term is given to this phenomenon?

    (a)   Habituation A
    (b) Screening B
    (c) Selectivity C

13. We gather and pattern the information received by our senses in
    meaningful ways. What is the term given to this psychological process?

    (a) Selective attention A
    (b) Perceptual organization B
    (c) Closure C

14. Only one of these statements is accurate: which one?

    (a) The 'halo effect' applies to person perception. A
    (b) The 'halo effect' applies to the perception of objects
        and events. B
    (c) The 'halo effect' can be applied to perception of both
        people and things. C

15. Which of these statements best highlights the organizational issues
    raised by the phenomenon of cultural stereotyping?

    (a) Cultural stereotypes are useful in giving us a basic
        understanding of the personalities of foreigners. A
    (b) Cultural stereotypes are potential barriers to effective
        interpersonal communication. B
    (c) Multicultural project teams are more effective because
        they include a rich variety of perspectives. C

4.1 LGA: Individual differences

Objectives

- To examine personal motives, and the link between motives and behaviour.
- To illustrate the concept of *individual differences* in motivation and to explore the reasons for such differences.
- To clarify the major elements of the Maslow's hierarchy of needs theory of motivation.
- To clarify the major elements of the expectancy theory of motivation.
- To highlight different content and process theories of motivation.

Introduction

The subject of motivation has retained prominence in organizational and managerial thought throughout the second half of the twentieth century. If we understand what motivates people at work, and in particular if we understand what motivates people to work hard and to work well, we can arrange for those who turn up on time and who do perform well to receive more of what they value, and for the latecomers and poor performers to receive less. Unfortunately, establishing such simple links between desirable behaviour and rewards is not a straightforward matter.

Motivation can be *extrinsic* – concerning rewards provided by others, such as praise and money – or *intrinsic* – concerning the rewards we give ourselves, such as feelings of achievement and self-confidence. Organization structures, management style and behaviour, work design, reward systems and interpersonal relationships can all be manipulated to provide people with increased extrinsic and intrinsic motivation – if that is what is required. The distinction between extrinsic and intrinsic motivation leaves open the question concerning the motivating potential of monetary reward, which is usually considered an extrinsic motivator.

The point we would like to make in the activities that follow is that people at work are potentially motivated by a range of factors, and money is only one of these, and for some people it may not be the most significant element of their working experience. Financial reward can also be related to the satisfaction of other intrinsic needs, as a symbol of personal accomplishment, for example.

Motivation theorists are also divided between those who believe that all people have a mental package of motives (the content theorists), and those who believe that they do not (process theorists). The activities highlight the differences between these two approaches. The instructor will indicate whether the class will engage in mode A or mode B.

Procedure: Activity A: Content theory

Step 1   Read the briefing, answer the three individual job characteristics question, then complete the *Individual motivation* questionnaire.

Step 2   Complete the short *Group estimation* task that follows the questionnaire.

Step 3   Complete the *Scoring* procedure and compare responses with colleagues sitting round about you.

Step 4   Work through the five analysis questions, following your instructor's guidelines, and depending on the time you have available.

Procedure: Activity B: Process theory

Expectancy theory is an approach that attempts to explain human motivation. It is based on the premise that employees choose to release energy at work, as a function of two factors; valence and expectancy. Valence (V) is the degree to which a reward is preferred, liked or desired. Expectancy (E) is the probability that a person's performance will lead to the achievement of that reward. High motivation (M) is believed to result when an employee both values the reward and expects that their performance will achieve it. That is,

Motivation (F) = Expectancy x Valence

Step 1   Four possible combinations of high and low (or uncertain) levels of expectancy and valence are shown in the table below. When instructed to, use the *Predicted motivation sheet* to rate the predicted effect of each combination in terms of their probable motivation; (A=high; B = medium; C= low)

Step 2   Watch the demonstration run by your instructor, and notice how the level of performance (motivation) of the volunteer changes as the expectancy and valence change.

Predicted motivation sheet

Situation	Expectancy	Valence	Probable motivation (A, B or C)
1	High	High	
2	Low	High	
3	High	Low	
4	Low	Low	

Mode A: Individual motivation questionnaire

You are invited to complete the following questionnaire with respect to your current (full or part time) job, or with respect to a job that you have held recently, or if neither of these possibilities applies to you, to complete the questionnaire with respect to the kind of job you expect to have when you do start work. Before you do this, however, reflect on and write down the three main features of your *ideal* job – this may include easy money, challenge and excitement, extended leisure time, opportunities for travel – whatever you personally look for from work.

The three main characteristics of my ideal job would be:

1: _____

2: _____

3: _____

The questionnaire describes a number of attributes or characteristics of work. Simply rate the importance of each of these attributes, to you personally, using this scale:

1 not important for me
2 a little important for me
3 below average importance for me
4 moderately important for me
5 above average importance for me
6 quite important for me
7 very important for me

_____   1.   The opportunity to develop close relationships with others

_____   2.   The opportunity for me to develop further my personal capabilities

_____   3.   The feeling that all the basics in life are provided for

_____   4.   The feeling of achievement and reputation that comes with this job

_____   5.   The knowledge that my job is secure and that I can probably stay here for as long as I like

_____   6.   The feeling of working alongside a number of good, close friends

_____   7.   The prestige and importance with which other people view this job

_____   8.   The knowledge that I will not go without the things I really need the most

_____   9.   The feeling that I belong here

_____   10.   The feeling of self-fulfilment that comes from using my capabilities effectively

_____   11.   The predictability of that regular pay cheque

_____   12.   The knowledge that I am achieving something really worthwhile

_____   13.   The feeling of self confidence that goes with doing the job well

_____ 14. The feeling that I will not go short of food and shelter

_____ 15. The feeling that things will be pretty much the same tomorrow as they are today

Group estimation

This questionnaire is designed to explore and measure, approximately, the strength of your needs under the following five headings, drawn from the motivational theory of Abraham Maslow (see *ORBIT3* Chapter 4):

physiological needs	H	M	L
safety needs	H	M	L
affiliation needs	H	M	L
esteem needs	H	M	L
self actualization needs	H	M	L

How do you think your group will have rated those five sets of needs? Given what you know about their ages, backgrounds and current circumstances, which of these needs will they rate as important, and which do you think will be less significant? Use the H for high, M for medium and L for low indicators above, and ring the letter that for each need reflects your estimation of its strength for your group.

Scoring

Now score your own responses by entering your rating on each item against the item numbers:

Physiological:
3 _____
8 _____
14 _____   total: divided by 3: _____   PHY

Security:
5 _____
11 _____
15 _____   total: divided by 3: _____   SEC

Affiliation:
1 _____
6 _____
9 _____   total: divided by 3: _____   AFF

Esteem:
4 _____
7 _____
13 _____   total: divided by 3: _____   EST

Self-actualization:

2 ____

10 ____

12 ____   total: divided by 3: ____   SAC

Now write these needs down in order of importance, with your highest scoring or most important need as number 1, and your lowest scoring or least important need as number 5:

most important need: 1 _____

                       2 _____

                       3 _____

                       4 _____

least important need: 5 _____

Analysis

- Compare the ranking of your needs with the characteristics that you identified for your ideal job. Are these consistent? In other words, if your most important need is affiliation, is that reflected in your ideal job characteristics or not? If not, why not?

- Having completed this questionnaire, what would you say are the strengths and limitations of this approach to the *measurement* of human motives?

- The scoring should reveal at least some (and occasionally some striking) differences in motivational priorities. How can you *explain* the differences found in your group?

- From a show of hands, find out how many in your group rated physiological needs as most important, how many rated security needs as most important, and so on. Any surprises in the revealed pattern of priorities in this particular group, or is it much as you estimated?

- If different individuals have different needs and motives, should work be organized accordingly? Consider, for example, how work could be organized to match the needs of those with high security needs on the one hand and those with high esteem needs on the other.

Note

Activity B is based on 'Expectancy Theory' in Keith Davis and John W. Newstrom, *Organizational Behaviour: Readings and Exercises*, McGraw Hill, 7/E, 1985, pp. 514–6.

4.2 SGA: Which motivation theories fit?

Objectives

- To provide students with practice in applying different motivation theories to real-life situations.
- To provide a structured opportunity to apply a particular theoretical framework to a practical organizational setting.
- To analyse critically the work organizational approach of a specific company.
- To demonstrate the use of a critical, theoretical analysis as the basis for assessing organizational strengths and weaknesses.

Introduction

Because the subject of motivation has received so much prominence in organizational and managerial thought during the last fifty years, there are numerous theories which stand beside, on top of, and under each other. Many overlap.

Part A of this activity invites students to match motivation theories with organizational situations to discover which might apply and why. The work of six motivation theorists is considered. Abraham Maslow, Frederick Herzberg and Victor Vroom are to be found in *ORBIT3*'s Chapter 4; B.F. Skinner in Chapter 5; David McClelland in Chapter 6; and Douglas McGregor in Chapter 11. Students should be familiar with their ideas before starting this activity.

Part B of this activity is based on the *job characteristics model* which is illustrated on page 88 of *ORBIT3* and which is explained in detail on pages 87 to 91. Detailed reference to this model will be required to complete this prepared assignment. The model was published in the 1970s, but the thinking behind it remains current today. Can it be applied to the analysis of contemporary company practice? This activity provides an opportunity to find out.

Procedure: Part A

Step 1 Read the *Background summaries* to remind yourself of the main features of each motivation theory.

Step 2 Individually, read through the six situation descriptions. Make notes on which motivation theory fits and why. Remember that more than one theory will be applicable in each situation. Because the situation descriptions are short, make explicit your assumptions or interpretations, when identifying the relevant theories.

Step 3 When all members have completed their individual assessments, each group then tries to come to a consensus on which motivation theories fit and why.

Background summaries

Maslow: A hierarchy of needs theory going from biological requirements (food, water, shelter), up through safety, affiliation, esteem, knowing and understanding, aesthetics, self-actualization, right through to transcendence. As each need is sequentially satisfied, the next becomes dominant and hence a motivator.

McGregor: Based on Maslow's theory, this theory holds that the style of management, and hence the style of motivation adopted by a manager, is a function of their assumptions about human nature, and their attitudes towards their subordinates. Theory X managers assume workers dislike work, are lazy, and need to be controlled, coerced, directed or threatened with punishment. Theory Y managers, in contrast, believe that employees like work, are creative, seek responsibility, and exercise self-direction.

Herzberg: The motivation-hygiene theory describes motivators, which are intrinsic to the job, and are responsible for motivation (responsibility, recognition, achievement, advancement opportunity, work itself, learning or growth opportunity). He distinguishes these from hygiene factors, which meet lower level needs, and which, if met, only prevent job dissatisfaction (pay, benefits, working conditions, supervision, interpersonal relations).

McClelland: His theory of needs holds that achievement (nAch), power (nPow) and affiliation (nAff) are three important needs that help us understand behaviour. All exist in each person, but to different levels.

Skinner: Theory of reinforcement and behaviour modification. It recommends rewarding desired behaviour (positive reinforcement) and generally ignoring poor behaviour (extinction). Other behaviour modification techniques include negative reinforcement and punishment.

Vroom: The expectancy theory of motivation states that the amount of work that a person puts into a job will depend on the outcome or reward that they expect to get, and how much they value it. For example, if an employee believes that by working hard they will be promoted to supervisor, and they value being a supervisor, they will put in the extra effort.

Situation descriptions

1. You have been designated a student syndicate leader by the course lecturer. One member of your group, an engineering student, repeatedly fails to turn up to meetings. She does not do her share of work, and you are often left to complete it for her. This confirms your view of people like her being fundamentally untrustworthy. Which theories apply?

2. There is a last minute rush to complete the re-equipment of the university computing centre. Overtime payments have been authorised for both departments involved. The head of hardware reports that his staff have responded well and will meet the deadline. The software manager complains that she is unable to induce her staff to work late or work weekends. They complain of having to do the 'same old stuff'. When they are there, they spend their time chatting, and not getting on with the job. It looks as if she'll have to threaten to cut their overtime bonus if they don't shape up! Which theories explain this?

3. Your syndicate group is preparing a two-person presentation for a course. Two members want to be the presenters, but have no experience (they want the practice), while the other two have excellent communication skills and would do an excellent job. Which theories would you use to ensure that everybody remains motivated?

4. One of your courses is very hard. Hardly anyone gets an 'A' for their course work essays, there are a few 'Bs', but mostly 'Cs' and 'Ds'. The course lecturer has complained about

essays, there are a few 'Bs', but mostly 'Cs' and 'Ds'. The course lecturer has complained about the standard of the work, complaining that, 'students are lazy these days'. Which theories explain how much time the student will devote to this course? Which theories suggest what the lecturer should do to improve student commitment?

5. Many of your friends are encouraging you to run for Student Union President. You are quite interested in pursuing it, but you know that it will detract from your studies, and your course work marks will probably drop. What do you decide? Which theories are relevant?

6. You have joined International Widgets as a graduate management trainee. The sector has witnessed wide rises and falls in demands for widgets (with attendant consequences for recruitment and redundancy). Your company has relocated assembly to new, purpose-built premises; re-organized workers into teams of six, and empowered them to make their own decisions about work arrangements. The response has been mixed. Some teams perform very well, while others do not. Team leaders have reported that some team members are slowing the others down. What theories are relevant?

Procedure: Part B

Step 1 Read the short article, *The managerless shop*.

Step 2 In your group, answer the following four questions with respect to the Job Characteristics Model:

1. Which *implementing concepts* have been used in the organization of work in this shop, and in what ways?

2. Which *implementing concepts* have not been used, and how could they now be applied?

3. What evidence is there that the *predicted critical psychological* states have been achieved?

4. What would you expect to be the main organizational problems and disadvantages of such an approach to shop management (think, for example, of your own local supermarket)?

The managerless shop

An experiment in team-working without managers has been launched by the Body Shop at its latest branch in London's West End. The 25 full-time and three part-time staff are split into four teams, and will rotate between teams over the first year that the Oxford Street outlet is open. All receive the same salary – £10,000 a year for a 37.5 hour week or pro rata for part-timers – and are described by the company as 'performers' in an attempt to draw parallels between retail and theatre.

Each team looks after an aspect of the business: storeroom, personnel, front of shop or finance. There are no managers or team leaders, although elected press spokesperson Debbie Greenwood said leaders were emerging. The idea for the staff structure came from Body Shop's central management group, but the day-to-day running of the store is being left entirely to the 'performers'. They make decisions, for instance, on the type and volume of stock, training, discipline and shift patterns. They will also make recommendations on recruitment once the initial intake is in place.

operations, said that the lack of management and equal salaries were selling points in advertising the jobs and appeared to draw more applicants. There were 1,000 initial enquiries, compared with a maximum of 600 on previous London trawls. She said that she had initiated the system because of 'a feeling that there was a lot more we could do to develop our staff'.

Source: *Personnel Management Plus*, 1991, vol. 2, no. 11, November, p. 3.

4.3 PREP: Plastic inserts

Objectives

- To develop understanding of the practical application of the job enrichment and work organization approaches to job design.
- To develop understanding of the strengths and weaknesses of these approaches.

Introduction

Some work is boring. Managers often claim that the nature of the task is such that few meaningful changes can be made to reduce boredom levels. It may also be the case that the kinds of changes that would make a difference would be too expensive and raise costs to uncompetitive levels. In this exercise, you are invited to consider the problems of a specific work location, and to apply the job enrichment approach in an attempt to find solutions.

Procedure

Step 1   Ensure that you are familiar with Chapter 4 *ORBIT3*, dealing with job enrichment and the job characteristics model, and with Chapter 13 on technology and work organization. The sections on the characteristics of mass production and socio-technical system design are the most relevant.

Step 2   Read the *Plastic inserts* case which follows, and prepare a response for the consultancy assignment.

Step 3   Produce a consulting report according to your Instructor's requirements. You may in addition be asked to present your conclusions in a class session.

Plastic inserts

The factory makes plastic 'inserts' for boxes of biscuits and chocolates. The inserts are actually made on vacuum forming machines. There are fifteen such vacuum forming machines in operation, all similar in design and operation, but all capable of being set up to manufacture a range of different types and sizes of inserts. Once set up and running, however, to change a machine over from one product to another takes a maintenance crew about an hour and a half.

A roll of plastic sheet of the correct colour is first loaded onto the back of the vacuum former. The sheet is then pulled over a special metal former, and is heated as it does so. The warm plastic sheet is then drawn into the former by evacuating the air between former and sheet through small holes in the former. The plastic sheet thus takes on the shape of the design of the former. Typically up to a dozen plastic 'inserts' for a box of chocolates or biscuits can be made on one draw in this way, depending on the size of each insert. The sheet is then passed off the machine. Half a dozen sheets are then 'nested' before being passed, by hand, through a guillotine which cuts the individual inserts from their sheets. The individual inserts are then separated from the scrap plastic, from around the edges, and are placed manually in cardboard boxes for despatch to customers.

The machines are set up and loaded with plastic roll by one of the two maintenance crews, each with four members, including a crew leader (who is the most experienced member of the crew). The plastic rolls are manufactured in a separate production area adjacent to the vacuum forming bays. Each vacuum forming machine is operated by three women. One takes the formed sheets from the machine and nests them, and generally observes the operation of the machine in case a problem arises and maintenance have to be called. The second passes the nested sheets through the guillotine and removes the scrap. The third packs the inserts into cardboard boxes. There are three Supervisors, one for each bank of five machines. The Supervisors are machine operators who have been promoted and thus understand the work. Their main jobs are to make sure that the machines are properly loaded and staffed, to ensure that production targets are fulfilled, and to liaise with maintenance when problems arise. The supervisors allow the machine operators to rotate roles if they become bored with any one particular task.

Counting supervisors, maintenance crews and machine operators, there should be 56 people on each of the two shifts. However, there is a very high rate of absenteeism among machine operators in particular, and management actually employ 65 machine operators on each shift to make sure that there are enough staff available to run the machines. The Supervisors spend a lot of their time early in each shift making sure that enough operators are allocated to each of the machines. There is also some absenteeism among maintenance staff, and this sometimes leads to delays in machine set-up and repair, and this in turn leads to lost production. The past twelve months has in addition seen a steady rise in the volume of scrap material being produced. This is strange, because the insert nests are guillotined in a predetermined manner which machine operators cannot directly influence, and management are puzzled as to the sources and causes of the increased scrap level. Automation of the machine set-up and operation tasks would be difficult and prohibitively expensive. The absenteeism is also expensive, but is much less costly than investment in new automated equipment would be.

The consulting assignment

You have been asked to advise management on what action, if any, they can take to reduce the absenteeism problems with respect to machine operators in particular, and perhaps with respect to maintenance personnel as well.

- How would you diagnose the problems here? Base your diagnosis on the work of Charles Walker and Robert Guest (Chapter 19).

- How would you address the problems here? Base your recommendations on the job enrichment (Chapter 4) and *work organization approach* (Chapter 19) to job design.

- Conclude your consulting report with a realistic assessment of the strengths and weaknesses of your proposals.

4.4 REV: Concepts, concepts

Objective

- To test your understanding of concepts relating to the theory and practice of motivation.

Introduction

It is essential to be clear about the way in which we use language in any social scientific context. Precision reduces confusion and dispute, and allows us to share and compare experience in a systematic manner. This review covers material introduced in Chapter 4 of the *ORBIT3* textbook.

Procedure

Write down the concept label attached to each of the following definitions. For example, the definition:

> the extent to which research findings from one setting can be applied to other broadly similar settings

would be attached to the concept label:

> external validity

The concept label may be a single word, or it could be a short phrase; you are given no indication which it might be. Complete this *review* without reference to the textbook. If you have read and understood the chapter, you will have no difficulties with what follows.

Concepts, concepts

1. The extent to which an individual feels accountable for the results of their efforts.

2. The social character type whose dominant values include mastery, control, and autonomy.

3. Breaking down a complex task into its simple component steps.

4. Work groups that have front-to-back responsibility and allocate their tasks themselves.

5. A supervisory style based on the use of punishment, profanity and threat.

6. Giving employees responsibilities normally carried out by supervisors or foremen.

7. A technique for changing the design of work to improve employee need satisfaction and performance.

8. An influential theory of motivation that takes into account the different values that we each attach to the different outcomes of our behaviour.

9. The innate biological factors influencing our behaviour.

10. An approach to work organization that seeks to improve performance by manipulating critical psychological states.

11. Characteristics of the context of work, like salary and company policies.

12. Influences on our behaviour arising from social learning.

13. The individual's expectation that a particular behaviour will lead to a particular outcome.

14. The job dimension concerned with giving the individual independence and discretion.

15. A measure of how effectively a job has been designed with respect to its core dimensions.

16. The innate desire to know better who and what we are.

17. The term used to describe our desires for confidence, independence, reputation and achievement.

18. Motivation theories that assume the existence of a given internal 'package' of needs or desires.

19. The degree to which a job involves a 'whole' or meaningful piece of work.

20. Giving employees responsibility for making personal contact with others both within and outside the organization.

21. The social character type whose dominant values include balancing knowledge and achievement with fun and play.

Chapter 5
Learning

5.1 LGA: The learning curve

Objectives

- To demonstrate the learning curve.
- To identify factors affecting the process of learning.
- To identify ways of improving the effectiveness of the learning process.

Introduction

Learning can be measured in many different ways. The learning of subject matter in an educational context is traditionally measured using examinations, essays, projects or assignments, and oral presentations. The learning process unfolds through time, and we establish whether learning has taken place by identifying changes in behaviour. When estimating how long it will take us to acquire proficiency in the use of a new computer software application, we often refer to moving 'up the learning curve'. We can assess, realistically, our own individual rates of learning by considering the extent to which our behaviour in this respect may or may not have changed.

The first activity allows you to experience moving up the learning curve. The second asks you to assess your own learning process, to identify factors that inhibit your learning, and to identify what you, your colleagues, and your Instructor could do to improve the effectiveness of your learning in this subject area. If you reached the *STOP!* exercise on page 108 of *ORBIT3*, you may have already thought through some of these issues for yourself. This is an opportunity to share your thinking with colleagues, and to give critical and constructive feedback to your instructor.

Procedure: Activity A

Step 1 Cover the *Numbers form* so that you cannot see the placement of the numbers.

Step 2   When directed by your instructor, remove the cover, and working on sheet 1, use a pen or pencil to draw a line from number 1 to 2 to 3 and so on until the instructor says stop. You will have 60 seconds for this.

Step 3   You will be asked to do this several more times by the instructor. Each time, use the next sheet on your Numbers form.

Step 4   Insert your score for each of the eight trials on the graph below:

Learning curve graph

Highest
number
attained

35								
30								
25								
20								
15								
10								
5								
	1	2	3	4	5	6	7	8

Trial

Numbers forms: Sheets 1-4

(1) 53   16   54
39
27   15   28   40   6
51   5   2   26   52
13   17
29   3   41   14   50   30
38
37   49   25   18   8   42
7   23   55   46   36
31   34
35   43   22   44   12
11   19   57   8   24
32   58
47   33   45   20   56
60
21   9   59   48   10

(1) 53   16   54
39
27   15   28   40   6
51   5   2   26   52
13   17
29   3   41   14   50   30
38
37   49   25   18   8   42
7   23   55   46   36
31   34
35   43   22   44   12
11   19   57   8   24
32   58
47   33   45   20   56
60
21   9   59   48   10

(1) 53   16   54
39
27   15   28   40   6
51   5   2   26   52
13   17
29   3   41   14   50   30
38
37   49   25   18   8   42
7   23   55   46   36
31   34
35   43   22   44   12
11   19   57   8   24
32   58
47   33   45   20   56
60
21   9   59   48   10

(1) 53   16   54
39
27   15   28   40   6
51   5   2   26   52
13   17
29   3   41   14   50   30
38
37   49   25   18   8   42
7   23   55   46   36
31   34
35   43   22   44   12
11   19   57   8   24
32   58
47   33   45   20   56
60
21   9   59   48   10

Numbers forms: Sheets 5-8

(1) 53 39 16 54
27 15 28 40 6
51 5 2 26 52
13 17
29 3 41 14 50 30
38
37 49 25 18 4 42
7 23 55 46 36 34
31
35 43 22 12 44
11 19 57 8 24 58
47 33 45 20 32
60 56
21 9 59 48 10

(1) 53 39 16 54
27 15 28 40 6
51 5 2 26 52
13 17
29 3 41 14 50 30
38
37 49 25 18 4 42
7 23 55 46 36 34
31
35 43 22 12 44
11 19 57 8 24 58
47 33 45 20 32
60 56
21 9 59 48 10

(1) 53 39 16 54
27 15 28 40 6
51 5 2 26 52
13 17
29 3 41 14 50 30
38
37 49 25 18 4 42
7 23 55 46 36 34
31
35 43 22 12 44
11 19 57 8 24 58
47 33 45 20 32
60 56
21 9 59 48 10

(1) 53 39 16 54
27 15 28 40 6
51 5 2 26 52
13 17
29 3 41 14 50 30
38
37 49 25 18 4 42
7 23 55 46 36 34
31
35 43 22 12 44
11 19 57 8 24 58
47 33 45 20 32
60 56
21 9 59 48 10

Procedure: Activity B

Using the example of a learning curve on page 107 of the textbook, construct a graph that will plot your learning on this organizational behaviour course. On the vertical axis, put *percentage of course material read and understood*, on a scale from 0 to 100 per cent. The horizontal axis represents *number of weeks into the course*.

Step 1 Now consider your overall approach to this subject and to your personal studying methods and learning pattern. Draw a line on the graph that honestly and realistically portrays your learning curve. This will, of course, start at week one, and at 0 per cent. It may not, however, reach 100 per cent by the time the course is complete.

Step 2 Compare your learning curve with those of colleagues sitting next to you. Note similarities and discuss differences.

Step 3 Now consider an 'ideal' learning curve for you and for this particular course. Plot your ideal learning curve on the same graph, perhaps using a different pen or colour. Compare your ideal also with that of colleagues sitting next to you.

Step 4 In buzz-groups of three people, compare your actual with your ideal learning and study patterns, and identify three things that you and fellow students could do to improve the effectiveness of your learning on this course:

1 _____

2 _____

3 _____

Step 5 Still in buzz-groups of three people, identify three things that your Instructor could do to improve the effectiveness of your learning on this course (be realistic):

1 _____

2 _____

3 _____

Note

Activity A taken from J.W. Newstrom and Edward E. Scannell, *Games Trainers Play*, McGraw Hill, 1980, pp. 153–9.

5.2 SGA: Making modifications

Objectives

- To demonstrate the practical dimensions of applying behaviour modification techniques.
- To explore the benefits and limitations of behaviour modification techniques.

Introduction

The theory and practice of behaviour modification appears to have significant potential in organizational settings. Organizations are concerned with eliciting 'appropriate behaviours' from all employees, at all levels. Managers typically occupy positions from which a wide range of different kinds of rewards and punishments can be manipulated. The scope for changing working methods and practices through behaviour modification techniques thus appears to be wide. In this exercise, you are invited to design and assess a behaviour modification approach that deals with specific problems of organizational behaviour – problems with which you may be familiar. An understanding of Chapter 5, *Learning*, in the textbook is a precondition for tackling this exercise.

Procedure

Step 1   Ensure that you are familiar with the behaviour modification approach explained in Chapter 5 of *ORBIT3*, including theoretical background and practical applications.

Step 2   Read the *Making modifications* brief below and, working on your own, make preliminary notes in answer to the questions that follow.

Step 3   In syndicates with three or four members each, design a practical, realistic behaviour modification programme that addresses at least some of the issues in the brief; you may feel that you cannot tackle all of them. Your design must clearly define the target behaviour(s), the nature and pattern of reinforcement, and the anticipated behaviour change(s). Think *creatively* with respect to appropriate reinforcement regimes.

Step 4   Now that you have completed your design, make a realistic practical assessment. What are the three main *strengths* of your behaviour modification approach that give it a chance of working as intended? What are the three main *weaknesses* in your approach that might make it less effective? Don't forget to nominate a spokesperson to present your approach and assessment to the whole group.

Step 5   Present solutions and assessments to the whole group for comparison. To avoid repetition, perhaps have only two groups presenting designs, with the third and fourth groups presenting their strengths and weaknesses respectively, and with the audience each time commenting only on differences between their analysis and that presented. In this manner, a class of, say, twelve members can quickly build an elaborate picture of behaviour modification design options and of the strengths and weaknesses in the approach.

Making modifications

Your organizational behaviour Instructor, Lesley, has been experiencing some problems recently. She has asked you to design a behaviour modification programme to help her.

Lesley has become particularly concerned about the increase in undesirable behaviours in one of her large organizational behaviour student groups. There are around two hundred students in this class, and organizational behaviour is one of the first courses they take as part of their qualification. The problem this year seems to be worse than in the past, but things are running much the same as they always have been. Lesley is not sure what is causing the increase in undesirable behaviours.

Many students are arriving late for lectures, sometimes by as much as ten minutes. This is very disruptive, as Lesley has to stop for each new noisy bunch of arrivals. This also effectively cuts down the lecture duration, and some material has been covered more superficially than Lesley had planned. There has also been an increase in students talking during lectures. This is not confined to the back rows, and there does not seem to be any acoustic problem; Lesley's voice can be heard clearly from all seats in the lecture theatre. The crosstalk is usually quiet, but it is loud enough to be distracting for Lesley and annoying for students listening to the lecture. The attitudes which students reveal in tutorial discussions, through their apparent lack of interest, lack of ideas and lack of willingness to get involved, are also disappointing. Lesley is accustomed to more positive attitudes; she regularly uses practical, interesting, stimulating tutorial exercises.

There are no explanations – or excuses – to be found in the conditions surrounding the course. Lecture rooms are all close to each other, so there is little delay in getting from one class to another. Lesley's sessions are not at awkward times (not first thing Monday, not last thing Friday), so students are not particularly tired or preoccupied in her sessions. In summary, we can assume that the undesirable behaviours are within the control of the students themselves, and are thus amenable to behaviour modification.

1.   What target behaviour(s) would it be realistic to consider modifying in this situation?

2.   What reinforcement regime could be developed and applied to achieve the desired behaviour change(s)?

3.   What behaviour changes would you hope to see?

5.3 PREP: Induction or indoctrination?

Objectives

- To illustrate the practical issues concerned in the design of a systematic organizational induction programme.
- To explore the benefits and limitations of socialization techniques used in an organizational setting.

Introduction

The previous activity explored ways of eliminating undesirable behaviours and encouraging desirable behaviour through behaviour modification techniques. The purpose of this activity, in contrast, is to consider how similar results can be achieved through techniques based on *social learning theory*. This is also described as *socialization*, and finds expression in organizational settings in the form of *induction programmes* for new employees. Consider Lesley's problems in the previous activity. How could those problems be overcome with a systematic, planned socialization process? This activity invites you to answer that question. In other words, we will be dealing again with the same Instructor's problems, but from an entirely different perspective. An understanding of Chapter 5, *Learning*, in the textbook, particularly pages 122 to 125, is again a precondition for tackling this activity.

Procedure

Step 1   Ensure that you are familiar with the social learning theory and the socialization approach explained in Chapter 5 of *ORBIT3*.

Step 2   Remind yourself of Lesley's problems explained in the briefing for the 5.2 SGA, *Making modifications*. In this activity, you are invited to consider resolving these same problems from a different perspective.

Step 3   Use the framework below to organize your thoughts concerning the desired key behaviours you are seeking to encourage (column 1); the reason these are sought (column 2); what effect the change in behaviour will have (column 3); and how your induction programme will communicate these (column 4).

Do not forget to indicate any recommended changes in the behaviours of administrators, secretaries and instructors in the institution as you feel appropriate to support the induction programme. Your approach will affect the next student intake. Consider how this approach could be used to help solve Lesley's current problems.

Hint: Do not make any changes to Lesley's lecturing or tutorial content or style. These are to remain exactly the same. If your induction programme involves any hint of rewarding or punishing students then you are on the wrong track. You are seeking to change students' attitudes, beliefs, values and norms so that they conform to those of the university with regard to proper student behaviour.

Step 4   Write a 1,000 word report describing your systematic, planned induction programme for new students. Conclude with a paragraph that weighs the costs of your programme against the anticipated benefits and answers the question, 'is it worth doing this?'.

Submit or present your report according to the directions of your instructor who may use this activity for a number of different purposes.

1 Desired key behaviours	2 These included because …	3 Benefit if current behaviour changed	4 Induction technique to be used

5.4 REV: True or false?

Objective

- To test students' understanding of the main arguments and concepts of Chapter 5 in *ORBIT3* concerning the psychology of learning.

Procedure

Simply write T or F beside each statement number to indicate whether you believe that statement to be either true or false respectively.

_____ 1. The power of intermittent reinforcement is demonstrated by anglers and gamblers who continue to fish and to feed slot machines respectively despite only occasional success.

_____ 2. One difference between behaviour modification and other techniques of performance improvement is that it does not depend on an understanding of employee attitudes.

_____ 3. Behaviour modification methods fail to recognize that employee performance is influenced by contingent consequences.

_____ 4. Behaviours that are emitted in the absence of identifiable stimuli were termed *respondents* by B.F. Skinner.

_____ 5. The law of effect states that people tend to repeat behaviours that have favourable consequences for them and to avoid behaviours that have unpleasant outcomes.

_____ 6. Negative reinforcement can be just as influential as positive reinforcement in changing behaviour at work.

_____ 7. Socialization in the norms and standards of an organization is a naturally occurring process with which managers cannot hope to interfere.

_____ 8. Fragmenting a task into meaningful segments for training purposes can cause boredom, lack of interest, and low motivation to learn.

_____ 9. Once desirable behaviours have been demonstrably established using effective behaviour modification techniques, reinforcement can be withdrawn.

_____ 10. Punishment for poor work indicates to learners what they are doing wrong and what they have to do to improve.

_____ 11. Behaviourist methods for learning and conditioning are based on the assumption that human beings have an innate desire for discovery and competence.

_____ 12. The process through which employee behaviour at work is changed through carefully selected supervisory feedback is known as 'shaping'.

_____ 13. Learners need time to reflect on their experience, and delayed feedback from supervisors is thus more effective than concurrent feedback.

_____ 14. Punishment can effectively change human behaviour when it is perceived as socially legitimate by the victim.

_____ 15. Negative reinforcement can be considered a form of social blackmail because the person will behave in a certain way to avoid receiving unpleasant consequences.

_____ 16. Where there are complex behaviours, then there will be 'nested' TOTE units.

_____ 17. Both positive and negative reinforcement strengthens desirable behaviour and increases the possibility of it being repeated.

_____ 18. New experiences always lead to changes in behaviour.

Chapter 6
Personality

6.1 LGA: Personality profiling

Objectives

- To demonstrate how individual differences in personality traits can be characterized.
- To develop understanding of the links between personality and behaviour.

Introduction

In the English language, there are over 17,000 adjectives which we use to describe individual behaviour. We thus have a rich vocabulary with which to explore and document the concept of personality, and through which to examine individual differences. From the perspective of organizational behaviour, there are two overarching questions of interest in this area. First, how can we measure personality? Second, can we predict a person's job performance in the future from knowledge of their current personality? If we can measure personality, and if we can use that measurement to predict behaviour and performance, then we can use personality assessment as part of the selection process for new recruits. This has been the thinking behind the development of *psychometrics*, the topic discussed in Chapter 6 of *ORBIT3*. In this exercise, we invite you to consider how personality can be described and characterized, and to consider further how personality profiles can be used to predict behaviour.

Procedure

Step 1 Read the *Personality profiling* brief below, and draw a personality profile for yourself across the sixteen personality traits listed. Compare your profile with one or two neighbours. Note and discuss similarities and differences.

Step 2 Work through the remaining analysis activities, identifying behaviours that illustrate some of your personality traits, and considering with colleagues the five 'prediction' questions.

Step 3 Consider what this analysis and discussion has revealed about the extent to which someone's behaviour can be predicted from knowledge of their personality profile.

Personality profiling

This is an opportunity for you to make a rapid self-assessment of your personality, on sixteen main *personality traits*. These are the kinds of traits measured by personality assessment questionnaires currently in use in organizational selection procedures. The assessment which this exercise is based on is known as the '16PF' – where PF stands simply for personality factors. These personality characteristics are described in terms of 16 continua.

In each case, ask yourself first where on the continuum you lie, for example between reserved on the one hand and outgoing on the other. Be honest. There is no point in 'cheating'. There is no such thing as a good or a bad profile; the one that is correct is the profile that is correct for you. Put a dot on the line to represent where you feel your personality lies.

reserved, detached .... outgoing, easygoing

concrete thinker .... abstract thinker

emotional .... emotionally stable

mild, accommodating .... assertive, aggressive

serious, reflective .... lively, happy-go-lucky

flexible, rule-breaker .... conscientious, persevering

shy, restrained .... venturesome, bold

tough-minded .... tender-minded

trusting, adaptable .... suspicious, self-opinionated

practical, conventional .... imaginative, creative

forthright, unpretentious .... astute, worldly

confident, complacent .... worrying, insecure

conservative, traditional .... experimenting, free-thinking

group-dependent 'joiner' .... self-sufficient, resourceful

less controlled .... controlled, exacting

relaxed, tranquil .... tense, frustrated

Analysis

1. When you have worked your way down this list, join up the dots to construct your individual *personality profile*. Compare this with one or two neighbours sitting close to you. Note and discuss differences.

2. Now choose three traits on which you have given yourself a more or less 'extreme' score (very tense, very reserved, very conscientious, for example). For each of these three traits, think of an incident where your behaviour offers a good illustration of that personality characteristic 'in action'. Make brief notes on each of these three incidents, noting the behaviours which illustrate aspects of your personality.

3. When you have done this, compare your three examples with one or two neighbours sitting close to you.

4. Working in pairs, exchange profiles, and consider the following questions. Considering what you now know about your colleague's personality profile:

   (a) Can you predict whether or not they would make a good organizational behaviour instructor? Explain your judgement.

   (b) Can you predict whether or not they would make a good policeman or policewoman? Explain your judgement.

   (c) Can you predict how they would behave if given an opportunity to cheat on an examination with only a small chance of being discovered? Explain your judgement.

   (d) Can you predict how effective they are likely to be in a leadership role in a large organization? Explain your judgement.

   (e) What other aspects of their future behaviour do you feel you could confidently predict?

5. Share your predictions with your partner in this exercise.

6.2 SGA: Measuring up

Objectives

- To develop understanding of how personality characteristics and other individual attributes can be assessed.
- To develop understanding of the value of different assessment strategies.
- To identify the limitations of selection interviewing and to explore how other approaches can improve the validity and reliability of the organizational selection process.

Introduction

The decision to select somebody for a job is always a *prediction*. This is a prediction that this particular candidate will perform in this job well, and that this candidate will perform the job better than the competing candidates. On what information should this prediction be based? Virtually all organizations still rely on the selection interview, at least to make preliminary assessments of suitability of candidates. Some organizations have introduced refinements to their interview process for particular occupations; this includes 'life themes analysis' and 'situational interviewing' in which questions are researched and are geared to job-specific activities and behaviours. During the 1990s, the use of *psychometric assessment* became more widespread in the search for valid and more reliable predictors of job behaviour. The available evidence seems to show that *assessment centres*, which use a variety of behavioural observation, psychometric, and interviewing methods, can generate the most valid and reliable evidence of all. So, should we recommend the general use of assessment centres in all selection contexts? Interviews are still quick to organize and cheap to conduct, and the candidate can meet and talk with the person or people with whom they will be working. Assessment centres can be extremely expensive, consume large amounts of costly professional time, and may use trained assessors instead of the candidates' superiors or colleagues who simply get a final report. In choosing an assessment strategy, therefore, there are typically a number of trade-offs to be considered. The choice is not simple.

In this exercise, we would like to invite you to consider a strategy for selecting five graduate management trainee recruits from a candidate pool of twenty. The company has specified the attributes required in these candidates. What methods are you going to use to find out which five candidates fit this requirement most closely?

Procedure

Step 1 Ensure that you are familiar with Chapter 6 on the subject of *Personality* in the *ORBIT3* textbook. This Chapter discusses the relative effectiveness of different selection approaches.

Step 2 Working in syndicates with three to five members, design a selection strategy according to the *Measuring up* brief. You will then be asked to evaluate the *validity* and the *reliability* of your methods and the confidence you are likely to place in the results. Nominate a spokesperson to give an account of your strategy, and of its strengths and limitations.

Step 3 Present your strategy and assessment.

Measuring up

You are a member of the personnel department of ScotSouth Bank plc, a medium sized national bank. Each year, the bank recruits five graduate management trainees who will begin their career with the bank at the head office in Edinburgh, but who can be rotated through and posted to branches anywhere in the country. Like other financial services sector institutions, the bank is facing increasingly rapid change and this is forcing changes in the way in which the company is managed. The bank's research, influenced by some recent American thinking, has identified a number of 'high-performance competences' which are believed to be required by managers now and into the future to enable them to operate effectively in a dynamic, turbulent organizational climate. These individual high-performance competences are:

information search:	uses a range of sources and a variety of information before reaching decisions.
concept formation:	uses information to detect patterns, form concepts, build models, to identify trends and cause and effect relationships.
conceptual flexibility:	seeks out and evaluates a range of options when planning and deciding.
interpersonal search:	effective in getting good information from others through appropriate questioning, and good at seeing others' viewpoints.
managing interactions:	builds effective, cooperative teams by involving and empowering others.
developmental orientation:	encourages others to develop by helping them become aware of their own strengths and limitations, and by providing appropriate coaching, training and resources.
impact:	uses a range of influencing techniques to get support for plans and ideas.
self-confidence:	willing to take a stand, willing to commit when required, expresses confidence in success.
presentation:	good at presenting ideas to others in interesting and persuasive manner.
proactive orientation:	takes responsibility, structures tasks for others, implements actions.
achievement orientation:	sets high personal standards, sets ambitious but realistic goals, wants to do things better, has targets against which progress is measured.

Your task is as follows:

1. Design a selection strategy, using whatever combination of selection methods you consider appropriate, to identify the five candidates who measure up best against this list

of competences. Design this strategy on the assumption that, as a central plank of current company policy, you are faced with no time or resource constraints.

2.   Prepare a realistic evaluation of the main strengths and limitations of the selection strategy that you have now designed. Assess how *valid* and how *reliable* your methods are. In addition, indicate the level of confidence (high, medium, low) you will place on your assessment of your candidates on those competences using those methods.

3.   You have just heard a leaked rumour about the company's next quarterly financial results, due to be published in about ten days time. They are not good, you have been told, and your department's budget looks like it will be a prime target. Assuming that you could be faced with severe resource constraints, design a fall-back selection strategy that would enable you to complete the selection procedures within a week at a fraction of the cost of your original plan.

4.   Prepare a realistic evaluation of the main strengths and limitations of your fall-back strategy. Once again, consider the *validity* and *reliability* of your methods. Assess also the impact of these changes on the confidence you will place in your assessments.

5.   Be prepared to present and justify your plans to your whole group in plenary session.

Notes

This exercise draws on the following article: Cockerill, T., 1989, 'The kind of competence for rapid change', *Personnel Management*, September, pp. 52–6. The author was management development adviser for the National Westminster Bank, and the article identifies eleven 'high performance managerial competences', based on some American research. The article defends vigorously the position that such competences can be assessed reliably through behavioural observation – using a range of approaches. Cockerill further argues that these are the competences required by managers operating in increasingly turbulent, dynamic, changing organizational environments.

This exercise could be based instead on an article in the same series: Dulewicz, V., 1989, 'Assessment centres as the route to competence', *Personnel Management*, November, pp. 56–9.
This article introduces twelve 'independent performance factors' or 'supra competences'. Any similar list of management attributes, characteristics, capabilities or competences could serve in this case.

6.3 PREP: DIY Personality assessment

Objectives

- To develop an understanding of the way in which nomothetic personality assessment methods are constructed.
- To illustrate the pitfalls and hazards of personality assessment using this approach.

Introduction

You too can design your own personality assessments. In this exercise, you are invited to do just that. Behind the theoretical façade and the statistical sophistication of most personality assessment instrumentation, there lies a creative process in which the statements or questions that find their way into the questionnaire are generated. In this exercise, you are invited to work through that process, and to get a feel for what is involved, giving you a better understanding of the sources and limitations of the assessments to which you are likely to be subjected in a job-hunting context.

Procedure

Step 1   Familiarize yourself with Chapter 6 in the *ORBIT3* textbook. The section that begins on page 147 is particularly important, as it outlines the methods used in the construction of personality questionnaires.

Step 2   Identify *two* personality traits in which you have a particular interest. Choose traits the measurement of which would be of *practical value* to you, in choosing syndicate team members, for example, or in selecting the residents for a corridor in an accommodation block. You could use some of the traits identified by Hans Eysenck, such as self-esteem, impulsiveness, or sociability. You could use a couple of the scales found in the Occupational Personality Questionnaire, such as change-oriented, emotional control, or competitiveness. You could choose other personality characteristics that carry particular significance to you at this time for personal reasons. The choice is yours. Before you proceed, *define* the two traits whose labels you have now chosen.

Step 3   Modelling your instructions on the questionnaire in the box on page 148 of the textbook, think of between 10 and 20 statements or questions that could be used to measure each of the two traits you are working with. This will give you a questionnaire of 20 to 40 items. You can word items simply as statements which invite a yes or no, agree or disagree response. You can word items as questions, and invite responses on a three, five or seven point scale, perhaps from 'strongly disagree' to 'strongly agree'. Note that this is a creative exercise, and that the scoring system and item wording have to be designed together.

Step 4   Design your questionnaire and its accompanying scoring system. You will have to choose whether to mix together the items which apply to the two traits, or to put them each into a separate section. If you mix them, will respondents get confused? If you separate them, will you 'give the game away'? Remember to have a cover page stating your name, the name of your institution, the title or name of the questionnaire you have designed, and instructions for completing the questionnaire.

Step 5   Photocopy a neat (preferably typed) version of your questionnaire, and ask up to 20 friends, colleagues, fellow students and/or relatives to fill them in. Calculate their scores on their behalf once they have done this for you, and not their reaction to your conclusions about their personalities.

Step 6   Write a report for your organizational behaviour instructor, explaining the purpose of your personality questionnaire, and explaining its design and scoring system. Include in your report the (anonymous) scores of your 20 respondents, and indicate what changes you would make to the questionnaire to refine it further based on that trial experience. Conclude your report with an assessment of the practical value of your questionnaire in achieving its intended purpose, and identify what you now see as its main limitations.

6.4 REV: Associations and definitions

Objectives

- To enhance your ability to associate correctly key writers in the psychology of personality with their concepts, theories and products.
- To check your understanding of concepts and ideas relevant to the psychology of personality and the application of that thinking to organizational selection procedures.

Introduction

This review of Chapter 6 of *ORBIT3* consists of two activities. The first encourages you to review the chapter, in order to match correctly the names of the key writers with their particular output. This may be a concept which they developed and which is associated with them; a theory on some aspect of personality; or a procedure used to measure personality in some way. The second activity allows you to consider the definitions of key concepts in greater depth.

This review activity should be graded independently either by another member of your student group or by your instructor. You can of course grade this yourself, but the temptation and the opportunity artificially to inflate your score is likely to be high if you approach the exercise in this way. You should check your incorrect or partially correct responses for yourself afterwards in any circumstances. This can be done by using the index at the back of the textbook to locate the relevant page in Chapter 6.

Procedure

Activity 1: Matching

In the left column of the table that follows are numbered 12 concepts, theories and questionnaires mentioned in Chapter 6. In the right hand column, are lettered a list of authors also mentioned in that chapter. Use the grid beneath the table to match correctly the author(s) with their theory, concept or questionnaire. There are more entries in the right hand column than in the left. Which are redundant?

Table

1. 'I' and 'me' theory	A. Gordon Allport
2. Thematic apperception test	B. Phineas Taylor Barnum
3. 'Big Five' personality types	C. John Campbell and Charles Hawley
4. Somototype personality theory	D. Charles Horton Cooley
5. Fallacy of personal validation	E. Paul Costa and Robert McRae
6. Extroverts and introverts	F. Hans Eysenck
7. Type A and Type B personality theory	G. Meyer Friedman and Ray Rosenman
8. Body humours theory of personality	H. Hippocrates
9. Looking glass self	I. Carl Gustav Jung
10. Occupational personality questionnaire	J. George Herbert Mead
11. E and N dimensions personality theory	K. Henry Murray
12. Personal self and social self	L. Irving Rein
	M. William Sheldon
	N. Carl Rogers
	O. Saville and Holdsworth
	P. William H. Whyte

1	2	3	4	5	6	7	8	9	10	11	12

Activity 2: Insert blanks

In the left column below are definitions of concepts mentioned in Chapter 6. Most are single words, some are phrases. The number of letters in the single, or the multiple words, are identified in the brackets at the end of the definition. Insert the correct concept name answer in the right hand column.

Concept	Label
1. A personality disposition that is strong, and which occurs frequently in an individual is called _____ (11).	
2. One of the 'Big Five' (8).	
3. Term used when measuring aptitude or intelligence, when high scores are judged to be better than low ones (11, 4).	
4. A form of selection method in which candidates are asked how they would respond to hypothetical, work-related situations (11, 12).	
5. A pre-determined category containing individuals with common patterns of behaviour (11, 4).	
6. School of thought which holds that our thoughts, behaviours and feelings are determined genetically (6).	
7. A person's condition, cognitive appraisal, and hardness are all examples of stress _____ which influences how they will respond to stress (10).	

8. Term used when measuring aspects of personality when high or low scores are not 'better' than others. (11, 10).	
9. Set of expectations that a person believes that others have of them (11, 5).	
10. A type of test which gives the subject freedom of response, not tying them down into pre-determined categories (10).	
11. Properties of personality which appear in different situations and continue over time (6).	
12. Any type of personality theory which is not precisely defined, formally articulated, or supported by data (8).	
13. An approach to personality which sees it as composed of discrete and identifiable elements (10).	
14. School of thought which holds that our thoughts, behaviours and feelings are determined by environmental, social and cultural factors (7).	
15. A behaviour syndrome characterised by relaxation, calm and the ability to enjoy leisure (4, 1).	
16. An enduring or habitual behaviour pattern which occurs in a variety of different circumstances (11, 5).	
17. A term which describes the positive aspects of stress (8).	
18. To see if a job candidate can do the job, get them to do the job. What is the name of this selection method? (4, 6).	
19. The image that we each have of ourselves (4, 7).	
20. That part of an individual's self-concept that concerns the way that they see themselves, and what they expect of others (8, 4).	
21. View that personality is the result of a process in which individuals learn who they are by interacting with others in society (7, 5, 4).	
22. Observation that, following the completion of a personality test, the same, single personality profile, if sufficiently vague and generalised, will be readily accepted as valid, by all the different testees (6, 6).	
23. Psychological qualities that consistently distinguish one person's behaviour from that of others, in different situations, and on an on-going basis (11).	
24. A viewpoint that holds that a person's personality is unique, and hence incapable of being measured or compared on the same dimensions as another's (11).	

PART II

GROUPS IN THE ORGANIZATION

Chapter 7
Group formation

7.1 LGA: Where are we now?

Objectives

- To introduce the model of group development phases.
- To apply the model to a group with which students are familiar.

Introduction

Tuckman and Jensen suggest that all groups which form can move through a number of phases. Such a journey however is not guaranteed, and any group can become 'stuck' in one of the non-productive stages. This model of group development can help us understand why some groups perform better than others. It also provides us with guidance as to what group leaders, group members and outside consultants can do to move a group from an unproductive phase into a productive one.

Procedure

Step 1   Think of a group of which you are a member. This may be an on-going syndicate group at university; a project team at work; or some other regularly-meeting group such as a social club, sports club or society. This group has some kind of objective to achieve. Write the name of your group in the space below:

Step 2   Keeping the behaviour of this group in your mind as a focus, answer the questions set out in the Group development phases questionnaire.

Step 3   Score the questionnaire as directed by your instructor.

Step 4   Locate your group on the graph as instructed by your instructor.

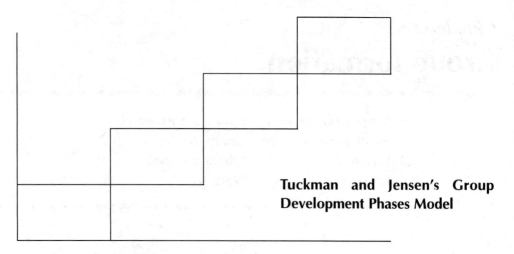

Tuckman and Jensen's Group Development Phases Model

Group development phases questionnaire

S

1. Members are unclear as to what the group's goals are.	T	F
2. At each meeting there is always a lot of talk about who is supposed to do what.	T	F
3. Members frequently look to the official chairperson or informal leader for guidance.	T	F
4. There is rarely, if ever, any discussion of how members feel about things.	T	F
5. When direction is provided by someone in the group, the others are reluctant to follow.	T	F
6. Members seems reluctant to tell others what they really think about things.	T	F
TOTAL		

F

7. People are discussing what part each will play in meeting the goal.	T	F
8. The group has developed a 'game plan' for achieving its priority objectives.	T	F
9. Measures are being produced to allow the checking of progress.	T	F
10. Group members look to others for direction as to what to do next.	T	F
11. Members argue a lot about what the group should be doing.	T	F
12. There are at least two people who want to be the group leader.	T	F
TOTAL		

N

13. Members comment intermittently on how well or badly the group is operating.	T	F
14. Information relevant to the task at hand is widely shared; little is kept hidden by individuals.	T	F
15. Most people are working for the group, rather than themselves.	T	F
16. There is a sense of 'togetherness' among the group.	T	F
17. Members trust and support each other.	T	F
18. Relationships between group members are for the most part amicable.	T	F
TOTAL		

P

19. The group is becoming good at identifying obstacles to achieving its goal.	T	F
20. We can diagnose problems in the way we work as a team and fix them.	T	F
21. We often develop creative solutions to achieve our objectives in different ways.	T	F
22. In this group, I feel able to risk expressing new ideas.	T	F
23. I feel able to express my disagreement within the group, without others taking it personally.	T	F
24. Members take the lead as the situation requires it.	T	F
TOTAL		

7.2 SGA: Group theatre

Objectives

- To experience the stages of group development under time pressure.
- To enable group members to evaluate the contributions made to the group activity, both by themselves and the other group members.

Introduction

Group working is a feature of organizational life. Budget committees, project teams, marketing groups, and customer-focused task forces are just some of names given to them. In all these situations, individuals from different departments are brought together to perform a set task, to a given standard, within a given time. Whether or not they succeed can depend to a large degree of how the group manages to develop through a collection of individuals into an effective single working unit. This activity simulates, in an accelerated form, that process of group development.

Procedure

Step 1   The instructor divides the class into groups of six to seven people. Ideally, these should be of students who do not know each other well. Next, a leader and an observer are arbitrarily identified by the instructor.

Step 2   The instructor introduces the activity. Each group is to create and perform an improvised, unwritten drama lasting six to eight minutes, which demonstrates the resolution of a management problem or issue of their choice. Each person is given a brief, depending on their role.

Step 3   Each group is, ideally, allocated a separate room where they can discuss the task and rehearse their performance. The instructor identifies in which room the performances and plenary discussion will take place, and what the 'come-back' time will be. This is approximately 35–40 minutes later.

Step 4   The instructor briefs the observers while the group members are reading their own notes. Observers are asked to make notes on the questions set; to sit aside from the group they are observing and not get involved in the activities of their group; and to be prepared to report back their observations during the plenary, de-briefing session.

Step 5   Once in their groups, members decide the scene and the problem to be improvised. Their briefs explains what they are to do, and the schedule allows them 15 minutes for this.

Step 6   Improvising and rehearsing. Members practise what they have agreed. The briefs which follow explain what they have to do. The schedule allows about 25 minutes for this.

Step 7   Having returned to the main room, all the students sit in a circle, and observe the groups perform their dramas, in the order indicated by the instructor.

Step 8   The observers give feedback to the class about what they observed of the processes occurring in their group, and the contributions of the individual members. The feedback is structured around the six themes highlighted in the observer's brief. The members of the different groups are then free to make comments, respond to observations, and raise further issues. At the end of the session, the whole class, including the observers, should list what they have learned.

Brief for leaders and groups

You and your group are to create and perform an improvised and unscripted drama lasting 6 to 8 minutes. It must be of as high a quality as possible. It should involve movement, be of interest to, and engage the audience. For example, a group of people sitting and talking around a table would not be interesting to an audience. The group must be able to perform within the time period.

Leader's role

Each group has a formal leader. As well as participating in the performance, the leader is responsible for ensuring that the group meets its objective, and does the best it can within the time limits.

The scene and the issue

You are managing a group effort or project which is quickly approaching its deadline. Consequently, your team is under time pressure. Suddenly, something happens which threatens the success of the project, work or idea. There is a danger that it will fail in some way. You and your team have to show a way out of the problem.

The process (15 minutes)

As a group you have to decide:
1. What the project is.
2. What problem you have to deal with.
3. How the problem is to be solved.
4. Who will play which part. (Everyone in the group including the leader must have a role, but the observer is excluded.)

The rehearsal (25 minutes)

You should allocate time to get up, and start rehearsing. Ensure that everyone participates, and knows their role in the improvisation. This can help you to check that your audience will be clear as to what is going on, what the problem is, and how the solution resolves it. Finally, the rehearsal allows you to check that you will remain in the time limit.

The performance (6–8 minutes)

When your preparation and rehearsal time is up, you will be asked to reconvene, and take turns to perform your short, improvised dramas.

Observer's brief

Your job is to observe the group processes, so that after the performances you can report back on what you observed. Sit a little way away from the group, and do not become involved in any aspect of the group's preparation, They may find your presence a little inhibiting at first, but they will soon get used to you and ignore you. Do not share your observations with anyone other than the instructor until after the performances.

When reporting back and describing *what* people do, you will need to use precise, objective language. When suggesting why they did it, your language will necessarily be more symbolic. Here, you will be trying to interpret the reasons why people behaved in particular ways, and the feelings that they appeared to be experiencing ...You may find similes helpful when doing this; e.g. it looks like, feels like, sounds like, it is as if ... Equally, metaphors may help; e.g. relating the group's behaviour to a family, a conflict or a sports team.

Take particular notes on the following areas:

1. Team development stages

Groups can go through four of these before they disband: forming, storming, norming and performing.

Forming is the stage of getting together, and finding out a bit about each other.

Storming is the ideas stage, when there is a lot of discussion, argument and conflict.

Norming is the stage of coming to an agreement about how to proceed.

Performing is the effective, production phase.

Observe the time each stage takes, and whether or not the group goes back over stages, either because they were not fully completed the first time, or because a new idea was generated. Did the group observed actually reach the performing phase, or did it get stuck in an earlier one?

2. Individual member contributions and team member roles

What did each person contribute to their group? (Who encouraged others to contribute? Who was prepared to differ to improve the drama? Who was prepared to differ just to get their own way?)

Did people begin to make the same broad type of contribution, i.e. taking a role in the team (suggestion-giver, information-sharer, idea evaluator) so that others began to look to them for that contribution? What roles seemed to develop and who performed them?

3. Leadership and decision-making

What style did the formal leader adopt, and how did this affect the way in which decisions were made in the group (autocratically by one person, democratically by all agreeing?) Were the decisions made acted on or ignored?

Did an informal leader emerge? What contribution did s/he make? If there were two leaders, how were the responsibilities divided up?

Did leadership pass between members rather than reside in one or two formal or informal leaders. What factors determined who took that lead?

4. Group structure

Did differences start to emerge between the group members to signal the emergence of group structures?

Were some members' ideas accorded higher value and adopted?	(status structure)
Were some individuals more influential than others?	(power structure)
Did some people work more closely with others and did cliques form?	(liking structure)
Did some people make specific, repeated types of contributions?	(role structure)
Were some leaders and other followers?	(leadership structure)
Did some talk more than others?	(communication structure)

5. Mood changes

Did the mood of the group change as it sought to achieve its task. Try to interpret and account for any mood changes observed.

Source: This activity was devised by Phillipa Brozson. The instructions for it are taken from D. Marcic, 'Additional Exercise: Improvised Drama and Creative Think: The art of building groups and teams', in *Instructor's Manual to accompany Organizational Behaviour: Experiences and Cases*, 4th edition, 1995, West Publishing Company, pp. 183–5. Used with permission.

7.3 PREP: Labour turnover

Objective

- To apply Elton Mayo's human relations perspective in analysing a work problem.

Introduction

The human relations perspective developed by Elton Mayo and his colleagues at the Harvard Business School has had a profound effect on social science in general, and on management in particular. It meant that 'people problems' in organizations came to be perceived in particular ways; that some causes of employee behaviour were given greater weight than others; and that some solutions were advanced in preference to others. What follows is a real life case study, based upon research carried out by Elton Mayo and his colleagues during the Second World War. Students are invited to carry out an analysis of the case from the human relations perspective.

Procedure

Step 1   Imagine that you are a management consultant who adopts a human relations approach to consulting. Using this perspective, read the case and identify the main problems, decide on their likely causes, and propose possible solutions. Bring this case and your notes to the class as directed by your instructor.

Step 2   In the class, form groups of four to six students.

Step 3   As a team of consultants, you have twenty minutes to discuss the case as a group, and collectively highlight the causes of, and possible solutions to, the high turnover problem in the factory.

Step 4   Your instructor will conduct a plenary session to elicit the views of different group members.

Case

Late in 1943, Elton Mayo and certain members of staff of the Harvard Graduate School of Business Administration, were asked to study the problem of labour turnover in the aircraft industry in southern California. The social setting was full of dramatic changes. Small aircraft plants had grown into large industries in a period of a few years. The drafting of workers into the army was a constant drain on the labour force since it necessitated the constant induction of new workers. These new workers migrated to California in their thousands. The staff at the Los Angeles War Manpower Commission estimated that in every month of 1943, approximately 25,000 people moved into southern California, and between 12,000 and 14,000 moved out. With this level of migration, it was not surprising to discover that labour turnover in the industry was running at 70 to 80 per cent. Mayo, however, refused to believe that this unsettlement alone was sufficient explanation for the turnover.

Like others aircraft companies in the area, Company A had applied scientific engineering knowledge technical skill to the product, and had systematised its operations. Analysing turnover, it found that with 40,000 employees, there were more than 30,000 departures in a twelve month period, 65,000 transfers within the plant, and approximately 150,000 'loans' or temporary transfers of a day or less, from one department within the plant to another. Thus, labour turnover was running at 75%, transfers at 157% and loans at 360%. Comparable data from other industries in the state suggested that the unsettlement in itself was insufficient to explain this problem.

Ignoring the departmental and shift organization, Mayo directed his attention at the smaller groups of people who were in daily working contact with each other. Seventy-one such groups were identified, and these differed in terms of their attendance record from no absence at all to high absence. This confirmed Mayo's suspicion that the dislocation caused by employee movement in and out of the industry could only provide a partial answer to the problem.

Sociometric studies led to the identification of 'natural groups'. These were very small groups varying in size from 3–7 workers. Twelve such groups were found, and each had a nearly perfect attendance record.

0   0

0   0

A researcher, acting as a non-participant observer of one of the natural groups, submitted the following report:

Research report

Group feature: excellent attendance record.

Productivity: 25% higher than average for plant.

Others' perception of this group:
- reputation for 'working like beavers'
- considered somewhat clannish by other groups.

Report of participant observer:

- Group members made references to what 'we' are doing and 'our' efficiency.

- Commented that 'other groups were not performing'.

- Group received only very occasional visits from the departmental foreman; his senior assistant popped his head in only once a day.

- One of the ordinary workers seemed to be in actual charge. This 'leadman' was a college graduate and had considerable experience of steel mills.

- He dealt with the minor hour-to-hour interruptions in the operations of the group.

- He introduced himself to new employees, and found them people they liked working with.

- After a few days he took new arrivals to the assembly line and showed them where the part that they had made fitted into the completed machine.

- He dealt with complaints listening to what people said: those he couldn't settle, he would discuss with the senior assistant foreman.

- He anticipated emergencies and shortages, and worked hard to get materials for his department.

- He dealt with inspectors and efficiency men who visited the group.

- Requests by group members for raises were channelled through him.

- He had the support of the senior assistant foreman in his actions.

Note

Based on: Elton Mayo and George F.F. Lombard, *Teamwork and Labour Turnover in the Aircraft Industry of Southern California*, Graduate School of Business Administration, Harvard University, Boston, 1944.

7.4 REV: Word search

Objective

- To assess student familiarity with the concepts, research and authors contained in *ORBIT3*'s Chapter 7 on group formation.

Introduction

This test encourages students to read the chapter on group formation in detail. Remembering key social science concepts and the details of empirical research studies forms the basis for understanding the subject of organizational behaviour. The inability to identify correctly the names of well known organizational behaviour writers or researchers indicates that the student is insufficiently familiar with the material. Many students, especially those from a science or engineering background, erroneously believe that social science has 'no right answers'. While it is true that there are many debates, schools of thoughts, and different interpretations of various issues and topics, it is also true that there is agreement on the key concepts, main writers and their research studies.

Procedure

Find the answers to the thirteen questions. These are hidden in the table below, and are presented horizontally, vertically, diagonally or backwards.

T	N	E	M	I	T	N	E	S
U	O	O	T	H	W	G	Q	W
C	E	B	R	O	O	U	I	T
K	T	E	O	M	E	Y	L	R
M	Y	C	W	A	I	F	A	E
A	H	R	B	N	E	N	O	K
N	W	E	T	S	L	T	G	I
B	R	F	I	A	O	R	R	L
E	T	A	G	E	R	G	G	A

Clues	Answers
1. Not a psychological group.	_____
2. Developed a theory of how groups formed.	_____
3. The boys place (initials).	_____
4. Feeling about a group.	_____
5. Third stage of group development.	_____
6. Tired plank at work (initials)?	_____

7. Minimum required for a group.   _____

8. Keen on linking the pins.   _____

9. Ladies smell a Roland (initials).   _____

10. Based on position in an informal group. _____

11. Said the group offered 'total integration'. _____

12. Can only be achieved if members work together. _____

13. He sells sweets as groups develop at school. _____

Chapter 8

Group structure and process

8.1 LGA: Tutorial pie

Objective

- To encourage students to see their organizational behaviour tutorial class as a group, and to analyse its structure.
- To raise students' awareness of the bases on which they differentiate members of the groups to which they belong.

Introduction

Group structure is a somewhat abstract concept. Yet each person who is a member of a group, automatically and unconsciously rates the other member on the basis of some criteria. Having done so, they then interact with them accordingly. This rating or ranking of group members on some criteria is at the heart of the concept of group structure. Perhaps the most confusing aspect is the mistaken belief that a group has only one structure. In reality, there are a number of parallel rankings operating, and people high on one may be low on another. This activity seeks to highlight these different ranking scales.

Procedure

Imagine that the circle below is a pie-chart which represents the members of the tutorial group of which you are a member, and which accompanies this course. This group is scheduled to meet several times a term, and you will have already participated in some of the discussions.

Step 1   Divide the pie into slices – one for each member of your tutorial group. Be sure to include a slice for yourself, and for the tutorial instructor. The size of each slice should represent each person's contribution to the class. Label each slice by inserting the individual's name or initials.

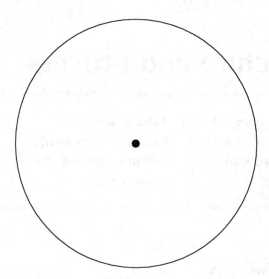

Step 2   Form a pair with the person sitting next to you. Take turns to explain your division of your pie-chart to them. Your explanation should focus on the following four questions:

a)   What criteria did you use to decide on the size of each person's 'contribution slice' to the tutorial class?

Step 2   b)   Describe the way in which you divided up the pie.

c)   Which 3 people did you give the largest slices to?

d)   How did you evaluate yourself in relation to the others in your tutorial group?

Note

This is an amended version of the exercise 'Class Pie' which appears in A. Pines and C. Maslach, *Experiencing Social Psychology: Readings and Projects*, Alfred A. Knopf Inc., 1979, pp. 217–8.

8.2 SGA: Group process analysis

Objectives

- To introduce a framework for describing and classifying different verbal behaviours in a group.
- To understand the difference between the content and process levels of a group's operation.
- To provide practice in using this framework to analyse verbal behaviour in a group.

Introduction

Every group works at two levels. The task or content level is concerned with the substantive issues being discussed by the group members. For example, how much money to spend, how to solve the problem, whom to appoint, etc. It also operates at the process level. This concerns issues of who communicates with whom, how frequently each person contributes, how they contribute, how group decisions are made. The latter level affects the former. For example, group problems may not be resolved (content level), because each member contributes to the discussion by pushing their own views, rather than trying to build on others' (process level). The group members can be seen as competing rather than co-operating.

In order to study how people communicate and behave in groups, we need a precise and reliable way to describe what is going on. Psychologists have devised a procedure for describing and analysing behaviour which consists of a series of categories which are used to classify each group member's speech. This exercise gives you the opportunity to use a simplified classification system. You are asked to analyse and contrast the behaviour of two discussion groups.

Procedure

Step 1   A group's performance is based on how its members choose to express themselves: for example, whether they make proposals, ask others for information, summarise what others have said, and so on. Below is a simple framework to help you analyse and categorize the behaviour contributions of members in groups. Familiarise yourself with the five verbal behaviour categories that will be used in the first discussion:

Verbal behaviour category	Explanation
Proposing	Any behaviour which puts forward a new suggestion, idea or course of action.
Supporting	Any behaviour which declares agreement with or support for any individual or their idea.
Disagreeing	Any behaviour which states a criticism of another person's statement.

Verbal behaviour category	Explanation
Giving	Any behaviour which gives facts, ideas, opinions or information, or clarifies these.
Seeking	Any behaviour which asks for facts, ideas, opinions or information from others.

Step 2 Use Record Sheet A to analyse transcript A. Read the verbal contribution made by Alan (No. 1) to the discussion. At the end of it, decide into which of the five verbal behaviour categories, described in the introductory section, it fits best. Insert the initial of that category into the square brackets provided [P, S, D, GI or SI]. Repeat this for all the other contributions in transcript A. Then put Record Sheet A aside temporarily.

Step 3 Repeat the procedure, but this time using Record Sheet B to analyse transcript B. This record sheet uses six behaviour categories. *Building* as an extra category is included.

   Building: Any behaviour which develops or extends an idea or suggestion made by someone else.

Again, write the initial of the appropriate behaviour category in the square brackets [P, B, S, D, GI or SI] for the contributions that make up transcript B.

Step 4 Now analyse the discussions depicted in Transcripts A and B. Referring to your Record Sheets A and B, add up the totals for each of the different categories. That is, add up all the Ps (proposals made), Ss (statements of support) and so on. Insert these in Record Sheet C.

Compare your scores to those produced by your instructor.

Record Sheet A

Category	Participants' Names				
	Jackie	Alan	Sue	Peter	Kate
Proposing					
Supporting					
Disagreeing					
Giving information					
Seeking information					

Record Sheet B

Category	Participants' Names				
	Jackie	Alan	Sue	Peter	Kate
Proposing					
Building					
Supporting					
Disagreeing					
Giving information					
Seeking information					

Record Sheet C

Category	Discussion A	Discussion B
Proposing		
Building		
Supporting		
Disagreeing		
Giving information		
Seeking information		
Total		

Transcript A

1. *ALAN*: I really feel that, over the two years I've been a university student, one of the greatest deficiencies of the whole system has been the lack of clarity of roles between the personal student counsellor and the course instructor. I feel they've been rather confused. Counsellors have been advising academically; instructors are rather aloof, and kind of descend on you like some great sage. [   ]

   I would certainly prefer the two roles to be combined in future years. I don't know what other people think? [   ]

2. *PETER*: You don't feel then that the instructor has been playing solely an academic role? As students, we go to tutorials to learn, in depth, a particular item from the course content. I think that there is a specialised role for the instructor, and that the counsellor is a separate unit completely. [   ]

   So I tend to disagree with you there Alan, and don't see the two roles as synonymous at all, and feel they should be kept separate. [   ]

3. *SUE*: No, I would disagree up to a point. I still think that there should be two roles. [   ]

   But the instructors and counsellors should coordinate what they are doing more and work together. [   ]

   They don't seem to do this at the moment. If you've got problems, you go to a counsellor; if you're worried about something academic, you go to your tutor. I'm not sure how much feedback there is between the two. [   ]

4. *KATE*: I think that the personal counselling should be expanded rather than reduced, especially when you get beyond foundation level. Because I think the problems become greater ... [   ]

5. *SUE*: After the first year, I never saw my counsellor. [   ]

6. *KATE*: I think the counsellor has a very specific role, which really should not be academic [   ]; they should be a personal advisor. [   ]

7. *ALAN*: Some students have problems, others don't. Obviously everybody has problems, but some have more than others. What I'm concerned about is that the counsellor won't have enough work entirely solving personal problems. [   ]

   After the first year, I think the counselling role should be undertaken by the tutor, and there should be contact between the tutor and the student. [   ]

8. *KATE*: But the tutor has a formal structure to follow in his tutorial sessions, hasn't he? [   ]

9. *JACKIE*: I don't think you feel that you can waste everybody's time by bringing up your personal problems in an hour's session. [   ]

10. *ALAN*: Maybe there should be time afterwards. [   ]

11. *PETER*: As a group, we seem to be saying, you know, that there is a separate identity between the counsellor and the instructor. And your particular point Alan, may be one

that goes along university lines, but down at student level, isn't necessarily a viable situation. [   ]

12. *JACKIE*: I think that most students would like to see more liaison between their own counsellors and tutors. [   ]

We tend to think that the tutor and counsellor have separate views of the student, and that their only contact in relation to the student is in the passing of papers about assignments. [   ]

Perhaps an extension of the tutorial session, to include a discussion of personal problems with the students' own counsellors present, would be helpful in creating a congenial atmosphere. [   ]

13. *SUE*: The situation as it stands leads to this argument and disagreement between these two roles because students are drawn in different directions, particularly with regard to academic work. If you want to quibble about that, you often go to the counsellor because you know them better, they're more approachable, they've build up a relationship with you [   ], and as you say, the two should come together more and have joint sessions probably lasting much longer. [   ]

14. *PETER*: One of the main problems is that students often miss tutorials. They're just not getting out of the course what they could. [   ]

15. *SUE*: Yes, but why don't people attend? Maybe they've been unable to attend, they think they missed something last time, and think, 'I won't bother going'. If instructors took the initiative to tell students what happened at the last tutorial, and outline what will happen next [   ], I think that there would be better group interaction, people would get together more, they'd be more group identity, and there wouldn't be splinter cliques which I think destroy the set up. [   ]

16 *KATE*: I think that smaller tutorial groups would be a good idea as well, then you could relate better to your tutor and other students. It would give the opportunity for the more timid ones to come in. [   ]

17. *JACKIE*: There are disadvantages with small groups. I have personal experience of where a personality clash between a pupil and a tutor, or between two pupils, can entirely disrupt a tutorial session. [   ]

Transcript B

18. *ALAN*: I think that one of the main problems of the university courses is the division between the tutor and the counsellor and the fact that you often get different advice from each. [   ]

19. *SUE*: Well, I agree. [   ]

I think it would be a good idea if there was more liaison between tutors and counsellors. If students go to one or other of those people, they should tell each other what was said, so that they can work together. [   ]

20. *PETER*: I think that this can be taken a little further. Perhaps after the meeting of the

tutor and the counsellor there should be more feedback to the student, because often they are left in a total vacuum. [   ]

21. *JACKIE*: Do you think what we need are a series of more informal meetings between counsellors, tutors and the students themselves, to keep the students aware of how the tutors are reacting to their written assignments, and keep the tutors aware of the students' problems? [   ]

22. *PETER*: At the moment the communication between the tutor and the counsellor is done mainly by correspondence. I'd like to be a little bit more positive and suggest that these two meet face-to-face so that there is an exchange of information between them. [   ]

23. *SUE*: Yes. [   ]

Possibly too, there could be a facility for there to be meetings other than formal tutorials. I know these happen at foundation level, but later, when you speak to people, they feel very much in isolation. Perhaps there could be meetings between tutorials, involving both the tutor and the counsellor. [   ]

24. *JACKIE*: I support Sue's proposal and can visualise the situation. [   ]

I think we need to avoid imposing an increased workload on our counsellors and tutors who already have a heavy student commitment. Should we suggest that students themselves form meaningful self-help groups? [   ]

25. *ALAN*: I think that's exactly right, Jackie. [   ]

I think it's absolutely essential that the university develops the concept of self-help groups, and give more publicity to their advantages as so much learning, I think, can be gained by students from other students. [   ]

26. *PETER*: Are we thinking of increasing the value of the self-help situation itself? [   ]

In these self-help groups, why not have a tutor there in an advisory capacity, rather than a tutorial capacity? [   ]

27. *KATE*: Do you mean or a regular basis? [   ]

28. *PETER*: Yes. [   ]

29. *KATE*: Yes. [   ]

If students could help to choose some of the tutorial topics, then we would be incorporating the self-help concept. [   ]

30. *SUE*: Talking about the groups, do you think we should advocate they should be smaller? [   ]

In these smaller groups, the two roles could be combined with one staff member doing both the counselling and tutoring. Do you think that that would have any value? [   ]

31. *JACKIE*: If we are considering smaller groups and specialist advice from tutors and counsellors, let's add an element of student mobility so that students can move between groups to gain the specialist advice they need at any particular time. [   ]

32. *SUE*: Yes, I think that's a very good point. [   ]

I think it would be useful if students were allowed to consult other tutors. I think this could be done easily if all tutorials were held on the same day, and if students were told what each individual tutor's speciality was, and actually told that if they had a problem, they could consult that person. [   ]

8.3 PREP: Belbin's team role theory

Objectives

- To analyse which roles individuals play in groups and teams.
- To introduce Meredith Belbin's Team Role Theory.

Introduction

A great deal of work in organizations is now carried out through team effort. Technical change projects, marketing task forces and appointments committees are just a few examples. In these circumstances, the composition of the team is crucial, and it cannot be guaranteed that they will always work well together, and succeed in the task that they have been set. The research of Meredith Belbin suggests that the chances of successful team performance are increased if group members play eight key roles. This inventory will allow students to assess the roles that they tend to play in a team or a group.

Procedure

Step 1   Students remind themselves of Belbin's Team Role Theory which is described in Chapter 8 of *ORBIT3*, especially the definition of team role which is that person's tendency to behave, contribute and interrelate with others in a particular way.

Step 2   Below will be found a definition of each of the nine team member roles. Briefly go through each role description highlighting and clarifying its main features, and predict the two team roles that you feel you carry out most often when a member of a group or a team. Write the two role names below:

Most often: _____

Next often: _____

Step 3   Students complete the Team Role Inventory before coming to the next session. There are no right or wrong answers.

Step 4   Score your Team Role Inventory by adding up your totals for the nine columns in the table. Each column refers to one of Belbin's nine team roles, and your instructor will indicate which is which. Insert the symbol for that role at the top of each of the nine columns.

Step 5   Divide into groups of 4–5, and:

- Compare and contrast your own team role scores (predicted and actual) with those of the other members of their group.

- Reflect on your experiences of participation in teams in the past. How well do these scores reflect your preferred team roles?

- Decide to what extent your preferred team roles are a reflection of your personality.

- Identify which roles in this team are preferred and which are avoided, rejected or are missing.

Points table for Belbin's team role inventory

Section	Total								
I	c	e	i	h	a	g	b	d	f	= 10
II	a	g	f	d	i	b	c	e	h	= 10
III	i	c	h	a	d	f	g	b	e	= 10
IV	d	b	c	e	f	h	a	g	i	= 10
V	e	h	i	c	g	a	f	d	b	= 10
VI	b	e	g	f	c	d	i	h	a	= 10
VII	h	d	a	i	e	g	b	f	c	= 10
Total									= 70

If this was a real management or project team, what could be done to cover the avoided or rejected roles?

- Decide whether certain roles are more important in certain phases of a team's operation? For example, which two team roles are likely to be crucial in the getting-started phase of a team's work; the generating-ideas phase; the developing-the-ideas phase; or the implementing-the-decision phase?

Team Role Descriptions

Implementor (IM)

Implementors need clear objectives, procedures, and direction. They may be uncomfortable with new ideas, but are the solid members who can make a practical plan to achieve the goal. They are the 'engineers' of the group, turning concepts and ideas into practical working procedures. They can carry out agreed plans, using their self-control self-discipline, realism and practical 'common sense'. However, they can have inflexible attitudes, and can be unresponsive to new, untested ideas.

Co-ordinator (CO)

This group member likes organising people, co-ordinating their activities, mapping their strengths, and using them productively. Co-ordinators tend to work to produce consent and develop agreement among different interests, making sure everyone has their say. They command respect, inspire enthusiasm, communicate easily, and usually demonstrate good timing and balance. Co-ordinators need not necessarily be charismatic leaders or intellectuals.

Shaper (SH)

Shapers are the behind-the-scene facilitators, who like to influence group decisions, and make their mark in meetings covertly. They are people who are willing to risk unpopularity to get their ideas across. They pay a lot of attention to setting priorities and objectives, making sure the group's discussion and action take on the preset shape that they have in their mind. The Shaper's drive and self-confidence are likely to be offset by a certain intolerance for vague ideas and vague people.

Plant (PL)

Plants are the group's innovators. They are original, independent, imaginative individuals, who sometimes can frustrate in-group work. They are sources of new approaches to old problems, providing new ideas and new strategies. They likes puzzles, brainstorms, patterns, problem-solving, and are valued (and tolerated) for their independent outlook as well as their intelligence and imagination. Plants can also be impractical, or weak at communicating their newfledged ideas to members with different attitudes and outlooks.

Resource Investigator (RI)

This is the member who operates at the group boundary, bringing in people and ideas from the outside. Resource Investigators have a network of personal contacts which they can draw upon. They like new techniques, and work well by phone. They are likely to have an outgoing, relaxed personality, strong on curiosity and willing to see the possibilities in anything new. At the same time, they can become over-enthusiastic, creating diversions from the task in hand, or fail to follow-up the initiatives that they have taken.

Monitor Evaluator (ME)

The Monitor Evaluator is the group's critical member who takes nothing for granted. Often slow, they carefully and thoroughly evaluates any new concepts or proposals put forward by the team. This person's judgement wins over their feelings. A Monitor Evaluator can find weaknesses in unsound proposals, and will ask for any missing information to be provided before a decision is made. As a team member, the Monitor Evaluator's key contribution is critical thinking and objectivity, but they can be overserious, overcritical, and perhaps too careful on behalf of their group. Their analyses can be counter-productive at the early, creative stages in a team's work.

Team Worker (TW)

The Team Worker is the group's nurturing mother figure, and thus plays a role directly opposite the Shaper, who acts as the team's father figure. This person likes people and works easily with them, even when they express ideas which are different from their own. Team Workers support other members in their strengths and underpin their weaknesses. They try to get consensus between different members in the group. Their strengths lie in their flexibility, popularity, and listening skills. However, they may lack decisiveness or toughness, and may be unable to tolerate competition and friction within the group.

Completer Finisher (CF)

This is the practical member who cares about meeting targets and deadlines, and can bring the group task to a successful completion. The Completer Finisher is the perfectionist who uses their fine eye for detail to notice any mistakes or omissions. They help their team to keep track of the portions of the task that need extra attention. They can create a sense of urgency in the team, and are natural worriers. The Completer Finisher has a strong sense of order, purpose and concern, but will suffer from impatience with other team members who have more casual habits or dispositions.

Specialist (SP)

This is the person who provides the team with the information that it needs at any point in time. Specialists make their contribution on a narrow front, and are proud of their technical skills and special knowledge. Their primary orientation is to advance their own knowledge of their field and maintain professional standards. In consequence, they may show little interest in other people or their work. Some writers have argued, that because of their specific and limited input, Specialists are not true team role members comparable with the previous eight.

Team role inventory

Instructions

For each section, distribute a total of ten points among the sentences which you think best describe your behaviour. The points may be distributed among several sentences: in extreme cases they might be spread among all the sentences or ten points may be given to a single sentence. Enter the points alongside each sentence in the space provided.

I. What I believe I can contribute to a team:

(a) ___   I think I can quickly see and take advantage of opportunities.

(b) ___   I can work well with a very wide range of people.

(c) ___   I can usually sense what is realistic and likely to work.

(d) ___   My capacity to follow through has much to do with my personal effectiveness.

(e) ___   My ability rests in being able to draw people out whenever I detect they have something of value to contribute to group activities.

(f) ___   My technical knowledge and experience is usually my major asset.

(g) ___   I can offer a reasoned case for alternative courses of action without introducing bias or prejudice.

(h) ___   Producing ideas is one of my natural assets.

(i) ___   I am ready to face temporary unpopularity if it leads to worthwhile results in the end.

II. If I have a possible shortcoming in teamwork, it could be that:

(a) ___   I am not at ease unless meetings are well structured and controlled and generally well-conducted.

(b) ___   My objective outlook makes it difficult for me to join in readily and enthusiastically with colleagues.

(c) ___   I find it difficult to lead from the front, perhaps because I am over-responsive to group atmosphere.

(d) ___   I am apt to get too caught up in ideas that occur to me and so lose track of what is happening.

(e) ___   My colleagues tend to see me as worrying unnecessarily over detail and the possibility that things may go wrong.

(f) ___   I am sometimes seen as forceful and authoritarian if there is a need to get something done.

(g) ___   I am inclined to be too generous towards others who have a valid viewpoint that has not been given a proper airing.

(h) ___   I am reluctant to contribute, unless the subject being discussed deals with an area I know well.

(i) ___   I have a tendency to talk too much once the group gets on to new ideas.

III.   When involved in a project with other people:

(a) ___   I can be counted on to contribute something original.

(b) ___   My general vigilance prevents careless mistakes and omissions being made.

(c) ___   I have an aptitude for influencing people without pressurising them.

(d) ___   I am keen to look for the latest in new ideas and developments.

(e) ___   I try to maintain my sense of professionalism.

(f) ___   I believe that my capacity for judgements can help to bring about the right decisions.

(g) ___   I am always ready to back a good suggestion in the common interest.

(h) ___   I am ready to press for action to make sure that the meeting does not waste time or lose sight of the main objective.

(i) ___   I can be relied upon to see that all essential work is organized.

IV.   My characteristic approach to group work is that:

(a) ___   I have a quiet interest in getting to know colleagues better.

(b) ___   While I am interested in all views, I have no hesitation in making up my mind once a decision has to be made.

(c) ___   I am not reluctant to challenge the views of others or to hold a minority view myself.

(d) ___   I think I have a talent for making things work once a plan has to be put into operation.

(e) ___   I have a tendency to avoid the obvious and I come out with the unexpected.

(f) ___ I am ready to make use of contacts outside of the group itself.

(g) ___ I bring a touch of perfectionism to any job I undertake.

(h) ___ I can usually find a line of argument to refute unsound propositions.

(i) ___ I contribute when I know what I'm talking about.

V. I gain satisfaction in a job because:

(a) ___ I enjoy analysing situations and weighing up all the possible choices.

(b) ___ I feel that I am using my special qualifications and training to advantage.

(c) ___ I like to find a field that stretches my imagination.

(d) ___ I feel in my element when I can give a task my full attention.

(e) ___ I am interested in finding practical solutions to problems.

(f) ___ I like to feel I am fostering good working relationships.

(g) ___ I can meet people who may have something new to offer.

(h) ___ I can get people to agree on a necessary course of action.

(i) ___ I can have a strong influence on decisions.

VI. If I am suddenly given a difficult task with limited time and unfamiliar people:

(a) ___ I tend to read up as much as I conveniently can on the subject.

(b) ___ I would retain a steadiness of purpose in spite of the pressures.

(c) ___ I would open up discussions with a view to stimulating new thoughts and getting something moving.

(d) ___ I believe that I would keep cool and maintain my capacity to think straight.

(e) ___ I would find some way of reducing the size of the task by establishing what different individuals might best contribute.

(f) ___ I would feel like retiring to a corner to devise a way out of the impasse before developing a line.

(g) ___ I would be prepared to take a positive lead if I felt the group was making no progress.

(h) ___ My natural sense of urgency would help ensure that we did not fall behind schedule.

(i) ___ I would be ready to work with the person who showed the most positive approach.

VII. With reference to the problems to which I am subject in working in groups:

(a) ___ I am apt to show my impatience with those who are obstructing progress.

(b) ___   I hesitate to get my points across when I run up against real opposition.

(c) ___   I am inclined to feel I am wasting my time and would do better on my own.

(d) ___   I am conscious of demanding from others the things I cannot do myself.

(e) ___   I tend to get bored rather easily and rely on one or two stimulating members to spark me off.

(f) ___   My desire to ensure that work is properly done can hold up proceedings.

(g) ___   Others may criticise me for being too analytical and insufficiently intuitive.

(h) ___   I find it difficult to get started unless the goals are clear.

(i) ___   I am sometimes poor at explaining and clarifying complex points that occur to me.

Note

Belbin's original team role theory described eight distinct roles. Later, he added a ninth role – Specialist. Some commentators argue that this is not a true team role at all. However, its inclusion is useful to remind us that any team may need a specialist, or outside input, at some time in its deliberations.

Source: This team role inventory was developed by Dr Meredith Belbin. It is reprinted, with adaptations, and by permission, from R.M. Belbin, *Management Teams: Why They Succeed or Fail*, Butterworth-Heinemann, London, 1981, pp. 153–6.

8.4 REV: Name check

Objective

- To familiarise students with the names of researchers and theorists contributing to the fields of group formation, structure and process.

Introduction

The ability to assign correctly the names of organization behaviour scholars to their theories and studies is part of the task of learning this subject. It also provides a shorthand that is useful when completing course assignment reports and examinations. It allows students to write, 'Brown's studies of the Grimsby fish factory showed that ...' This activity develops your ability to link specific theories, research, writings and ideas with their authors. Although considered in the context of groups here, it is an ability which needs to be demonstrated in all the other subject fields.

Procedure

Read chapters 7 and 8 of *ORBIT3* paying particular attention to the names of authors as you encounter them. Then, put the book aside, and answer the questions below. Insert the surnames of the people associated with the studies described. If two researchers were involved, only the surname of the first is required.

Description	Surname
1. Studied group leadership styles on boys' clubs in Iowa.	
2. Used the concepts of sentiments, activities and interaction to explain how groups formed.	
3. Distinguished the different types of power that could be exerted by individuals within groups.	
4. Conducted laboratory experiments which sought to relate communication to different group leadership styles.	
5. Considered the psychological and social environment as one of the three variables which determined group structure.	
6. Studied street gangs in Chicago.	
7. Conducted empirical studies into the process of group formation.	
8. Studied communication patterns in restaurants.	
9. Devised a technique for categorising the verbal contributions of the different members of a group.	
10. Considered the challenges posed by globally distributed teams.	
11. Described the group orientation of Japanese companies.	
12. A member of the Hawthorne studies research team who became the first professor of organizational behaviour.	

13. Conceived of group leadership as a social exchange process.	
14. Developed the theory of supportive relationships.	
15. Distinguished between task and maintenance behaviours in a group.	
16. Compared different communication structures in a group on the criteria of speed, accuracy, leadership and satisfaction.	
17. Distinguished between a person's team role and their functional role in the company.	
18. Originated a method for mapping human relations based on personal choices.	

Chapter 9

Group control

9.1 LGA: Glasgow gangs

Objective

- To sensitize students to the key concepts relevant to understanding group control.

Introduction

The dynamics of group control of individual behaviour are similar whether one is considering the members of a board of management of a major company, or a gang of youths. This activity offers students who have no previous contact with the subject of group control, an opportunity to identify some of the key elements which will be examined in greater depth in the course.

Procedure

Step 1   Turn to the appropriate page in your workbook. There they will find a short article from the Glasgow Evening News of 1929. Read it through quickly now on your own.

Step 2   Working with the person next to you, answer the ten questions below.

1. Were the Glasgow gangs 'psychological groups' or 'aggregates'?
2. Were the gangs formal or informal groups?
3. List the objectives of the gangs.
4. Give an example of a gang norm.
5. Give an example of a gang sanction to enforce that norm.
6. On what criteria were gang leaders chosen?
7. What enhanced the status of individuals in the gang?
8. What contributed to each gang's unique identity?
9. What features distinguished gang members?
10. What could happen to the most effective gang member?

Note   The article appeared in the *Glasgow Evening News* on 10 May 1929.

THE EVENING NEWS, GLASGOW, FRIDAY, MAY 10, 1929.

NTS
AL
SALE

ve already been furnished ... made
ces and on terms well within the

ly good furniture at greatly reduced
ant's *now* ... while these amazing
howrooms and compare prices and

ut a few examples of the
at present. There are
ing your inspection.

CREDIT

sh out-of income, on our famous "No
y instalment, all the furniture you have
account can be cleared by weekly or
rs, according to your requirements. In
icult for you to continue payments you
rate treatment that has made our name

/6   with Order and 12 6 monthly secures delivery of
this luxurious Three-Piece Suite.

s Three-Piece Suite, covered in best quality Hide effect
hinished a richly toned Brown colour, and complete with
Brown Velveteen Cushions, filled feathers. This Suite is
very comfortable, and being soundly constructed of good
materials, eminently suited for hard wear. Usual Price,

E **£17 15/-**   Or No Deposit
and 12/6 monthly

/-   with Order and 10 - monthly secures delivery of
this Handsome Living-Room Suite.

Living Room Suite made of figured Oak, beautifully
rich Brown colour, comprising 4ft. wide Sideboard with
were interlined with Green baize for cutlery) and two roomy
below 5ft. by 3ft extending Dining Table and four
built small chairs with loose seats covered in Rexine.
19 Gns.

E **£14 12/6**   Or No Deposit
and 10/- monthly.

GLASGOW GANGSTERS.

Youthful Hooligans Terrorise Small Shopkeepers.

BID TO RIVAL CHICAGO.

GIRL MEMBERS LEAD TO MANY DISPUTES

A special investigation into the activities of the Glasgow gangs was conducted by a representative of The Evening News. The inquiry revealed that these gangs constitute a serious menace to the community.

Their activities are not confined to one city area, but they are specially and notoriously active in Bridgeton and in Govan. The " Nud'e Boys " of Bridgeton almost rival the gangsters of Chicago in their threats to the safety of the citizens.

BOTTLES BETTER THAN RAZORS.

The blackmailing activities of some of the Glasgow gangs were revealed to an Evening News representative who carried out an investigation in the areas principally affected. They terrorise the whole community, and particularly the small-shopkeeping class, in order that they may make an easy livelihood without doing any work themselves.

Most of the members of such gangs are unemployed or unemployable youths between 17 and 22. The leader is generally a few years older than his followers, and is chosen principally for his weight and fighting ability. A system of transfers (similar to that which obtains in the football world) is in operation, and when two rival gangs are about to stage a battle good fighters are transferred from one gang to another. Heavy fees are reported to be paid, and as much as £20 has been paid for a single "transfer."

GIRLS OR "MOLLS."

A girl is known to the gangsters as a "Moll." Each gang has a number of such girls attached to it and over these "fair" followers many disputes arise.

For example: Not long ago the sweetheart of the leader of one gang went off to a certain picture house with a member of another gang. They were discovered by the outraged leader, who also happened to attend the cinema that night, and he immediately remarked: "That gang can have the leavings of our gang any time they want." There was no verbal reply, but he woke up to find himself in the infirmary with a terrible slash, inflicted with a razor.

THEIR METHODS.

It is not to be thought that these gangs are formed for the mere purpose and from the love of fighting. That is not the case. They are formed in order that they may obtain an easy livelihood at the expense of their more peaceful neighbours.

The small shopkeeper they hold in a state of terror, and they extract from him a weekly payment of two shillings. Should he fail to pay, the gang burgle his premises or smash the shop window. Publicans are also victims, although they do not usually pay in cash.

AFRAID TO COMPLAIN.

To complain to the police would seem the obvious course, but this they are afraid to do, because (so effective is the organisation of the gangs), if they do, the gangs immediately take reprisals, smash a window, and loot the premises.

One reason why it is very difficult to deal with these gangs is that a rival gangster never gives the members of an opposing gang away. There is honour among gangsters. One member of a gang who did turn on his erstwhile companions not so long ago went soon after to hospital—as the result of an "accident"—and he is still there. His former colleagues seized him, broke his ribs, and left him lying on the street unconscious.

THE LEADING GANG.

The leading and by far the worst gang is that which operates in Bridgeton under the somewhat inexplicable title of " The Nudie Boys." Other well-known gangs are the "Pikers," and the "Billy Boys." A good fighter (a man who carries a big transfer fee) is one who can " gouge," and who is an expert bottle-thrower. " Gouging " is the most fiendish activity of the gangs. It is an operation whereby one damages an opponent's eye by using the pressure of the forefinger and the thumb.

A bottle-thrower is a particularly useful member of a gang. He throws a bottle in order to strike, and the experts can use two bottles at a time. A member of one gang stated that bottle-throwing was more effective than razor slashing. " Besides," he pointed out, " one only gets a bigger sentence if one is found in possession of a razor.

MENACE TO THE COMMUNITY.

It will be readily seen that these gangs constitute a serious menace to the community. They are particularly a menace to the young people in the district in which they operate. Very often a young man who has refused to join a gang is seized upon by members and mauled to such an extent that he finally agrees to become one of the desperadoes.

The police—who are known in the terminology of the gangs as "splits"—find great difficulty in suppressing these gangs. Even when a fight takes place in the public streets it is difficult to draw batons and lay around them because of the danger of innocent bystanders being involved.

There appears to be only one remedy. A fine is not enough. Very often the necessity of paying a fine is just another reason for further terrorism against the small shopkeepers. Imprisonment is not enough. Most of the members rather glory in the fact of having been in prison.

The use of the " cat " would appear to be the only remedy. If legislation is needed to allow of its use, that legislation should be passed, and passed as quickly as possible.

MO

Motoring

Spee
wit

Messrs WY
Garage at Be
with all those
cars in the co

Accommodat

No matter w
overhaul, M
carried out i

We specialise
to Motor Ca
dynamo or b

Coachbuildin

9.2 SGA: United Chemical Company

Objective

- To explore issues of socialization in groups.

Introduction

Joining any new group can be a stressful experience. The new member has their own needs, standards and objectives. The group possesses its already established ones, and wants the new recruit to adopt these. Sometimes there is a clash, and the problem of how it is to be resolved arises.

Procedure

Step 1   Read the case study, *United Chemical Company*, and make individual notes to the six questions below:

1. Does Sue value her membership in the group? Explain.
2. What is Sue seeking from membership in the design group?
3. What are the other members seeking from membership in the group?
4. How do you rate the way Max handled his meeting with Sue?
5. Discuss this situation in terms of the stages of group development.
6. Discuss this situation in terms of structural dimensions of the group.
7. What should Sue do next? What should Max do next?

Step 2   In the groups assigned by your instructor, discuss your individual responses, and agree a group response to each of the six questions.

Step 3   The instructor leads a discussion. Class members contribute their group and individual insights.

United Chemical Company Case

The United Chemical Company is a large producer and distributor of commodity chemicals with five chemical production plants in the United States. The operations at the main plant in Baytown, Texas, include not only production equipment but also is the site of the company's research and engineering centre.

The process design group consists of eight male engineers and the supervisor, Max Kane. The group has worked together steadily for a number of years, and good relationships have developed among all members. When the workload began to increase, Max hired a new design engineer, Sue Davis, a recent master's degree graduate from one of the foremost engineering schools in the country. Sue was assigned to a project whose goal was expansion of one of the existing plant facility's capacity. Three other design engineers were assigned to the project along with Sue: Jack Keller (aged thirty-eight, fifteen years with the company); Sam Sims (aged forty, ten years with the company); and Lance Maddison (aged thirty-two, eight years with the company).

As a new employee, Sue was very enthusiastic about the opportunity to work at United.

She liked her work very much because it was challenging and it offered her a chance to apply much of the knowledge she had gained in her university studies. On the job, Sue kept fairly much to herself and her design work. Her relations with her fellow project members were friendly, but she did not go out of her way to have informal conversations during or after working hours.

Sue was a diligent employee who took her work quite seriously. On occasions, when a difficult problem arose, she would stay after hours in order to come up with a solution. Because of her persistence, coupled with her more recent education, Sue completed her portion of the various project stages usually a number of days before her colleagues. This was somewhat irritating to her because on these occasions she went to Max to ask for additional work to keep her busy until her fellow workers caught up with her. Initially, she had offered to help Jack, Sam and Lance with their portion of the project, but each time she was turned down very tersely. About five months after Sue had joined the design group, Jack asked to see Max about a problem the group was having. The conversation between Max and Jack was as follows:

MAX: Jack, I understand you wanted to discuss a problem with me.

JACK: Yes, Max, I didn't want to waste your time, but some of the other design engineers wanted me to discuss Sue with you. She is irritating everyone with her know-it-all, pompous attitude. She is just not the kind of person we want to work with.

MAX: I can't understand that, Jack. She's an excellent worker whose design work is always well done and usually flawless. She's doing everything the company wants her to do.

JACK: The company never asked her to disturb the morale of the group or to tell us how to do our work. The animosity of the group can eventually result in lower quality work for the whole unit.

MAX: I'll tell you what I'll do. Sue has a meeting with me next week to discuss her six-month performance. I'll keep your thoughts in mind, but I can't promise an improvement in what you and the others believe is a pompous attitude.

JACK: Immediate improvement in her behaviour is not the problem; it's her coaching others when she has no right to engage in publicly showing others what to do. You'd think she was lecturing an advance class in design with all her high-power, useless equations and formulas. She'd better back off soon, or some of us will quit or transfer.

During the next week, Max thought carefully about his meeting with Jack. He knew that Jack was the informal leader of the design engineers and generally spoke for the other group members. On Thursday of the following week, Max called Sue into his office for her mid-year review. Certain excerpts of the conversation were as follows:

MAX: There is another aspect I'd like to discuss with you about your performance. As I just related to you, your technical performance has been excellent; however, there are some questions about your relationships with the other workers.

SUE: I don't understand – what questions are you talking about?

MAX: Well to be specific, certain members of the design group have complained about your apparent 'know-it-all attitude' and the manner in which you try to tell them about how to do their job. You're going to have to be patient with them and not publicly call them out about their performance. This is a good group of engineers, and their work over the years has been more than acceptable. I don't want any problems that will cause the group to produce less effectively.

SUE: Let me make a few comments. First of all, I have never publicly criticized their performance to them or to you. Initially, when I was finished ahead of them, I offered to help them with their work, but was bluntly told to mind my own business. I took the hint and concentrated only on my part of the work.

MAX: Okay, I understand that.

SUE: What you don't understand is that after five months of working in this group, I have come to the conclusion that what is going on is a 'rip-off' of the company. The other engineers are 'goldbricking' and setting a work pace much less than they're capable of. They're more interested in the music from Sam's radio, the local football team, and the bar they're going to after work. I'm sorry, but this is just not the way I was raised or trained And finally, they've never looked on me as a qualified engineer, but as a woman who has broken their professional barrier.

MAX: The assessment and motivation of the engineers is a managerial job. Your job is to do your work as well as you can without interfering with the work of others. As for the male-female comment, this company hired you because of your qualifications, not your sex. Your future at United is quite promising if you do the engineering and leave the management to me.

Sue left the meeting very depressed. She knew that she was performing well and that the other engineers were not working up to their capacity. The knowledge frustrated her more and more as the weeks passed.

Source: Andrew D. Szilagi and Marc J. Wallace, *Organizational Behaviour and Performance*, 1983, Scott, Foresman and Co. Used with permission.

9.3 PREP: Discovering the norms

Objectives

- To raise students' understanding of the effect of group norms on behaviour in a non-university and a university environment.
- To demonstrate the link between behaviour in groups and the creation of group norms.
- To enable students to identify group norm enforcement strategies.

Introduction

Often group norms are implicit rather than explicit, and are difficult to identify. Nevertheless, individuals' behaviour may be influenced by norms of which they may not be fully conscious. When people become aware of the norms that affect them, the more they are able to understand their own behaviour. This activity seeks to make group norms explicit.

Step 1   Before the class, write down in the space below, the THREE most salient norms that operate in a group of which you are a member. This should be a non-university group.

Norm A

Norm B

Norm C

Step 2   For each of the three norms, respond to the three sets of questions below:

(a) How was this group norm communicated to newcomers to the group including yourself?

(b) What happens to people who violate this norm? How does the group 'police' itself? How does any individual feel who 'goes against' this group norm?

(c) Is this norm still relevant to the group? What purpose does it serve for the group members?

Bring your notes to class, and be ready to discuss them with your fellow students in syndicates.

Step 3   In the class, in your syndicates, compare and discuss the answers to the four questions about the operation of norms of groups of which you are a member *outside* of the university.

Step 4   The focus now switches to the *class group* itself. Within the same syndicate groups, identify three student behaviours which may provide the basis of class or group norms. Your instructor will provide you with some examples if you get stuck. A norm is usually based on an actual behaviour experienced by the class or the group about which they have feelings. For each behaviour, insert below the norm that operates.

Example:

Behaviour: absence from class
Associated norm: ask fellow student to apologise to instructor for your absence

Behaviour 1

Norm:

Behaviour 2:

Norm:

Behaviour 3:

Norm:

Step 5 After you and your group have identified three behaviours and their associated norms:

(a) Agree a rank order of importance for these norms to the group. Insert the ranking in the spaces on the right of each norm.
(b) Discuss how you would feel if you broke the norms? Would different group members have the same feelings?
(c) Discuss how this group might react if one of its members behaved in a way that broke these norms. What would the others do?

Note

This activity is based on and was influenced by a similar one by Peter B. Smith, entitled 'Norms and roles in the small group' in Breakwell, G.M., Foot, H. and Gilmour, R. (eds) (1982), *Social Psychology: A Practical Manual*, Macmillan, London, pp. 244–55.

9.4 REV: Essay marking

Objective

- To assess students' understanding of factual information group research contained in Chapters 2, 7, 9 and 10 of *ORBIT3*.

Introduction

This review exercise gives the student the opportunity to check their understanding of research design and research methods from Chapter 2, with their understanding of research into group behaviour described in Chapters 7, 9 and 10. Additional factual errors are included. Readers are put into the position of an instructor marking an essay, and are asked to identify the mistakes.

Procedure

Assume that the student who wrote this essay began with 25 marks. Deduct one mark for each factual error, highlight it in the space on the right hand side of the page, and write in the correction. What mark out of 25 should this essay receive?

Essay question:

What empirical evidence is there to suggest that the behaviour of individuals is influenced by the group to which they belong?

Student answer	Error

1. Through its studies, social psychology has conclusively demonstrated the effect on the individual of the group to which they belong. Early studies documented the phenomena of social facilitation, that is, the altering of individual behaviour by the presence of others. Additionally, British industrial psychologists discovered that a person's boredom level while at work doing a repetitive task was more likely to be reduced if that individual worked in a group. Earlier, Frederick Winslow Taylor, the 'father of scientific management' realised that workers had feelings and associated with others in the factory, but did not consider that this affected their work performance.

2. Most research, however, was carried out in the post-1945 period. Much of this was focused on individuals and groups in organizations. Before addressing the question, some of the key terms will be defined. The question refers to the group. Social scientists reserve the term 'social

group' to denote two or more people who regularly interact and are aware of each other, irrespective of whether they perceive themselves to be a group. Large social groups possessing these characteristics (of 12 or more people) are designated 'aggregates'. It is because, amongst other things, group members share common goals and a common communication network, that the group is able to to influence its individual members.

3. Such an informal group always meets both the work needs and the social needs of its members. Group members will comply with group demands because they want to satisfy their love and esteem needs. These were highlighted by the motivation theorist Frederick Herzberg. His hierarchy of needs theory broadly located these needs in the middle of the pyramid. Both personal experience and anecdotal accounts suggest that individual behaviour is influenced by groups in this way. However, the question asks for empirical evidence to confirm such beliefs. Since empirical evidence is obtained from properly conducted research investigations, it is to these that we turn for supporting evidence.

4. Perhaps the best known studies in the behaviour of groups at work were carried out in the 1940s by Elton Mayo, an industrial psychologist and employee of the Western Electric Company's Research Division. One of Mayo's studies was of women assembling electrical relays. In this laboratory-type research study, changes were introduced to the dependent variables; the rest and lunch breaks and work stopping times. The effects of these modifications on the independent variable – the women's output – were measured. Although these results were not conclusive, Mayo suspected that by being allowed to select co-workers, the positive internal relations between the women translated itself into improved productivity.

5. More convincing evidence of group effects on the individual were obtained by Mayo's studies of the men working in the Bank Wiring Observation Room. This research revealed that three separate informal groups existed. Each one had its own norms, and applied sanctions to enforce individual behaviour to the norm. These related to acceptable production output limits, how to dress while at work, what you were allowed to tell a supervisor about a fellow worker, and how to behave if you were an inspector.

6. The research studies of Asch are also relevant to our understanding of group influence on the individual. His

findings revealed the speed of norm formation in a group. Using the illusion of the autokinetic effect, he discovered that initially wide estimates of movement by a group of experimental subjects soon narrowed to form an acceptable group norm. In a related experiment, Sherif demonstrated how group pressure led individuals to distort their perception, judgement or action. His matching-the-length-of-lines experiment revealed that 55% of those studied succumbed to group pressure.

7.   The work of Stoner on risk-taking in groups represents yet another empirical demonstration of group influence on individual behaviour. He asked subjects to study scenarios described in a questionnaire indicating how much risk they were prepared to accept. Subjects first completed the instrument on their own, and then produced a group decision. Stoner found that groups made riskier decisions than individuals. The explanations offered included that younger group members were swayed by more experienced older ones; that in a group, individuals had the opportunity to compare and reassess their level of caution vis-a-vis others; that risk-taking was culturally accepted and esteemed behaviour; and that in a group, the responsibility for a risky course of action was diffused among several members.

8.   The studies quoted so far, those of Mayo, Asch, Sherif and Stoner represent the most often cited empirical evidence for the proposition that groups do influence individual behaviour. However, the findings of these studies have not gone unchallenged by their critics. The entire Hawthorne study results have been questioned because of their weaknesses in Mayo's research design and research methods.

9.   The research of Asch and Sherif was conducted on random individuals who were prepared to participate in the study. The real subject in each group joined what was in fact a group of the researcher's assistants. The subjects therefore did not represent real groups or teams. Similarly, Stoner's research was carried out on liberal arts students. Apart from the respondents not constituting real groups, the questionnaire required respondents to select a 1-in-10, 1-in-20 or 1-in-30 chance level. This does not represent the way people normally evaluate risk. Since the findings cannot be applied to other groups, the internal validity of this research is highly suspect.

10. Additionally, one might mention a field study carried out by Stanley Milgram. This involved a set of experiments aimed at testing the extent to which people will obey the instructions of an authority figure. One version of Milgram's experimental set-up involved two stooges refusing to continue administering the electric shocks required by the white-coated experimenter. On seeing the two refuse, all real subjects tested also refused. The design of Milgram's experiment suggested that internal variables in the test situation had been controlled, and that the stooges' refusal could be considered to be the cause of the subject's behaviour. The external validity of this study could therefore be claimed to be high.

11. In conclusion, one can say that personal experience and observation strongly suggest that groups influence individual behaviour, and this is supported by the empirical psycho-logical research. However, some of this research on which this finding is based could be improved. Specifically, more experimentation should be done with real groups in companies, where people have to live with the consequences of their decisions, and where the personal and political realities of organizations play a part.

Mark out of 25: _____

Group effectiveness

10.1 LGA: Nightingale Hospital

Objective

- This activity will consider how group effectiveness is influenced by organizational and managerial decisions.

Introduction

Research suggests that group cohesiveness has a major effect on group productivity and group member satisfaction. Actions that are taken by management, whether consciously or unconsciously, can damage cohesiveness, and result in lower productivity and a drop in morale.

Procedure

Step 1   Read the case on your own, and then:
a) Identify the possible causes of the problem.
b) Suggest possible solutions for each cause.

Step 2   Once you have done that, compare your responses with those of the person next to you.

Nightingale Hospital

The domestic service arrangements in a large hospital had, for many years, been based on the permanent allocation of domestic staff to specific wards. When staff shortages occurred (due to sickness or leave), these were made up from a reserve pool of staff, or by overtime working. Permanent allocation to a ward thus carried status among the domestic staff. New entrants to the hospital's domestic department would begin as 'reliefs', and would then be 'promoted' to a permanent ward position on completion of a satisfactory probationary period. Domestic supervisors also operated an unofficial sanction system whereby staff off sick frequently, or for long periods of time, were penalised for their absences by being 'demoted' to the reserve pool, only returning to the permanent ward position when their record of attendance proved to be satisfactory.

The domestic staff had a permanent placement within a particular ward or two adjacent wards. Over time, the staff working on the same ward got to know each other well. They had their tea and lunch breaks together, during which time they discussed the patients on 'their' ward. Working in the same wards, these domestic staff also got to know the regular nursing personnel who had been assigned to their ward.

Getting the work done was achieved by group effort. Each domestic was expected to warn the others of the impending approach of a supervisor. Group members were required to support each other in the event of any 'harassment' by management. Bragging about the happenings on their ward was expected and acceptable. Different ward teams tried to outdo each other in terms of the dramas they had seen on their wards.

Shortly after the hospital had achieved Trust status, the hospital management called in Organization and Methods (O & M) consultants to review the working practices of these domestic staff. The consultants conducted numerous time and motion studies, and noted all the results. They recommended that efficiency could be increased, and overtime reduced, by changing work patterns, and the type of equipment used. Following these recommendations, the hospital management purchased the new equipment. Meanwhile, the changes in work patterns resulted in the dissolution of the reserve pool, and the allocation of staff to ward areas on a rotational basis. Each morning, domestic staff were allocated to different ward areas, to work alongside other staff. This was intended to increase flexibility in the transfer of staff on an ad hoc basis to any areas of shortage. These two changes resulted in the replacement of the old labour intensive system which depended on staff co-operation and co-ordination.

Much to the surprise of management, problems began to arise as soon as the revised system was put into operation. The levels of sickness and absenteeism amongst the domestic staff rose, their productivity and efficiency fell, and problems of liaison between domestic and nursing staff increased at ward level. Generally, a deterioration in working relationships between all concerned was observed.

Source: This case is based on research reported in Huczynski, A.A. and Fitzpatrick, M.J., *Managing Employee Absence for a Competitive Edge*, Pitman, 1989.

10.2 SGA: Supersew Ltd

Objectives

- To apply research and theoretical findings to a given work problem.
- To make recommendations for managerial actions which are supported by data.
- To use your understanding of organizational behaviour, to highlight gaps in knowledge.

Introduction

Knowing a theory is one thing, being able to apply it to a concrete situation is quite another. This case study gives students an opportunity to apply what they have learned on the course so far to a real management problem. However, difficulties of this nature do not come neatly parcelled and wrapped up. It is important to be able to use one's knowledge to identify what you don't know (but need to find out). This case also provides students with the opportunity to do this.

Procedure

Step 1   Divide into groups of 5–6 students, and select a leader.

Step 2   All groups are to put themselves in Trevor's shoes, and solve the problem described in the case. You are to do two things:

(a) Limiting yourself to the facts presented in the case, agree on three recommendations that you feel will solve the problem.

The recommendations should be in the form of specific actions for Trevor to take. Each recommended action should be supported by theoretical or empirical research evidence.

(b) Move beyond the facts given, and identify what additional information Trevor might obtain in order to implement an even more effective solution. Suggest how this information might be obtained.

Case

For the past six months Trevor has been the supervisor of a sewing room of 25 women in a garment factory which produces underwear and T-shirts. The firm's output is bought by two large chains of retail stores. The share of their orders that they place with Supersew depends largely upon the company's past record for high quality and punctual delivery. For this reason, output to target and a low reject rate are crucial.

The manufacture of T-shirts involves eleven operations. Predominantly, these involve cutting the material to shape, and then sewing the bits together. The material is cut by hand with scissors, whilst the sewing is done on electrically powered machines. Resembling domestic ones, these machines are more heavy-duty types which are built for long life, and can remain in service for a dozen years or even more. The old machines operate satisfactorily, but tend to become unreliable with age.

Sewing room layout

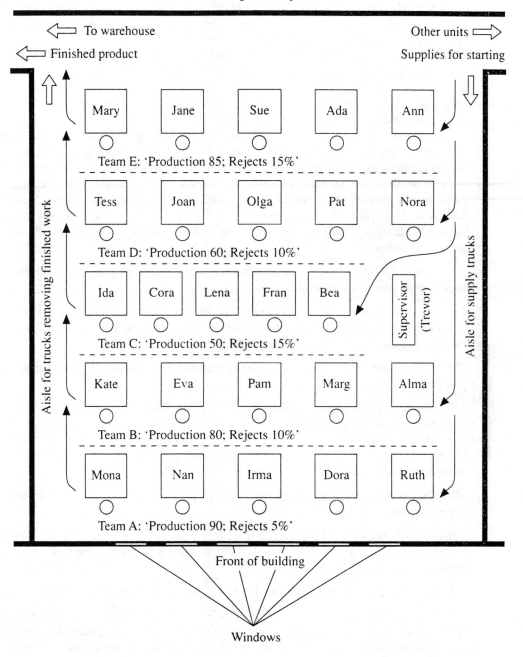

Front of building

Windows

The women doing the cutting and sewing are all union members. They are organized as five teams (A, B, C, D and E) of five workers (see sewing room layout). For the simpler operations, there is little loss of production when operators move from one type of garment to another. However, it takes about three months for a machinist doing one of the more complicated operations such as lockstitching, to achieve the performance standard assigned for the garment that she is working on.

Some of the women, Mary, Jane, Sue, Ada and Ann, had been working together at Shirtail Ltd before it closed down, and was taken over by Supersew. The managing director of Supersew, Mr Henderson, was keen to expand production facilities, and acted quickly to take advantage of the available skilled labour. The girls agreed to be recruited after being given an assurance that they could continue to work together.

Until recently, Trevor's problem had been getting out enough production. Three months ago, however, payment for all sewing machine operations was changed from an hourly-rate to a team piece-rate, and production output became fairly satisfactory. Quality now became the main problem. Not that there were too many rejects, but serious complaints had begun to come in from both the salesmen in the field, and from the chain store buyers. Since the women were not paid for rejected items, it was difficult to understand why they were not being more careful. Trevor has been called in by his department foreman, Mr Preston to discuss the matter.

MR P: Trevor, I want to talk to you again about the kind of work your unit is turning out. What's the matter down there anyway?

Trevor: Heaven knows! On the old hourly rate the girls weren't turning out anything, and now, on this new group piece-rate, a lot of the work that they do isn't any good. When I make them do it again, they say I'm picking on them.

MR P: Sylvia and Eddie aren't having the trouble with their girls that you are having with yours.

TREVOR: Well, I'm not having trouble with all of mine. There is just this small group of five or six who are the real problem. They all want to be finishers or anything but what they are. I've moved them near to my desk where I can keep an eye on them, and I've told them that I won't move them until they've improved their work. Even so, I'd like to see Sylvia or Ed or anybody else get any work out of them.

MR P: You're not trying to tell me that just a few girls out of more than two dozen make your department look that bad.

TREVOR: No, but they are the worst ones. I called all the girls in the 'C' and 'D' teams together last week and gave them a good talking to about how much worse they've become. Production and quality are both down.

MR P: I'm beginning to think that you don't have any workers that are any good.

TREVOR: No, that's not true. I'll take the girls in my 'A' team and put 'em up against any we've got in the factory. As a matter of fact, all of my finishers are a pretty decent bunch. The 'B' team has a couple of good workers in it, and there is nothing wrong with the 'E' team.

MR P: Yeah, but their rejects are too high.

TREVOR: Well, that might be true, but those girls certainly produce. Maybe if I can get them to slow down a bit, their quality may rise. It's going to annoy them, though.

MR P: That's your problem. You're not afraid of them, are you?

TREVOR: No, but they didn't even like it the other day when I bawled them out for talking on the job. Come to think of it, all that chattering may be the reason they don't pay any attention to quality.

MR P: Well, tell them that if they don't stop talking, you'll break up their little club. You're the boss down there, aren't you ?

TREVOR: Well, you've kind of got me there. Under Mr Henderson's instructions, I hired everybody in Team 'E' in one batch with the understanding that they could be together, and I hate to go back on my word.

MR P: Well, give them a good lecture and threaten to do it.

TREVOR: I know, but it's a headache. Those girls stick together and you can't locate the trouble maker. Even when they don't get on with one another, they still gang up on you. For example, I gave these girls in team 'C' a safety lecture the other day after one of them got her hands caught in the machine, and all they did was gripe and pick on me about everything under the sun. I never saw such a bunch of sour hens before in my life.

MR P: What's bugging them anyway? There must be something if they picked on you?

TREVOR: Oh, it was just the same old moaning about all of them wanting to be finishers. After they've been on the job a few weeks, they think they know everything.

MR P: Sounds like you've been giving some of those new girls a lot of half-baked ideas about the jobs around here. What's so special about being a finisher anyway? The pay is the same.

TREVOR: I don't know. I think its just a silly idea that they've got into their heads. You and I know the end job's no easier.

MR P: Was that all they moaned about, or do they want us to install a staff swimming-pool?

TREVOR: No, quite a few of them are annoyed because they said they couldn't make the standard. Most of the girls think it is too hard to hit anyway.

MR P: I haven't heard complaints from any other departments about it. After all, 80 isn't so high. Why should your girls complain when none of the rest of them do?

TREVOR: All I know is that they do. Except for Team 'A' and a few others who really turn the stuff out, they're just about the worst bunch of operators I've ever seen. I don't know why I have to have all of them in my department.

MR P: Trevor, we've been over all this before and I'm tired of listening to you feel sorry for yourself. Either get those girls on the ball, or we'll have to put somebody else down there who knows how to run things. I don't want to be tough about it, but that's the way it is. I'll give you thirty days to get this mess straightened out, and I'll back you up on anything that seems reasonable. If you can show me some results by the end of that time you can stay; if you don't, we'll have to find someone to replace you. Is that clear?

TREVOR: I suppose so. But after racking my brains for the past six months I don't know what you or I or anybody else can do with those girls. I've tried everything.

10.3 PREP: The Destructors

Objective

- To apply the concepts of group formation, structure, control and effectiveness to a fictional case study.

Introduction

Some novels can tell us a great deal about individuals and groups. This short story by Graham Greene is set in the post-war London of the 1950s. As a fictional account, it provides great scope for the consideration of group behaviour in general, and that of George Homans' theory in particular. Homans is important because he offers us an explanation of how a group forms and internally structures itself.

Procedure

Step 1   Before the session, read the short story in your own time. Then, referring to the *ORBIT3* chapters indicated, write short answers in response to the questions. Each answer should be one or two paragraphs in length.

1. Why does the Wormsley Common Gang constitute a psychological group? (Chapter 7).

2. Using Homans' theory, describe the formation of the gang, specifying the factors which compromise the 'external' or formal system. Specifically, the group's (a) physical environment; (b) cultural environment; (c) technological environment. How were the sentiments of the group members strengthened? (Chapter 7)

3. Using Tuckman and Jensen's model, describe the stages of the gang's development from the point when T joins them and the original gang has to reform. Use the headings: (a) storming; (b) forming; (c) norming; (d) performing. (Chapter 7)

4. What is group structure? Analyze the gang's structure on the following dimensions: (a) status; (b) power; (c) liking; (d) role. (Chapter 8)

5. What is group process? Identify the gang's (a) mode of decision-making; (b) T's leadership style; (c) communication structure. (Chapter 8)

6. How does the gang control the behaviour of its members? List specifically the norms and sanctions used by the gang. (Chapter 9)

7. What personal (psychological benefits) does each group member gain by adhering to the gang's norms? (Chapter 9)

8. Suggest how a gang of twelve, highly-spirited youngsters come to agree unanimously to carry out an action which breaks both criminal and moral laws. (Chapter 9)

9. Assess the gang's effectiveness and its members' satisfaction. (Chapter 10)

The Destructors

I

(1)   It was on the eve of the August Bank Holiday that the latest recruit became the leader of the Wormsley Common Gang. No one was surprised except Mike, but Mike at the age of nine was surprised by everything. 'If you don't shut your mouth,' somebody once said to him, 'you'll get a frog down it.' After that Mike kept his teeth tightly clamped except when the surprise was too great.

(2)   The new recruit had been with the gang since the beginning of the summer holiday, and there were possibilities about his brooding silence that all recognized. He never wasted a word even to tell his name until that was required of him by the rules. When he said 'Trevor' it was a statement of fact, not as it would have been with the others a statement of shame or defiance. Nor did anyone laugh except Mike, who finding himself without support and meeting the dark gaze of the newcomer, opened his mouth and was quiet again. There was every reason why T, as he was afterwards referred to, should have been an object of mockery – there was his name (and they substituted the initial because otherwise they had no excuse not to laugh at it), the fact that his father, a former architect and present clerk, had 'come down in the world' and that his mother considered herself better than the neighbours. What but an odd quality of danger, of the unpredictable, established him in the gang without any ignoble ceremony of initiation?

(3)   The gang met every morning in an impromptu carpark, the site of the last bomb of the first blitz. The leader, who was known as Blackie, claimed to have heard it fall, and no one was precise enough in his dates to point out that he would have been one year old and fast asleep on the down platform of Wormsley Common Underground Station. On one side of the car-park leant the first unoccupied house, No. 3, of the shattered Northwood Terrace – literally leant, for it had suffered from the blast of the bomb and the side walls were supported on wooden struts. A smaller bomb and incendiaries had fallen beyond, so that the house stuck up like a jagged tooth and carried on the further wall relics of its neighbour, a dado, the remains of a fireplace. T, whose words were almost confined to voting 'Yes' or 'No' to the plan of operations proposed each day by Blackie, once startled the whole gang by saying broodingly, 'Wren built that house, father says.'

'Who's Wren?'

'The man who built St. Paul's.'

'Who cares?' Blackie said. 'It's only Old Misery's.'

(4)   Old Misery – whose real name was Thomas – had once been a builder and decorator. He lived alone in the crippled house, doing for himself: once a week you could see him coming back across the common with bread and vegetables, and once as the boys played in the carpark he put his head over the smashed wall of his garden and looked at them.

(5)   'Been to the lav,' one of the boys said, for it was common knowledge that since the bombs fell something had gone wrong with the pipes of the house and Old Misery was too mean to spend the money on the property. He could do the redecorating himself at cost price, but he had never learnt plumbing. The lav was a wooden shed at the bottom

of the narrow garden with a star-shaped hole in the door: it had escaped the blast which had smashed the house next door and sucked out the window-frames at No. 3.

(6)   The next time the gang became aware of Mr Thomas was more surprising. Blackie, Mike and a thin yellow boy, who for some reason was called by his surname Summers, met him on the common coming back from the market. Mr Thomas stopped them. He said glumly, 'You belong to the lot that play in the carpark?'

Mike was about to answer when Blackie stopped him. As the leader he had responsibilities. 'Suppose we are?' he said ambiguously.

'I got some chocolates,' Mr Thomas said. 'Don't like 'em myself. Here you are. Not enough to go round. I don't suppose. There never is,' he added with sombre conviction. He handed over three packets of Smarties.

The gang was puzzled and perturbed by this action and tried to explain it away. 'Bet someone dropped them and he picked 'em up,' somebody suggested.

'Pinched 'em and then got a bleeding funk,' another thought aloud.

'It's a bribe,' Summers said. 'He wants us to stop bouncing balls on his wall.'

'We'll show him we don't take bribes,' Blackie said, and they sacrificed the whole morning to the game of bouncing that only Mike was young enough to enjoy. There was no sign from Mr Thomas.

(7)   Next day T astonished them all. He was late at the rendezvous, and the voting for that day's exploit took place without him. At Blackie's suggestion the gang was to disperse in pairs, take buses at random and see how many free rides could be snatched from unwary conductors (the operation was to be carried out in pairs to avoid cheating). They were drawing lots for their companions when T. arrived.

'Where you been, T?' Blackie asked. 'You can't vote now. You know the rules.'

'I've been *there*,' T said. He looked at the ground, as though he had thoughts to hide.

'Where?'

'At Old Misery's.' Mike's mouth opened and then hurriedly closed again with a click. He had remembered the frog.

'At Old Misery's?' Blackie said. There was nothing in the rules against it, but he had a sensation that T was treading on dangerous ground. He asked hopefully, 'Did you break in?'

'No. I rang the bell.'

'And what did you say?'

'I said I wanted to see the house.'

'What did he do?'

'He showed it me.'

'Pinch anything?'

'No.'

'What did you go for then?'

The gang had gathered round: it was as though an impromptu court was about to form and try some case of deviation. T said, 'It's a beautiful house,' and still watching the ground, meeting no one's eyes, he licked his lips first one way, then the other.

'What do you mean, a beautiful house?' Blackie asked with scorn.

'It's got a staircase two hundred years old like a corkscrew. Nothing holds it up.'

'What do you mean nothing holds it up. Does it float?'

'It's to do with opposite forces, Old Misery said.'

'What else?'

'There's panelling.'

'Like in the Blue Boar?'

'Two hundred years old.'

'Is Old Misery two hundred years old?'

(8) Mike laughed suddenly and then went quiet again. The meeting was in a serious mood. For the first time since T had strolled into the carpark on the first day of the holidays his position was in danger. It only needed the use of his real name and the gang would be at his heels.

'What did you do it for?' Blackie asked. He was just, he had no jealousy, he was anxious to retain T in the gang if he could. It was the word beautiful that worried him – that belonged to a class world that you could still see parodied at the Wormsley Common Empire by a man wearing a top hat and monocle, with a haw-haw accent. He was tempted to say, 'My dear Trevor, old chap,' and unleash his hell hounds. 'If you'd broken in,' he said sadly – that indeed would have been an exploit worthy of the gang.

'This was better,' T said, 'I found out things.' He continued to stare at his feet, not meeting anybody's eye, as though he were absorbed in some dream he was unwilling – or ashamed – to share.

'What things?'

'Old Misery's going to be away all tomorrow and Bank Holiday.'

Blackie said with relief, 'You mean we could break in?'

'And pinch things?' somebody asked.

Blackie said, 'Nobody's going to pinch things. Breaking in – that's good enough, isn't it? We don't want any court stuff.'

'I don't want to pinch anything,' T said. 'I've got a better idea.'

'What is it?'

T raised his eyes, as grey and disturbed as the drab August day. 'We'll pull it down,' he said. 'We'll destroy it.'

(9) Blackie gave a single hoot of laughter and then, like Mike, fell quiet, daunted by the

serious implacable gaze. 'What'd the police be doing all the time?' he said.

'They'd never know. We'd do it from inside. I've found a way in. He said with a sort of intensity, 'We'd be like worms, don't you see, in an apple. When we came out again there'd be nothing there, no staircase, no panels, nothing just walls, and then we'd make the walls fall down – somehow.'

'We'd go to jug,' Blackie said.

'Whose to prove?' and anyway we wouldn't have pinched anything.' He added without the smallest flicker of glee, 'There wouldn't be anything left to pinch after we'd finished.'

'I've never heard of going to prison for breaking things,' Summers said.

'There wouldn't be time,' Blackie said. 'I've seen housebreakers at work.'

'There are twelve of us,' T said. 'We'd organize.'

'None of us know how ...'

'I know.' T said. He looked across at Blackie. 'Have you got a better plan?'

'Today,' Mike said tactlessly, 'we're pinching free rides ...'

'Free rides.' T said. 'Kid stuff. You can stand down, Blackie, if you'd rather ...'

'The gang's got to vote.'

'Put it up then.'

Blackie said uneasily. 'It's proposed that tomorrow and Monday we destroy Old Misery's house.'

'Here, here,' said a fat boy called Joe.

'Who's in favour?'

T said, 'It's carried.'

'How do we start?' Summers asked.

(10)   'He'll tell you,' Blackie said. It was the end of his leadership. He went away to the back of the carpark and began to kick a stone, dribbling it this way and that. There was only one old Morris in the park, for few cars were left there except lorries: without an attendant there was no safety. He took a flying kick at the car and scraped a little paint off the near mudguard. Beyond, paying no more attention to him than to a stranger, the gang gathered around T; Blackie was dimly aware of the fickleness of favour. He thought of going home, of never returning, of letting them all discover the hollowness of T's leadership, but suppose after all what T proposed was possible – nothing like it had ever been done before. The fame of the Wormsley Common carpark gang would surely reach around London. There would be headlines in the papers. Even the gangs that ran the betting at the all-in wrestling and the barrow boys would hear with respect of how old Misery's house had been destroyed. Driven by the pure, simple and altruistic ambition for fame for the gang, Blackie came back to where T stood in the shadow of Old Misery's wall.

(11)   T was giving his orders with decision: it was as though his plan had been with him all his life, pondered through the seasons, now in his fifteenth year crystallized with the pain of puberty. 'You,' he said to Mike, 'bring some big nails, the biggest you can find, and a hammer. Anybody who can, better bring a hammer and a screwdriver. We'll need plenty of them. Chisels too. We can't have too many chisels. Can anybody bring a saw?'

'I can,' Mike said.

'Not a child's saw,' T said. 'A real saw.'

Blackie realized he had raised his hand like any ordinary member of the gang.

'Right, you bring one, Blackie. But now there's difficulty. We want a hacksaw.'

'You can get 'em at Woolworth's,' Summers said.

The fat boy called Joe said gloomily, 'I knew it would end in a collection.'

'I'll get one myself,' said T. I don't want your money. But I can't buy a sledge-hammer.'

Blackie said, 'They are working on No. 15. I know where they'll leave their stuff for Bank Holiday.'

'Then that's all,' T said. 'We meet here at nine sharp.'

'I've got to go to church,' Mike said.

'Come over the wall and whistle. We'll let you in.'

II

(12)   On Sunday morning all were punctual except Blackie, even Mike. Mike had a stroke of luck. His mother fell ill, his father was tired after Saturday night, and he was told to go to church alone with many warnings of what would happen if he strayed. Blackie had difficulty in smuggling out the saw, and then in finding the sledge-hammer at the back of No. 15. He approached the house from a lane at the rear of the garden, for fear of a policeman's beat along the main road. The tired evergreens kept off a stormy sun: another wet Bank Holiday was being prepared over the Atlantic, beginning in swirls of dust under the trees. Blackie climbed into Misery's garden.

There was no sign of anybody anywhere. The lav stood like a tomb in a neglected graveyard. The curtains were drawn. The house slept. Blackie lumbered nearer with the saw and the sledge-hammer. Perhaps after all nobody had turned up: the plan had been a wild invention: they had woken wiser. But when he came close to the back door he could hear a confusion of sound hardly louder than a hive in swarm: a clickety-clack, a bang bang, a scraping, a creaking, a sudden painful crack. He thought: it's true, and whistled.

(13)   They opened the back door to him and he came in. He had at once the impression of organization, very different from the happy-go-lucky ways under his leadership. For a while, he wandered up and down the stairs looking for T. Nobody addressed him: he had a sense of great urgency, and already he could begin to see the plan. The interior of the house was being carefully demolished without touching the walls. Summers,

with hammer and chisel, was ripping out the skirting boards in the ground floor dining room: he had already smashed the panels of the door. In the same room Joe was heaving up the parquet blocks, exposing the soft wood floorboards over the cellar. Coils of wire came out of the damaged skirting and Mike sat happily clipping the wires.

(14) On the curved stairs two of the gang were working hard with an inadequate child's saw on the bannisters – when they saw Blackie's big saw they signalled for it wordlessly. When he next saw them a quarter of the banisters had been dropped into the hall. He found T at last in the bathroom – he sat moodily in the least cared for room in the house, listening to the sounds coming up from below.

'You've really done it,' Blackie said with awe. 'What's going to happen?'

'We've only just begun,' T said. He looked at the sledge-hammer and gave his instructions. 'You stay here and break the bath and the wash-basin. Don't bother about the pipes. They come later.'

Mike appeared at the door. 'I've finished the wires, T,' he said.

'Good. You've just got to go wandering around now. The kitchen's in the basement. Smash all the china and glass and bottles you can lay hold of. Don't turn on the taps – we don't want a flood – yet. Then go into all the rooms and turn out the drawers. If they are locked get one of the others to break them open. Tear up any papers you find and smash all the ornaments. Better take a carving knife with you from the kitchen. The bedroom's opposite here. Open the pillows and tear up the sheets. That's enough for the moment. And you Blackie, when you've finished in here crack the plaster in the passage up with your sledge-hammer.'

'What are you going to do?' Blackie asked.

'I'm looking for something special,' T said.

(15) It was nearly lunch-time before Blackie had finished and went in search of T. Chaos had advanced. The kitchen was a shambles of broken glass and china. The dining room was stripped of parquet, the skirting was up, the door had been taken off its hinges, and the destroyers had moved up a floor. Streaks of light came in through the closed shutters where they worked with the seriousness of creators – and destruction after all is a form of creation. A kind of imagination had seen this house as it had now become.

Mike said, 'I've got to go home for dinner.'

'Who else?' T asked, but all the others on one excuse or another had brought provisions with them.

They squatted in the ruins of the room and swapped unwanted sandwiches. Half an hour for lunch and were at work again. By the time Mike returned they were on the top floor, and by six the superficial damage was completed. The doors were all off, all the skirtings raised, the furniture pillaged and ripped and smashed – no one could have slept in the house except on a bed of broken plaster. T gave his orders – eight o'clock next morning, and to escape notice they climbed singly over the garden wall, into the car park. Only Blackie and T were left: the light had nearly gone, and when they touched a switch, nothing worked – Mike had done his job thoroughly.

(16) 'Did you find anything special?' Blackie asked.

T nodded. 'Come over here,' he said, 'and look.' Out of both pockets he drew bundles of pound notes. 'Old Misery's savings,' he said. 'Mike ripped out the mattress, but he missed them.'

'What are you going to do? Share them?'

'We aren't thieves,' T said. 'Nobody's going to steal anything from this house. I kept these for you and me – a celebration.' He knelt down on the floor and counted them out – there were seventy in all. 'We'll burn them,' he said, 'one by one,' and taking it in turns they held a note upwards and lit the top corner, so that the flame burnt slowly towards their fingers. The grey ash floated above them and fell on their heads like age. 'I'd like to see Old Misery's face when we're through,' T said.

'You hate him a lot?' Blackie asked.

'Of course I don't hate him,' T said. 'There'd be no fun if I hated him.' The last burning note illuminated his brooding face. 'All this hate and love,' he said, 'it's soft, it's hooey. There's only things, Blackie,' and he looked round the room crowded with the unfamiliar shadows of half things, broken things, former things. 'I'll race you home, Blackie,' he said.

III

(17) Next morning the serious destruction started. Two were missing – Mike and another boy whose parents were off to Southend and Brighton in spite of the slow warm drops that had begun to fall and the rumble of thunder in the estuary like the first guns of the old blitz. 'We've got to hurry,' T said.

Summers was restive. 'Haven't we done enough?' he asked. 'I've been given a bob for slot machines. This is like work.'

'We've hardly started,' T said. 'Why, there's all the floors left, and the stairs. We haven't taken out a single window. You voted like the others. We are going to destroy this house. There won't be anything left when we've finished.'

(18) They began again on the first floor picking up the floor boards next to the outer wall, leaving the joists exposed. Then they sawed through the joists and retreated into the hall, as what was left of the floor heeled and sank. They had learnt with practice, and the second floor collapsed more easily. By the evening an odd exhilaration seized them as they looked down the great hollow of the house. They ran risks and made mistakes: when they thought of the windows it was too late to reach them. 'Cor,' Joe said, and dropped a penny down into the dry bubble-filled well. It cracked and spun among the broken glass.

(19) T was already on the ground, digging at the rubble, clearing a space along the outer wall. 'Turn on the taps,' he said. 'It's too dark for anyone to see now, and in the morning it won't matter.' The water overtook them on the stairs and fell through the floorless rooms.

It was then that they heard Mike's whistle at the back. 'Something's wrong,' Blackie said. They could hear his urgent breathing as they unlocked the door.

'The bogies?' Summers asked.

'Old Misery,' Mike said. 'He's on his way,' he said with pride.

'But why?' T said, 'He told me ... ' He protested with the fury of a child he had never been, 'It isn't fair.'

'He was down at Southend,' Mike said, 'and he was on the train coming back. He said it was too cold and wet.' He paused and gazed at the water. 'My, you've had a storm here. Is the roof leaking?'

'How long will he be?'

'Five minutes, I gave Ma the slip and ran.'

'We better clear,' Summers said. 'We've done enough, anyway.'

'Oh no we haven't. Anybody could do this – 'this' was the shattered hollow house with nothing left but the walls. Yet walls could be preserved. Facades were valuable. They could build inside again more beautifully than before. This could again be a home. He said angrily. 'We've got to finish. Don't move. Let me think.'

'There's got to be a way,' T said. 'We couldn't have got this far ...'

'We've done a lot,' Blackie said.

'No, no, we haven't. Somebody watch the front.'

'We can't do any more.'

'He may come in at the back.'

'Watch the back too.' T began to plead. 'Just give me a minute and I'll fix it. I swear I'll fix it.' But his authority had gone with his ambiguity. He was only one of the gang. 'Please,' he said.

'Please,' Summers mimicked him, and then suddenly struck home with the fatal name, 'Run along home, Trevor.'

T stood with his back to the rubble like a boxer knocked groggy against the ropes. He had no words as his dreams shook and slid. Then Blackie acted before the gang had time to laugh, pushing Summers backward. 'I'll watch the front, T,' he said, 'and cautiously he opened the shutters of the hall. The grey wet common stretched ahead, and the lamps gleamed in the puddles. ' Someone's coming, T No, it's not him. What's your plan, T?'

'Tell Mike to go out to the lav and hide close beside it. When he hears me whistle he's got to count ten and start to shout.'

'Shout what?'

Oh, 'Help', anything.'

'You hear, Mike,' Blackie said. He was the leader again. He took a quick look between the shutters, 'He's coming, T. '

'Quick, Mike. The lav. Stay here, Blackie, all of you, till I yell.'

'Where are you going, T?'

'Don't worry. I'll see to this. I said I would, didn't I?'

(20) Old Misery came limping off the common. He had mud on his shoes and he stopped to scrape them on the pavement's edge. He didn't want to spoil his house, which stood jagged and dark between the bomb-sites, saved so narrowly, as he believed, from destruction. Even the fanlight had been left unbroken by the bomb's blast. Somewhere somebody whistled. Old Misery looked sharply round. He didn't trust whistles. A child was shouting: it seemed to come from his own garden. Then a boy ran into the road from the carpark. 'Mr Thomas,' he called, 'Mr Thomas.'

'What is it?'

'I'm terribly sorry, Mr Thomas. One of us got taken short, and we thought you wouldn't mind, and now he can't get out.'

'What do you mean, boy?'

'He's got stuck in your lav.'

'He'd no business ... Haven't I seen you before?'

'You showed me your house.'

'So I did. So I did. That doesn't give you the right to ...'

Do hurry Mr Thomas. He'll suffocate.'

'Nonsense. He can't suffocate. Wait till I put my bag in.'

'I'll carry your bag.'

'Oh no you don't. I'll carry my own.'

'This way, Mr Thomas.'

'I can't get in the garden that way. I've got to go through the house.'

'But you *can* get in the garden this way, Mr Thomas. We often do.'

'You often do?' He followed the boy with a scandalized fascination. 'When? What right ...?'

'Do you see? ... the wall's low.'

'I'm not going to climb walls into my own garden. It's absurd.'

'This is how we do it. One foot here, one foot there, and over.' The boy's face peered down, an arm shot out, and Mr Thomas found his bag taken and deposited on the other side of the wall.

'Give me back my bag,' Mr Thomas said. From the loo a boy yelled and yelled. 'I'll call the police.'

'Your bag's all right, Mr Thomas. Look. One foot there. On your right. Now just above. To your left.' Mr Thomas climbed over his own garden wall. 'Here's your bag, Mr Thomas.'

'I'll have the wall built up,' Mr Thomas said. 'I'll not have you boys coming over here, using my loo.' He stumbled on the path, but the boy caught his elbow and supported him. 'Thank you, thank you, my boy,' he murmured automatically. Somebody shouted out again through the dark. 'I'm coming, I'm coming,' Mr Thomas called. He said to the boy beside him, 'I'm not unreasonable. Been a boy myself. As long as things are done regular. I don't mind you playing round the place Saturday mornings. Sometimes I like company. Only it's got to be regular. One of you asks leave and I say Yes. Sometimes I'll say No. Won't feel like it. And you come in at the front door and out at the back. No garden walls.'

'Do get him out, Mr Thomas.'

'He won't come to any harm in my loo,' Mr Thomas said, stumbling slowly down the garden. 'Oh my rheumatics,' he said. 'Always get 'em on Bank Holiday. I've got to be careful. There's loose stones here. Give me your hand. Do you know what my horoscope said yesterday? "Abstain from any dealings in first half of week. Danger of serious crash". That might be on the path.' Mr Thomas said. 'They speak in parables and double meanings.' He paused at the door of the loo. 'What's the matter in there?' he called. There was no reply.

'Perhaps he's fainted,' the boy said.

(21) 'Not in my loo. Here, you come out.' Mr Thomas said, and giving a great jerk at the door he nearly fell on his back when it swung open easily. A hand first supported him and then pushed him hard. His head hit the opposite wall and he sat down heavily. His bag hit his feet. A hand whipped the key out of the lock and the door slammed. 'Let me out,' he called, and heard the key turn in the lock. "A serious crash" he thought, and felt dithered and confused and old.

A voice spoke to him softly through the star-shaped hole in the door. 'Don't worry Mr Thomas, we won't hurt you, not if you stay quiet.'

(22) Mr Thomas put his head in his hands and pondered. He had noticed that there was only one lorry in the carpark, and he felt certain that the driver would not come for it before the morning. Nobody could hear him from the road in front, and the lane at the back was seldom used. Anyone who passed there would be hurrying home and would not pause for what they would certainly take to be drunken cries. And if he did call 'Help', who, on a lonely Bank Holiday evening, would have the courage to investigate? Mr Thomas sat on the loo and pondered with the wisdom of age.

(23) After a while there seemed to him to be sounds in the silence – they were faint and came from the direction of his house. As he stood and peered through the ventilation hole – between the cracks in one of the shutters he saw a light, not the light of a lamp, but the wavering light that a candle might give. Then he thought he heard the sound of hammering and scraping and chipping. He thought of burglars – perhaps they had employed the boy as a scout, but why should burglars engage in what sounded more and more like a stealthy form of carpentry? Mr Thomas let out an experimental yell, but nobody answered. The noise could not even have reached his enemies.

IV

(24) Mike had gone home to bed but the rest stayed. The question of leadership no longer

concerned the gang. With nails, chisels, screwdrivers, anything that was sharp and penetrating, they moved around the inner walls of the house worrying at the mortar between the bricks. They started too high and it was Blackie who hit on the damp course and realised the work could be halved if they weakened the joints immediately above. It was a long, tiring, unamusing job, but at last it was finished. The gutted house stood there balanced on a few inches of mortar between the damp course and the bricks.

(25) There remained the most dangerous task of all, out in the open at the edge of the bombsite. Summers was sent to watch the road for passers-by, and Mr Thomas, sitting on the loo, heard clearly now the sound of sawing. It no longer came from the house, and that a little reassured him. He felt less concerned. Perhaps the other noises had no significance.

A voice spoke to him through the hole. 'Mr Thomas.'

'Let me out,' Mr Thomas said sternly.

'Here's a blanket,' the voice said, and a long grey sausage was worked through the hole and fell in swathes over Mr Thomas's head.

'There's nothing personal,' the voice said. 'We want you to be comfortable tonight.'

'Tonight.' Mr Thomas repeated incredulously.

'Catch,' the voice said, 'Penny buns – we've buttered them, and sausage rolls. We don't want you to starve, Mr Thomas.'

Mr Thomas pleaded desperately. 'A joke's a joke, boy. Let me out and I won't say a thing. I've got rheumatics. I've got to sleep comfortable.'

'You wouldn't be comfortable, not in your house, you wouldn't. Not now.'

'What do you mean, boy?' But the footsteps receded. There was only the silence of night: no sound of sawing. Mr Thomas tried one more yell, but he was daunted and rebuked by the silence – a long way off an owl hooted and made away again on its muffled flight through the soundless world.

(26) At seven the next morning, the driver came to fetch his lorry. He climbed into the seat and tried to start the engine. He was vaguely aware of a voice shouting, but it didn't concern him. At last the engine responded and he backed the lorry until it touched the great wooden shore that supported Mr Thomas's house. That way he could drive right out and down the street without reversing. The lorry moved forward, was momentarily checked as though something were pulling from behind, and then went on to the sound of a long rumbling crash. The driver was astonished to see bricks bouncing ahead of him, while stones hit the roof of his cab. He put on his brakes. When he climbed out the whole landscape had suddenly altered. There was no house beside the carpark, only a hill of rubble. He went round and examined the back of the lorry for damage, and found a rope tied there that was still twisted at the other end round a part of a wooden strut.

The driver again became aware of somebody shouting. It came from the wooden erection which was the nearest thing to a house in that desolation of broken brick. The driver climbed the smashed wall and unlocked the door. Mr Thomas came out of the loo. He was wearing a grey blanket to which flakes of pastry adhered. He gave a sobbing cry. 'My house,' he said. 'Where's my house?'

'Search me,' the driver said. His eye lit on the remains of a bath and what had once been a dresser and he began to laugh. There wasn't anything left anywhere.

'How dare you laugh,' Mr Thomas said. 'It was my house. Mỳ house.'

'I'm sorry,' the driver said making heroic efforts, but when he remembered the sudden check of the lorry, the crash of falling bricks, he became convulsed again. One moment the house had stood there with such dignity between the bomb-sites like a man in a top hat, and then, bang, crash, there wasn't anything left. He said, 'I'm sorry. I can't help it, Mr Thomas. There's nothing personal, but you got to admit it's funny.'

Note

'The Destructors' was written in 1954 and appears in Graham Greene, *Twenty-One Stories*, Penguin Books, 1975, pp. 7–23 and is used with permission. The story analysis for the workbook was prepared by C. Ritchie Graham.

10.4 REV: Groupthink virus in PC support

Objectives

- To identify the symptoms of groupthink.
- To provide practice in applying a groupthink framework to the analysis of a work situation.
- To assess the relevance and potential usefulness of the groupthink framework for improving the performance of teams at work.

Introduction

This activity gives students the opportunity to apply their understanding of the concepts of groupthink to a real-life work situation. Janis' eight symptoms of groupthink are:

1. Illusion of invulnerability – members display excessive optimism that past successes will continue and tend to take extreme risks.

2. Collective rationalization – members collectively construct rationalizations that allow them to discount negative information about the assumptions upon which they base their decisions.

3. Illusion of morality – members believe that they, as moral individuals, are unlikely to make bad decisions.

4. Shared stereotypes – members dismiss disconfirming evidence by discrediting its source (e.g. stereotyping other groups and its leaders as evil or weak).

5. Direct pressure – imposition of verbal, non-verbal or other sanctions on individuals who explore deviant positions (e.g. those who express doubts or question the validity of group beliefs). Perhaps use of assertive language to force compliance.

6. Self-censorship – members keep silent about misgivings about the apparent group consensus and try to minimise their doubts.

7. Illusion of unanimity – members conclude that the group has reached a consensus because its most vocal members are in agreement.

8. Mindguards – members who take it upon themselves to screen out adverse information supplied by 'outsiders' which might endanger the group's complacency.

Procedure

Step 1 Form into groups as directed by your instructor. Read the definitions of Janis' eight symptoms of groupthink contained in the Introduction.

Step 2 Individually, read the Introduction and Case 1. Enter your answers in the space provided. Then, compare and discuss your answers to it with your fellow students.

Step 3 Continue with Cases 2 and 3. Again, write in your individual decisions to both. When all syndicate members have finished, compare your group answers for both.

Groupthink virus in PC support

The PC Support Unit at Universal Life Assurance offered advice and support to staff throughout the company. The members of the team were largely responsible for managing their unit (e.g. problem-solving, making technical adjustments). In consequence, there was a high level of interaction between members, and support from other members in order to make the necessary decisions and perform the required tasks that the unit was confronted with. Under these circumstances, there was a great potential for high group cohesion. The likelihood of individuals conforming to the general group view was also high. Group members worked as a unit on a daily basis, and depended on each other for the effective completion of group tasks. This increased the attractiveness of conforming in order to be accepted by the group. All these factors made the unit vulnerable to being infected by groupthink.

Case A

Owing to on-going work commitments, attendance at the unit's weekly meetings varied widely. This week, twelve out of the unit's eighteen staff were present. Not having been there the previous week, Peter raised the continuing issue of flexible working hours. Other members responded quickly by giving reasons why these should stay as they are. One objector said that anyone wanting to start at eight, 'must be mad'. The proposal involved having 'core' attendance hours of 103, and allowing members to arrive early or work late as they chose. Jane, a soft-ware engineer, said that such an arrangement would help her to organise the childcare facilities for her daughter. Brian retorted that she shouldn't put personal convenience ahead of company requirements. It was stated that a vote was 'the best way' of deciding, and that the group had previously voted against such a change. Maggie, the unit leader, then pointed out that the issue of working hours had been discussed at the last meeting and that 'nobody' disagreed with keeping the times as they were, so she had assumed that everybody was in agreement.

As the meeting progressed, it became clear that the flexitime proposal had been lost by a single vote at the last meeting. Peter added that, 'it doesn't seem fair because almost half of us want the change'. He suggested that perhaps a flexible attendance pattern could operate on alternating weeks allowing all the unit's members preferences to be met some of the time. However, Peter received little support from the others in the room, and with the pressure from the unit leader and the opposing group members, the subject was finally dropped. An observation of the body language of a number of the staff present indicated that they were not happy with the outcome, but that they were not expressing their views.

Identify which of the eight symptoms of groupthink were illustrated in the case.

Groupthink symptom				*Illustrated by*

Case B

The primary task of the six members of the unit's software support team is to help insurance staff who have difficulty in getting their software to function properly. During one of their meetings, Claire informed the others there had been a lot of complaints made about them, and that this should be discussed and acted upon. The ensuing discussion revealed that the Pensions Department had been dissatisfied with the length of time they had had to wait for assistance, and blamed it on them. Pensions felt that they were unable to achieve their customer care targets because they had to wait for their's to be rectified.

Various group members made comments. Jean admitted that there had been some significant delays. Others defended and supported their own position. One person said that few of the other company departments had complained. The senior programmer, who regularly liaised with the Pensions Department, said that, in his view, 'Pensions expect us to drop everything, anytime they whistle', and 'they don't understand how long it takes to de-bug the problems'. In the end, Claire did not push the issue, and indeed had not contributed to the discussion. The group dropped the topic without any solutions being suggested to the problems raised. The group members were confident that they were in the right, and that the complaints that they had received from Pensions were both unreasonable and unjustified.

Identify which of the eight symptoms of groupthink were illustrated in the case.

Groupthink symptom   *Illustrated by*

Case C

The eight members of the unit's hardware support group had a meeting which was attended by the Services Manager to whom Maggie, the unit leader, reports. The discussion concerned the quality of the hardware repairs that the group was carrying out. Participation in the problem-solving discussion was evenly spread, and most members appeared to be making a contribution. After a few minutes, however, the Services Manager made the statement, 'This is what I think you should do, does anybody here disagree?', and took charge of the rest of the meeting. From that point, the involvement of the others became limited. The manager outlined the steps he wanted the group to take, and the meeting ended once his instructions had been announced. As members left the meeting, their facial expressions indicated that although they would comply with the manager's instructions, they felt that they had neither contributed to the solution nor agreed with it.

Identify which of the eight symptoms of groupthink were illustrated in the case.

| *Groupthink symptom* | *Illustrated by* |

PART III

ORGANIZATION STRUCTURES

Chapter 11

Organization structures

11.1 LGA: Function or product based structure?

Objective

- To compare the effects of a chosen organization structure on related aspects of company functioning.

Introduction

A basic decision confronting every enterprise is how to organize. Which structure is most appropriate for it. There are a range of available structural forms (based on division by function, production, geography, client). Each have both advantages and disadvantages. Moreover, a choice of an organizational structure can have consequences that are not always immediately evident. In this example, function-based and product-based structures will be compared.

Procedure

Step 1 Read the description of the two structural arrangements (functional and product).

Step 2 Answer the seven questions that follow, giving a brief reason for your answer.

Pen Company

Assume a firm makes a biro, the manufacture of which involves three primary operations. These are making the plastic tube (operation T), the plastic cap (operation C), and the inkholder (operation I). Each biro requires a tube, cap and an ink holder. The machinery that manufactures these items varies in age, and is periodically replaced. The employees consist of a plant manager, three supervisors and nine operatives. Under these circumstances, the enterprise could be departmentalized either by function or product:

Function-based structure

Following a functional structure, the firm could be organized as three functional departments. In Department A, all the plastic tubes (T) would be made. In Department B, all the plastic caps (C) would be manufactured. Finally, Department C would make the ink tubes (I). Each department would make three units of their product per day. One supervisor (S) would be in charge of each department, and these would report to the plant manager as shown in the organizational chart below.

Manager

Supervisor 1	Supervisor 2	Supervisor 3
T T T	C C C	I I I
Operators	Operators	Operators

Product-based structure

Using a product-based structure, the firm could be organized into three separate, but identical, product departments. Within each of the departments, the three operations (tube manufacture, cap manufacture and inkholder manufacture) are duplicated. In this arrangement, each worker continually performs only one of the three operations. For example,

Manager

Supervisor 1	Supervisor 2	Supervisor 3
T C I	T C I	T C I
Operators	Operators	Operators

Questions

(Read all the questions before answering)   F = function   Reason
    P = product

1. In which structure is the job of the supervisor likely to be more difficult?

2. In which structure will supervisors be most qualified to be promoted to plant manager level?

3. Which structure produces a greater division of labour for operators?

4. In which structure is conflict between departments most likely to occur?

5. Which structure allows the better comparison of each supervisor's performance?

6. Which structure produces operators who can most easily be promoted to supervisor level?

7. With which structure will the firm be most affected if one department shuts down through equipment failure or a strike?

Source: This exercise is based on one developed by Arthur Bedian, *Management,* CBS Publishing, 1986, p. 269. Used with permission.

11.2 SGA: Words-in-sentences

Objectives

- To experiment with designing and running an organization.
- To compare production and quality outputs under different organizational structures and leadership styles.

Introduction

This exercise gives students the experience of structuring and managing a production company. Each student group forms a 'mini-company' which will be in competition with several others in their industry. Students therefore have the opportunity to think about and experiment with the best design for their organization before and between the actual production periods. Since the success of each company will depend on its structure, objectives, planning, quality control and leadership, this activity opens up a variety of topics for discussion.

Procedure

Step 1   Read pages 143–6 in this workbook to familiarize yourself with the rules and procedures of the activity. These are specified in the section headed Directions.

Step 2   Your instructor will divide you into small groups of roughly equal size, and will assign you to your workplaces. Each group should consider themselves a company. It is not important if group numbers are not exactly equal. The instructor may designate company managers – leaders, and give them additional instructions.

Step 3   Follow the statement of instructions and ask any questions for clarification. Each team will need to provide the instructor with a one-word company name, and the name of its quality control representative.

Step 4   Your team should prepare for production run 1 in two ways. First, by designing its organization structure, using as many of its members as it sees fit to produce its product – 'words-in-sentences'. There are many different ways of organizing. Some are more efficient than others. Each company will want to consider the following questions:

- What is its objective?

- How will that objective be achieved? How should the work be planned given the time allowed?

- What technology will you use?

- What division of labour, authority and responsibility is most appropriate, given the chosen objective, task and technology?

- Are certain company members more qualified to perform certain tasks than others?

    Second, it should do a short 'practice run' using a test word or phrase of its choice, to identify the possible production problems.

Step 5   Production Run 1 (10 minutes).

Once the raw material word/phrase is announced by the instructor, each company is to manufacture as many words as possible, and package them into sentences for delivery by their quality control representative to the Quality Control Board.

Step 6   Quality Control Board.

The quality control representatives from the various companies form the Quality Control Board. They review the output from each company in turn, ensuring that it meets the standards specified in the rules. Company performances are announced.

While this is going on, the other company members review their performance, and decide on any changes that they would like to make to their work methods or organizational arrangements for the next run. Companies may re-organize for Production Run 2.

Step 7   Production Run 2 (10 minutes).

Step 8   The Quality Control Board again reviews each company's output for Run 2.

While the Board is finalizing its figures, the other members prepare answers to the following questions:

1. How well did your company perform in the light of the scores of its competitors (excellent, good, medium, bad)?

2. How was the work divided? By task, by person, by time? Was this arrangement changed?

3. Overall, what factors contributed to your company's success (+) or failure (–)?

4. Did you have a formal leader? What was their leadership style? (*ORBIT3,* Chapters 8 and 20). What effect did it have on employee motivation and on production?

Directions

You are a small company that manufactures words and then packages them into meaningful (English language) sentences. Market research has established that sentences of at least three words, but no more than six words, are in demand. Therefore, packaging, distribution and sales should be set up for three-to-six word sentences.

The words-in-sentences (WINS) industry is highly competitive. Several new firms have recently entered an expanding market. Since raw materials, technology and pricing are all standard for the industry, your ability to compete depends on two factors: volume and quality.

Task

Your group must design and operate a WINS company. You should design your organization to be as efficient as possible during each 10 minute production run. After the first production run, you will have the opportunity to re-organize your company if you want to.

Raw materials

For each production run, you will be given a raw material word or phrase. The letters contained in the word or phrase serve as the raw materials available to you to produce new words for your sentences. For example, if the raw material word was *organization*, you could produce the following words that would form the following sentence, 'Nat ran to a zoo'.

Production standards

There are several rules that have to be followed in producing 'words-in-sentences'. If these rules are not adhered to, your sentences will not meet production specifications, will not pass the quality control specification, and will not count towards your output figure.

1. The same letter may appear only as often in a manufactured word as it appears in the raw material word or phrase. For example, 'organization' has two o's. Thus the word 'zoo' is acceptable, but 'zoology' is not because it has three o's.

2. Once a new word has been manufactured from the raw material letters, those letters become available immediately for the next new word. That is, raw material letters can be used again in different manufactured words.

3. A manufactured word may be used only once in a sentence, and only in one sentence during a production run. For example, if the word *zoo* is used once in a sentence, it becomes out of stock for the remainder of that production run.

4. A new word may not be made by adding an *s* to form the plural of an already used, manufactured word.

5. A word is defined by its spelling and not its meaning. For example, only one *land* is permissible, irrespective of whether it refers to what an aeroplane does, or where one grows wheat.

6. Nonsense words or nonsense sentences are unacceptable.

7. All words must be in the English language.

8. Names and places are acceptable.

9. Slang is not acceptable.

Measuring performance

The output of your WINS company is measured by the total number of acceptable words that are packaged in sentences. The sentences must be legible, listed on no more than two sheets of paper, and handed to the Quality Control Review Board at the completion of each production run.

Delivery

Delivery must be made to the Quality Control Review Board within 30 seconds of the instructor signalling the end of each production run.

Quality control

The Quality Control Review Board (composed of one member from each WINS company) is the final arbiter of sentence acceptability. If *any* word in a sentence does not meet the standards set out above, *all* the remaining words in that sentence will be rejected. In the event of a tie vote in the Review Board, a coin toss will determine the outcome.

Activity management

Talk through the instructions, especially the rules, answering any student questions. Stress the location of the quality control table and the 30 second delivery time. Explain that from each team you require a one-word company name, and the name of their quality control representative. After 5 minutes, the instructor goes round each 'company' in turn and gets them quickly to give their name and identify a quality control representative. While students are preparing, allocate a separate table with a card saying 'Quality Control' around which the QC reps will gather.

Words-in-sentences production sheet

To be completed by members of the Quality Control Review Board and handed back to the instructor.

Production Run No. ___

Company name	Total number of accepted words
1. _____	_____
2. _____	_____
3. _____	_____
4. _____	_____
5. _____	_____
6. _____	_____

Start Production Run 1 by writing up a raw material word or phrase such as *engineering management* on the board, and shouting 'Start!' The production run lasts 10 minutes, and is ended with a shout of 'Stop!' After announcing the end of production, the instructor stands by the QC table counting down the 30 seconds. Any arrivals after the half-minute deadline are deemed not have met the delivery schedule (as specified in the rules), and their output will not be counted in this round. A Production Sheet which lists the names of the companies, and the agreed scores for each company, is left on the Quality Control table for the reps to complete at the end of their deliberations. This is collected by the instructor who charts up the scores for that run. The procedure is repeated for Production Run 2, using a new word or phrase. This might be *no smoking by order* or *competitive advantage*.

Words-in-sentences company performance

Company name

Run 1				
Run 2				
Total				

Source: This activity is taken from R.J. Lewicki, D.D. Bowen, D.T. Hall and F.S. Hall, *Experiences in Management and Organizational Behaviour*, Wiley, Chichester, 1988, pp. 219–33. Used with permission.

11.3 PREP: Windworth University Business School

Objectives

- To introduce the dilemmas in designing an organization.
- To evaluate the costs and benefits of different organizational structures.
- To apply the theory of organizational design to a specific case.

Introduction

Most people fit into an existing organization structure. Indeed, they are unaware of it until external or internal factors trigger a re-design. Yet the arrangement of levels, responsibilities, job descriptions and reporting relationships is the scaffold that links organizational goals to human performance. An effective structure meets both employee and customer needs within the context of organizational goals. The exercise gives students an opportunity to address the issue of organizational structuring for the first time within a context with which they are familiar. The activity provides an opportunity to address the issue of different organizational structures.

Procedure

Step 1   Individually read the case, and understand the different 'products' of the business school:

U – teaching of undergraduate degree programmes
  (bachelor's, diploma and certificate)

P1 – teaching of postgraduate full-time (MBA) programmes

P2 – teaching of postgraduate part-time (MBA) programmes

(T – undergraduate and postgraduate teaching)*

R – research

D – doctoral supervision

C – in-company consultancy

S – short, non-graduating courses at WUBS

* Add this as an extra category to integrate the previous three.

Step 2   Imagine that you are Helen Bond. Decide on TWO different ways of organizing the staff at the business school. You are free to make any assignments that you feel are appropriate, as long as you do not change the assumptions of the case. Prepare an organizational chart showing your dispositions. What principles support your decision? What are the strengths and weaknesses of each of your two chosen structures?

Step 3   Submit your analysis as directed by your instructor.

Windworth University Business School

Windworth University is a large institution attracting students from all parts of the U.K. as well as from abroad. It was formed in the early 1990s by the re-naming of a polytechnic and the amalgamation of a number of smaller educational establishments. It has six faculties, including a business school which was formed by the merging of the polytechnic's departments of management, law, accounting and business studies; a semi-autonomous research institute; and a residential short course centre which came as a dowry when the college of commerce was incorporated into the newly formed university.

The main campus is on the western edge of the city; the research institute has premises in the city centre, and the residential centre is located some 18 miles east of the city on the road to the coast. The business school offers programmes leading to certificates, diplomas and bachelor's degrees in management. It teachers two Master of Business Administration degrees. One is a 12-month full-time programme for students from around the world. The second is a 2-year part-time programme for managers from local companies who study while continuing to work. WUBS supervises doctoral research, and has a research grant from a Research Council. It offers in-company consultancy, and also runs courses for managers from different firms at its residential centre.

Helen Bond, the newly-appointed director of the business school, was thinking about the best way to organise the 100 or so staff in the school. With the recent higher education reorganization, and the need to increase rapidly the productivity and quality of the services it offered, deciding on the appropriate organizational structure and implementing it swiftly was a priority for her. Otherwise, the opportunity to integrate the diverse staff from different backgrounds into an effective unit would be lost and morale would plummet. However, she also knew that if she chose the wrong structure, the effect would be divisive, and her job would be made more difficult.

She remembered her tasks when she was a lecturer. She was encouraged to apply for research grants, and when awarded, she and a senior colleague had to recruit their research team. She remembered how much time grant application had taken up. Even trickier had been the process of interviewing the short listed candidates. One appointee had turned out to be so awful that they had had to sack him. It was a long time before she developed her interviewing skills. Doing the actual research was relatively straightforward. The problem came towards the end of the contract when the researchers began looking for new jobs before their grants ran out. This rarely stopped the research itself being finished, but it did mean a delay in publications as absent staff were entreated to complete research papers and articles. It was rare that a book on the research ever got written. It seemed a waste of time doing the research if no-one was going to read the results. This problem of lack of output was particularly serious now as both the amount of research grant obtained, and the publication record of the school's staff, were being scrutinised much more closely.

Reflecting on the process, Helen remembered what difficulties her research staff had in communicating their research results to students. In the end, the research seminars had to be abandoned because of complaints from undergraduates. The research staff, they grumbled, seemed unable to explain their ideas succinctly to them. Helen had often wondered whether a good researcher could also be a good teacher, or whether an academic was drawn to one area rather than the other. Anyway, she was sure that the business school needed good teachers.

Good teaching attracted students, and students meant income for the business school. The new view of students as customers certainly put a premium on staff who were high quality performers. The boom in business education meant that there was a great demand for competent lecturers. Beyond the undergraduate level, staff had to teach course members who were managers with years of management experience, and these groups were often highly critical of both the material presented and of the lecturer. You had to be a certain kind of person to deal with a crowd like that. Those who succeeded ('showmen' as her previous boss had called them) did not score well on research and publications at the annual staff appraisal, often saying that they, 'weren't really into that sort of thing'.

One of the greatest frustrations that Helen had experienced as a researcher and teacher, was the lack of time to adapt her research findings into material suitable for teaching. Research formed the basis of up-to-date presentations to be communicated to students. She and her colleagues needed time to translate the findings into teaching materials such as case studies, exercises and role plays activities. Not least, new overhead transparencies and 35mm slides had to be prepared. In many cases, a short video film would help students understand the main ideas. Regrettably neither she nor her colleagues had the time or expertise to prepare one. In recent years, knowledge has become a commodity. It is no longer enough to discover it and teach it; you also have to sell it. That's what the vice-chancellor said at the last graduation ceremony. She had been thinking of establishing a business consultancy centre at the residential management centre to market the research expertise of the business school. The centre, specialising in short, non-graduating courses for experienced managers, was the part of the business school that was closest to the business frontline. However, Helen's predecessor had warned her that the teachers at the centre, mainly ex-managers who had switched to teaching as a second career, were not temperamentally suited to going around local businesses selling courses and explaining the consultancy services on offer. For this, he felt, you needed younger, more entrepreneurial individuals, who saw themselves primarily as marketing people.

At the end of last week, Helen had spoken to one of the top final year students who had accepted a place to do post-graduate work at another university. Asked why he had not stayed at WUBS, he said that although many of her staff were good teachers, few of them had any research reputation or a publications record. Earlier in the day, Helen had had a talk with Susan, a newly appointed member of staff. Although responsible for the undergraduate B. Accountancy programme, Susan had expressed the desire to be contribute to the postgraduate Master of Business Administration programme. She also hoped that Helen would ensure that she was given enough time to conduct her research. Without publications, Susan reminded her, the chances of promotion were limited. Helen thought about what kind of organizational structure she could develop which met all of these competing demands.

11.4 REV: Crossword

Objective

- To develop the ability to distinguish the main concepts and author names from Chapter 11, *ORBIT3*, which deals with organization structures.

Introduction

Understanding a topic in organizational behaviour involves a familiarity with the research, authors, theories and concepts in that field. This activity gives you practice in correctly linking these together in the management of conflict with their definitions or descriptions.

Procedure

The crossword below already contains some of the letters in the answers. The shading indicates where a word starts and ends. Use the clues to identify the 21 answers, and position them correctly in the crossword grid. Each clue indicates the length of the answer word.

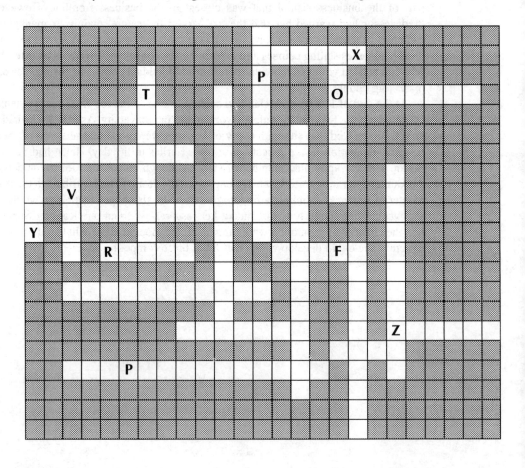

Clues

1. Few levels mean a flat _____ (9).

2. Department managers lean on these for specialist advice (5).

3. In this relationship, the manager has to accept the advice (10).

4. Perhaps he shouldn't touch an organizational objective (7).

5. Project leader directs pranks on the rug, say (6).

6. In this relationship, when the boss directs you, you have to tow-the- _____ (4).

7. Organizing begins with this (3, 10).

8. Fox stressed this view of organizations (10).

9. Visually depicts authority and responsibility relationships (5).

10. His formula for the future was 0.5 x 2 x 3 (5).

11. Another term for decentralization (11).

12. People have to report back to their bosses because of this (14).

13. The 'invisible' organization (8).

14. A structure which concentrates decision-making at the top (11).

15. The process of dividing up a large task into its component elements and distributing these among different individuals and groups to complete (8).

16. For Duncan, structure facilitated the flow of this (11).

17. Within an organization structure, employees performs _____ (5).

18. You get it with the application form when writing off for a job (12).

19. De-layering reduces the span of _____ (7).

20. She felt new technology would informate middle managers out of a job (6).

21. Requirement to act because of one's position in the structure (14).

Chapter 12
Scientific management

12.1 LGA: Improving library performance

Objective

- To introduce students to the scientific management approach.

Introduction

Working with the person next to you, imagine that you are a management efficiency expert. You have been called in by the local branch of your university or public library to help the chief librarian ensure that the performance of its lending department is at the maximum state of efficiency.

As a first step in your study, make a list of the type of information that you would wish to collect about (i) library tasks to be performed, and (ii) the layout of the library, so as to help you make suggestions for efficiency improvements.

12.2 SGA: Paper boat builders

Objectives

- Apply the principles of scientific management to a physical task.
- To experience the application of time and motion study of a given task.

Introduction

The focus of this activity is on time and motion study in particular. Its purpose is to give you the opportunity to apply the scientific management techniques of observing jobs, measuring their duration, and using that information to plan and organize production. Each team will seek to identify the 'one-best-way' of production and scientifically select its squad of workers.

Procedure

Step 1   The class will divide into teams of between six and eight students. Each team is identified by a letter (A, B, C, etc.) and has a team leader. At least one member of each team should have a watch with a stopwatch function.

Step 2   Note that:
1.   The purpose of this exercise is to apply scientific management techniques to production. The aim of each team will be to study the jobs of its members, and to make them as efficient as possible. This means ensuring:

- Maximum output.
- Minimum waste.
- Meeting quality control standards.
- Matching budgeted output to actual output.

2.   The same product, a paper boat, will be assembled in all three production runs by each team's members.

3.   An acceptable finished product is a completed boat whose mast tip is a point (not a curve) and which projects above its sides.

4.   During the production runs, only four students will be workers, while the remainder will be time-and-motion study experts. However, during the preparation phase, all team members will participate in the decisions about job design and production.

5.   There will be THREE production runs:

Run 1: All team members will use a craft system in which each of its four workers will complete all fourteen steps of the boat assembly process individually.

Run 2: All teams will use an assembly line system in which the fourteen production steps will be divided between the four workers.

Run 3: All team members will use an assembly line system modified by them in the light of their Run 2 experience.

6. Before each run, each team will have to specify how many boats it intends to make.

Step 3   Review your written instructions for making the paper boat which are located at the end of this exercise. Practise assembling the boat.

Step 4   Prepare for production run 1 (craft). Duration: 5 minutes.

1. Teams select workers for their four-person work squad.

2. Team leaders inform the instructor about their projected outputs.

Step 5   Production run 1 (craft). Duration: 5 minutes.

Step 6   Teams review actual production and compare with projected production.

Step 7   Prepare for production run 2 – (assembly line production). (Preparation time – 20 minutes.) In each team:

1. There is a selection of workers for their four-person work squad.

2. Each of the fourteen assembly steps is timed.

3. Time-and-motion study experts analyse some of the key motions so as to increase output.

4. Experts decide which steps will be carried out by which squad member in what manner.

5. The team leader informs the instructor of their projected output.

6. The team leader's decision on all these matters is final.

Attention should also be paid to how the semi-finished products will be transported between workers; how blockages or pile-ups will be avoided; and how the team will avoid being left with semi-finished products.

Step 8   Prepare for production run 2 (assembly line). Duration: 5 minutes.

Step 9   Teams review actual production and compare with projected production.

Step 10   Prepare for production run 3 (assembly line – modified). Preparation time: 10 minutes. They modify the arrangements they used in the previous run. For example, they place their four workers in a different order; they replace one or more workers entirely; they give extra or take away assembly steps from the four work stations to 'balance the line'; etc.

Step 11   Production run 3 (assembly line – modified). Duration: 5 minutes.

Step 12   Teams review actual production and compare with projected production.

Building the boat

These are the directions for making a paper boat. For each step there is a diagram showing what to do, and another showing what it should look like then. There are fourteen steps.

1. Hold the sheet of paper so the printing on it is facing up.

YOU

2. Fold AB to CD.

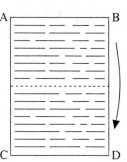

It should look like this:

3. Fold in along JG and JH so that E and F meet at point K.

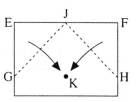

It should look like this:

Make sure there is a point here

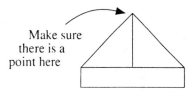

4. Fold one layer (up direction) along LM.

It should look like this:

5. Turn the boat over to the other side.
   It should look like this:

6. Fold (up direction) along NP.

It should look like this:

7. Tuck section Q (just the top layer) back around the edge of the boat, so it is between the back of the boat and the back layer of paper.

Fold section Q (back piece) towards you over the edge of the boat and press flat.

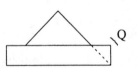

It should look like this:

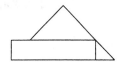

8. Do the same thing to the left end (don't turn it over). It should look like this:

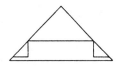

9. Pick up the boat and hold it in your hands with the open side (R) down. Open up R with your fingers and keep pulling it apart until points S and T meet.

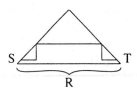

Turn the paper so that S is facing up and T is underneath. It should look like this:

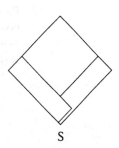

10. Fold S up to U.

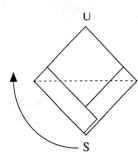

It should look like this:

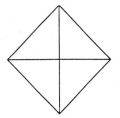

11. Turn over so that T is facing up. Fold T up to U.

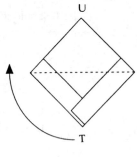

It should look like this:

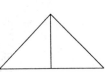

12. Pick up the boat and hold it in your hands, with the open side, V, down. Open V with your fingers and keep pulling apart so that W is facing up and X is underneath.
It should look like this:

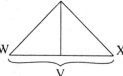

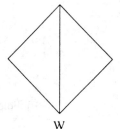

13. Fold W to A and then bring back down again to its original position. There should now be a crease at BC.

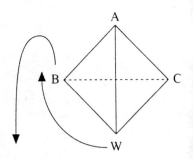

Turn over so that X is facing up. Fold X to A and then bring X down again to its original position. There should now be a crease at DE.

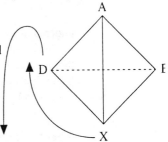

Hold Y (front and back at the top left point) with left hand, and Z (front and back at the top right point) with the right hand, and pull apart as far as it will go.

It should look like this:

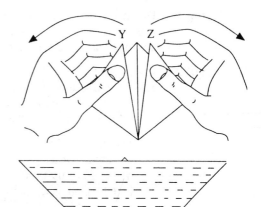

14. Stand it up. You have finished your boat!

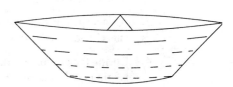

Quality control standards for the boat

- The middle point must be a point, not a curve.

- The middle point must be even with or above the sides of the boat.

- Only completed boats are accepted.

One person assembly times

Fast	(top 10%)	35–45 seconds
Average		45–55 seconds
Slow	(bottom 10%)	over 55 seconds

Materials for activity

Bring large amounts of scrap A4 paper to the classroom. These present the raw material for the product. The instructor should ensure that teams neither submit boats made during the practice sessions in the real production runs; nor hide away paper intended for practice sessions to 'top up' raw material deficiencies during the production runs. Both of these underhand practices have been used by students in the past. To avoid these problems, the instructor should make a careful check on the amounts of paper distributed to teams during the practice runs; and collect up all completed and part completed boats, as well as unused paper, before distributing fresh supplies for each production run. Ideally, different coloured paper can be used for each production run.

Procedure

Step 1   Divide the class into teams of between six and eight students. Allocate letters to identify teams – A, B, C, etc.). Identify a leader (at random) in each team. Organize and seat the teams ensuring that at least one member of each team has a watch with a stopwatch function.

Step 2   Explain that:
1.   The purpose of this exercise is to apply scientific management techniques to production. The aim of each team will be to study the jobs of its members, and to make them as efficient as possible. This means ensuring:

- Maximum output.
- Minimum waste.
- Meeting quality control standards.
- Matching budgeted output to actual output.

2.   The same product, a paper boat, will be assembled in all three production runs by all teams. HOLD UP A COMPLETED BOAT TO SHOW THE STUDENTS.

3.   An acceptable finished product is a completed boat whose mast tip is a point (not a curve) and which projects above its sides.

4.   During the production runs, only four students will be workers, while the remainder will be time-and-motion study experts. However, during the preparation phase, all team members will participate in the decisions about job design and production.

5.   There will be THREE production runs:

Run 1: All team members will use a craft system in which each of its four workers will complete all fourteen steps of the boat assembly process individually.

Run 2: All teams will use an assembly line system in which the fourteen production steps will be divided between the four workers.

Run 3: All team members will use an assembly line system modified by them in the light of their Run 2 experience.

6.   Before each run, each team will have to specify how many boats it intends to make.

Step 3   Refer students to their written instructions for making the paper boat. Distribute one piece of paper to each team member with which to practise assembly. While they are doing this, gather together the leaders from each team at a suitable table, and demonstrate the steps to them. Allow time for team leaders to return to their teams, then proceed.

Step 4   Teams prepare for 10 minutes for production run 1 (craft). During this time, they familiarise themselves with the paper folding sequence, time different workers, and select workers for their four-person work squad.

Just before production run 1, the instructor

1. Collects up the practice boats, and all the spare paper from the teams.

2. Asks for each team's projected output.

3. Writes it up in the left-hand column on the Production Chart (run 1).

4. Gives one non-squad member of each team their raw material (equal to their projected output).

Production chart

TEAM	A			B			C			D		
	Production			Production			Production			Production		
	Projected	Actual	Variation	Projected	Actual	Variation	Projected	Actual	Variation	Projected	Actual	Variation
Run 1												
Run 2												
Run 3												

Step 5   Production run 1 (craft). Duration: 5 minutes.

1. Signal start of the production period.

2. Count five minutes.

3. Signal end of production period.

4. Team leaders bring completed boats for assessment to instructor, together with any unused or spoiled paper.

5. The total of accepted boats for each team is written up on the Production Chart (run 1 – actual).

6. The variation from the projected is noted in the right-hand column.

7. Teams review actual production and compare it with projected production.

Step 6   Teams prepare for 20 minutes for production run 2 (assembly line).

1. Teams select their workers for their four-person work squad.

2. Work study experts time each of the fourteen assembly steps.

3. Time-and-motion study experts analyse some of the key motions so as to increase output.

4. Experts decide which steps will be carried out by which squad member in what manner.

5.   The team leader informs the instructor of their projected output.

6.   The team leader's decision on all these matters is final.

Just before production run 2, the instructor

1.   Collects up the practice boats, and all the spare paper from the teams.

2.   Asks for each team's projected output.

3.   Writes it up in the left-hand column on the Production Chart (run 1).

4.   Gives one non-squad member of each team their raw material (equal to their projected output).

Step 7   Production run 2 (assembly line). Duration: 5 minutes.

1.   Signal start of the production period.

2.   Count five minutes.

3.   Signal end of production period.

4.   Team leaders bring completed boats for assessment to instructor, together with any unused or spoiled paper.

5.   The total of accepted boats for each team is written up on the Production Chart (run 2 – actual).

6.   The variation from the projected is noted in the right-hand column.

7.   Teams review actual production and compare it with projected production.

Step 8   Teams prepare for 10 minutes for production run 3 (assembly line – modified). Teams make any modifications that they feel appropriate based on their experience of the previous run. For example, they may choose to place their four workers in a different order; replace one or more workers entirely; or give extra or take away assembly steps from the four work stations to 'balance the line'.

Just before production run 3, the instructor

1.   Collects up the practice boats, and all the spare paper from the teams.

2.   Asks for each team's projected output.

3.   Writes it up in the left-hand column on the Production Chart (run 3).

4.   Gives one non-squad member of each team their raw material (equal to their projected output).

Step 9   Production run 3 (assembly line – modified). Duration: 5 minutes.

1.   Signal start of the production period.

2.   Count five minutes.

3.   Signal end of production period.

4.   Team leaders bring completed boats for assessment to instructor, together with any unused or spoiled paper.

5. The total of accepted boats for each team is written up on the Production Chart (run 3 – actual).

6. The variation from the projected is noted in the right-hand column.

7. Teams review actual production and compare it with projected production.

Activity timings

Steps	Time (mins)	Total time elapsed (hr/min)
1. Divide students	5	0.5
2. Explain	15	0.20
3. Refer	10	0.30
4. Teams prepare	5	0.45
5. Production run 1	5	0.45
6. Teams prepare	20	1.05
7. Production run 2	5	1.10
8. Teams prepare	15	1.25
9. Production run 3	5	1.30
10. Plenary	30	2.00

Note

The exercise is based on D.A. Kolb, I.M. Rubon and J.A. McIntyre, *Organizational Psychology: An Experiential Approach*, Prentice Hall, Englewood Cliffs, NJ, 1974, 2nd edition, pp. 103–6.

12.3 PREP: Brave new management

Objective

- To identify the concepts of scientific management and rationalistic learning within the context of a science-fiction novel.

Introduction

Published in 1932, Aldous Huxley's book, *Brave New World*, ranks alongside H.G. Wells's *War of the Worlds* and George Orwell's *1984* as one of the world's most significant futuristic novels. At the start of his story, Huxley describes a society which is very different from today's. It is a society based on the theories of Frederick Taylor, Henry Ford and Ivan Pavlov. While examining this imaginary society of the future, it is interesting to consider to what extent the practices described are already used (in a modified and less intense form) in the real organizations of today.

Procedure

Step 1   Students should read the abridged section of *Brave New World* before coming to class. Then, referring to Chapters 1, 5, 12 and 13 of *ORBIT3*, they should make notes in response to the questions set out below:

Questions

1.   If the World State's motto is 'Community, Identity, Stability', what might be the motto of all organizations? (Hint: see Chapter 1.)

2.   Sum up the 'message' that Huxley seeks to convey in the case. Which commonplace and contemporary organizational processes, practices and procedures, would broadly serve the purposes of:
     (a) Ecto-genesis (Bokanovsky process)?
     (b) Pre-destination?
     (c) Neo-Pavlovian conditioning?

3.   What are the main points that the Director wants to impress upon his students?

4.   How is social stability achieved, and what kind of society is created?

5.   How is Henry Ford's deification in the novel linked to Frederick Taylor's principles of scientific management?

Note

The case is taken from Aldous Huxley, *Brave New World*, 1932. Abridged from p. 19–63 and 161–2.

Brave New World

I

(1) A squat grey building of only thirty-one storeys. Over the main entrance the words, CENTRAL LONDON HATCHERY AND CONDITIONING CENTRE, and, in a shield, the World State's motto, COMMUNITY, IDENTITY, STABILITY.

(2) The enormous room on the ground floor faced towards the north. Cold for all the summer beyond the panes, for all the tropical heat of the room itself, a harsh thin light glared through the windows, hungrily seeking some draped lay figure, some pallid shape of academic goose-flesh, but finding only the glass and nickel and bleakly shining porcelain of a laboratory. The overalls of the workers were white, their hands gloved with a pale corpse-coloured rubber. The light was frozen, dead, a ghost. Only from the yellow barrels of the microscopes did it borrow a certain rich and living substance, lying along the polished tubes like butter, streak after luscious streak in log recession down the work tables.

(3) 'And this,' said the Director opening the door, 'is the Fertilizing Room.'

Bent over their instruments, three hundred Fertilizers were plunged, as the Director of Hatcheries and Conditioning entered the room, in the scarcely breathing silence, the absentminded, soliloquizing hum or whistle, of absorbed concentration. A troop of newly arrived students, very young, pink and callow, followed nervously, rather abjectly, at the Director's heels. Each of them carried a note-book, in which, whenever the great man spoke, he desperately scribbled. Straight from the horse's mouth. It was a rare privilege. The DHC for Central London always made a point of personally conducting his new students round the various departments.

(4) 'Just to give you a general idea,' he would explain to them. For of course some sort of general idea they must have, if they were to do their work intelligently – though as little of one, if they were to be good and happy members of society, as possible. For particulars, as everyone knows, make for virtue and happiness; generalities are intellectually necessary evils. Not philosophers, but fret-sawyers and stamp collectors compose the backbone of society.

'Tomorrow,' he would add, smiling at them with a slightly menacing geniality, 'you'll be settling down to serious work. You won't have time for generalities. Meanwhile ...'

Meanwhile, it was a privilege. Straight from the horse's mouth into the note book. The boys scribbled like mad.

(5) Tall and rather thin but upright, the Director advanced into the room. He had a long chin and big, rather prominent teeth, just covered, when he was not talking, by his full, floridly curved lips. Old, young? Thirty? Fifty? Fifty-five? It was hard to say. And anyhow the question didn't arise; in this year of stability, A.F. 632, it didn't occur to you to ask it.

(6) 'I shall begin at the beginning,' said the DHC, and the more zealous students recorded his intention in their notebooks: *Begin at the beginning*. 'These,' he waved his hand, 'are the incubators.' And opening an insulated door he showed them racks of numbered test-tubes. 'This week's supply of ova. Kept,' he explained, 'at blood heat; whereas the male gametes,' and here he opened another door, 'they have to be kept at thirty-five

instead of thirty-seven. Full blood heat sterilizes.' Rams wrapped in thermogene beget no lambs.

(7)   Still leaning against the incubators he gave them, while the pencils scurried illegibly across the pages, a brief description of the modern fertilizing process; spoke first, of course, of its surgical introduction – 'the operation undergone voluntarily for the good of Society, not to mention the fact that it carries a bonus amounting to six mon...s' salary; continued with some account of the technique of preserving the excised ovary alive and actively developing; passed on to a consideration of optimum temperature salinity, viscosity; referred to the liquor in which the detached and ripened eggs were kept; and leading his charges to the work tables, actually showed them how the liquor was drawn off from the test-tubes; how it was let out drop by drop on to the specially warmed slides of the microscopes; how the eggs which it contained were inspected for abnormalities, counted and transferred to a porous receptacle; how (and he now took them to watch the operation) this receptacle was immersed in a warm bouillon containing free-swimming spermatozoa – at a minimum concentration of one hundred thousand per cubic centimetre, he insisted; and how, after ten minutes, the container was lifted out of the liquor and its contents re-examined ; how; if any of the eggs remained unfertilized, it was again immersed, and, if necessary, yet again; how the fertilized ova went back to the incubators; where the Alphas and the Betas remained until definitely bottled; while the Gammas, Deltas and Epsilons were brought out again, after only thirty-six hours, to undergo Bokanovsky's Process.

(8)   'Bokanovsky's Process,' repeated the Director, and the students underlined the words in their little note-books.

One egg, one embryo, one adult – normality. But a bokanovskified egg will bud, will proliferate, will divide. From eight to ninety-six buds, and every bud will grow into a perfectly formed embryo, and every embryo onto a full sized adult. Making ninety-six human beings grow where only one grew before. Progress.

'Essentially,' the DHC concluded, 'bokanovskification consists of a series of arrests of development. We check the normal growth and, paradoxically enough, the egg responds by budding.'

Responds by budding. The pencils were busy.

He pointed. On a very slowly moving band a rack-full of test-tubes was entering a large metal box, another rack-full was emerging. Machinery faintly purred. It took eight minutes for the tubes to go through, he told them. Eight minutes of hard X-rays being about as much as an egg can stand. A few died; the rest, the least susceptible divided into two; most put out four buds; some eight; all were returned to the incubators, where the buds began to develop; then, after two days, were suddenly chilled, chilled and checked. Two, four, eight, the buds in their turn budded; and having budded were dosed almost to death with alcohol; consequently burgeoned again and having budded – bud out of bud out of bud were thereafter – further arrest being generally fatal – left to develop in peace. By which time the original egg was in a fair way to becoming anything from eight to ninety-six embryos – a prodigious improvement – you will agree on nature. Identical twins – but not in piddling twos and threes as in the old viviparous days, when an egg would sometimes accidently divide; actually by dozens, by scores at a time.

'Scores,' the Director repeated and flung out his arms, as though he were distributing largesse. 'Scores.'

(9)   But one of the students was fool enough to ask where the advantage lay.

'My good boy!' The Director wheeled sharply around on him. 'Can't you see? Can't you *see*?' He raised a hand; his expression was solemn. 'Bokanovsky's Process is one of the major instruments of social stability!'

Major instruments of social stability.

Standard men and women; in uniform batches. The whole of a small factory staffed with the products of a single bokanovskified egg.

'Ninety-six identical twins working ninety-six identical machines!' The voice was almost tremulous with enthusiasm. 'You really know where you are. For the first time in history.' He quoted the planetary motto. 'Community, Identity, Stability.' Grand words. 'If we could bokanovskify indefinitely the whole problem would be solved.'

Solved by standard Gammas, unvarying Deltas, uniform Epsilons. Millions of identical twins. The principle of mass production at last applied to biology.

II

(10)   In the Bottling Room all was harmonious bustle and ordered activity. Flaps of fresh sow's peritoneum ready cut to the proper size came shooting up in little lifts from the organ store in the sub-basement. Whizz and then, click! the lift-hatches flew open; the Bottle-Liner had only to reach out a hand, take the flap, insert, smooth-down, and before the lined bottle had to travel out of reach along the endless band, whizz, click! another flap of peritoneum had shot up from the depths, ready to be slipped into yet another bottle, the next of that slow interminable procession on to the band.

Next to the Liners stood the Matriculators. The procession advanced; one by one the eggs were transferred from their test-tubes to the larger containers; deftly the peritoneal lining was slit, the morula dropped into place, the saline solution poured in ... and already the bottle had passed, and it was the turn of the labellers. Heredity, date of fertilization, membership of Bokanovsky Group – details were transferred from test-tube to bottle. No longer anonymous, but named and identified, the procession marched slowly on; on through an opening in the wall, slowly into the Social Predestination Room.

(11)   ... the sultry darkness into which the students now followed him was visible and crimson, like the darkness of closed eyes on a summer's afternoon. The bulging flanks of row and tier above tier of bottles glinted with innumerable rubies, and among the rubies moved the dim red spectres of men and women with purple eyes and all the symptoms of lupus. The hum and rattle of machinery faintly stirred the air.

'Give them a few figures, Mr Foster,' said the Director, who was tired of talking.

Mr Foster was only too happy to give them a few figures.

Two hundred and twenty metres long, two hundred wide, ten high. He pointed upwards. Like chickens drinking, the students lifted their eyes towards the distant ceiling.

Three tiers of racks; ground-floor level, first gallery, second gallery.

The spidery steelwork of gallery above gallery faded away in all directions into the dark. Near them, three red ghosts were busily unloading demijohns from a moving staircase.

The escalator from the Social Predestination Room.

Each bottle could be placed on one of fifteen racks, each rack, though you couldn't see it, was a conveyor travelling at the rate of thirty-three and a third centimetres an hour. Two hundred and sixty seven days at eight metres a day. Two thousand one hundred and thirty-six metres in all. One circuit of the cellar at ground level, one on the first gallery, half on the second, and on the two hundred and sixty-seventh morning, daylight in the Decanting Room. Independent existence – so called.

(12) 'But in the interval,' Mr Foster concluded, 'we've managed to do a lot to them. Oh, a very great deal.' His laugh was knowing and triumphant.

'That's the spirit I like,' said the Director once more. 'Let's walk round. You tell them everything Mr Foster.'

Mr Foster duly told them.

Told them of the growing embryo on its bed of peritoneum. Told them of the tests for sex carried out in the neighbourhood of Metre 200. Explained the system of labelling – a T for the males, a circle for the females and for those who were destined to become freemartins a question mark, black on a white ground.

He rubbed his hands. For, of course, they didn't content themselves with merely hatching embryos; any cow could do that.

'We also predestinate and condition. We decant our babies as socialized human beings, as Alphas or Epsilons, as future sewerage workers or future ... ' He was going to say future World Controllers, but correcting himself, said 'future Directors of Hatcheries' instead.

The DHC acknowledged the compliment with a smile.

(13) They were passing Metre 320 on Rack 11. A young Beta-minus mechanic was busy with a screw-driver and spanner on the blood-surrogate pump of a passing bottle. The hum of the electric motor deepened by fractions of a tone as he turned the nuts. Down, down ... A final twist, a glance at the revolution counter, and he was done. He moved two paces down the line and began the same process on the next pump.

'Reducing the number of revolutions per minute,' Mr Foster explained. 'The surrogate goes round slower; therefore passes through the lung at longer intervals; therefore gives the embryo less oxygen. Nothing like oxygen-shortage for keeping an embryo below par.' Again he rubbed his hands.

'But why do you want to keep the embryo below par?' asked an ingenuous student.

'Ass!' said the Director, breaking a long silence. 'Hasn't it occurred to you that an Epsilon embryo must have an Epsilon environment as well as an Epsilon heredity?'

It evidently hadn't occurred to him. He was covered with confusion.

'The lower the caste,' said Mr Foster, 'the shorter the oxygen.' The first organ affected was the brain. After that the skeleton. At seventy per cent of normal oxygen you got dwarfs. At less than seventy, eyeless monsters.

'Who are no use at all,' concluded Mr Foster.

'... in Epsilons,' said Mr Foster very justly, 'we don't need human intelligence.'

Didn't need and didn't get it. But though the Epsilon mind was more mature at ten, the Epsilon body was not fit to work till eighteen. Long years of superfluous and wasted immaturity. If the physical development could be speeded up till it was as quick, say, as a cow's, what an enormous saving to the Community!

'Enormous!' murmured the students. Mr Foster's enthusiasm was infectious.

(14) Their wanderings through the crimson twilight had brought them to the neighbourhood of Metre 170 on Rack 9. From this point onwards Rack 9 was enclosed and the bottles performed the remainder of their journey in a kind of tunnel, interrupted here and there by openings two or three metres wide.

'Heat conditioning,' said Mr Foster.

Hot tunnels alternated with cool tunnels. Coolness was wedded to discomfort in the form of hard X-rays. By the time they were decanted the embryos had a horror of cold. They were predestined to emigrate to the tropics, to be miners and acetate silk spinners and steel workers. Later on their minds would be made to endorse the judgement of their bodies. 'We condition them to thrive on heat,' concluded Mr Foster. Our colleagues upstairs will teach them to love it.'

'And that,' put in the Director sententiously, 'that is the secret of happiness and virtue – liking what you've *got* to do. All conditioning aims at that: making people like their inescapable social destiny.'

... the Director...looked at his watch. 'Ten to three,' he said. We must go up to the Nurseries before the children have finished their afternoon sleep.'

III

(15) Mr Foster was left in the Decanting Room. The DHC and his students stepped into the nearest lift and were carried up to the fifth floor.

INFANT NURSERIES. NEO-PAVLOVIAN CONDITIONING ROOMS, announced the notice board.

The Director opened the door. They were in a large bare room, very bright and sunny; for the whole of the southern wall was a single window. Half a dozen nurses, trousered and jacketed in the regulation white viscose-lined uniform, their hair aseptically hidden under their white caps, were engaged in setting out bowls of roses in a long row across the floor. Big bowls, packed tight with blossom. Thousands of petals, ripe-blown and silky smooth, like the cheeks of innumerable little cherubs, but of cherubs, in that bright light, not exclusively pink and Aryan, but also luminously Chinese, also Mexican, also apoplectic with too much blowing of celestial trumpets, also pale as death, pale with the posthumous whiteness of marble.

(16) The nurses stiffened to attention as the DHC came in.

'Set out the books,' he said curtly.

In silence the nurses obeyed his command. Between the rose bowls the books were duly set out – a row of nursery quartos opened invitingly each at some gaily coloured image of a beast or fish or bird.

'Now bring in the children.'

They hurried out of the room and returned in a minute or two, each pushing a kind of dumb-waiter laden, on all of its wire-netted shelves, with eight-month-old babies, all exactly alike (a Bokanovsky Group, it was evident) and all (since their caste was Delta) dressed in khaki.

'Put them down on the floor.'

The infants were unloaded.

'Now turn them so they can see the flowers and books.'

(17) Turned, the babies at once fell silent, then began to crawl towards those clusters of sleek colours, those shapes so gay and brilliant on the white pages. As they approached, the sun came out of momentary eclipse behind a cloud. The roses flamed up as though with a sudden passion from within; a new and profound significance seemed to suffuse the shining pages of the books. From the ranks of the crawling babies came little squeals of excitement, gurgles and twitterings of pleasure.

The Director rubbed his hands. 'Excellent!' he said. 'It might almost have been done on purpose.'

The swiftest crawlers were already at their goal. Small hands reached out uncertainly, touched, grasped, unpetalling the transfigured roses, crumpling the illuminated pages of the books. The Director waited until all were happily busy. Then, 'Watch carefully,' he said. And lifting his hand, he gave the signal.

The Head Nurse, who was standing by a switchboard at the other end of the room, pressed down a little lever.

There was a violent explosion. Shriller and ever shriller, a siren shrieked. Alarm bells maddeningly sounded.

The children started, screamed; their faces were distorted with terror.

'And now,' the Director shouted (for the noise was deafening), 'now we proceed to rub in the lesson with a mild electric shock.'

He waved his hand again, and the Head Nurse pressed a second lever. The screaming of the babies suddenly changed its tone. There was something desperate, almost insane, about the sharp spasmodic yelps to which they now gave utterance. Their little bodies twitched and stiffened; their limbs moved jerkily as if to the tug of unseen wires.

'We can electrify that whole strip of floor,' bawled the Director in explanation. 'But that's enough,' he signalled to the nurse.

The explosions ceased, the bells stopped ringing, the shriek of the siren died down from tone to tone into silence. The stiffly twitching bodies relaxed, and what had become the sob and yelp of infant maniacs broadened out once more into a normal howl of terror.

'Offer them the flowers and books again.'

The nurses obeyed; but at the approach of the roses, at the mere sight of those gaily-coloured images of pussy and cock-a-doodle-doo and baa-baa black sheep, the infants shrank away in horror; the volume of their howling suddenly increased.

'Observe,' said the Director triumphantly, 'observe.'

Books and loud noises, flowers and electric shocks – already in the infant mind these couples were compromisingly linked; and after two hundred repetitions of the same or a similar lesson would be wedded indissolubly. What man has joined, nature is powerless to put asunder.

(18)   'They'll grow up with what the psychologists used to call an 'instinctive' hatred of books and flowers. Reflexes unalterably conditioned. They'll be safe from books and botany all their lives.' The Director turned to his nurses. 'Take them away.'

One of the students held up his hand; and though he could see quite well why you couldn't have lower-caste people wasting the Community's time over books, and that there was always the risk of their reading something which might undesirably decondition one of their reflexes, yet ... well, he couldn't understand about the flowers. Why go to the trouble of making it psychologically impossible for Deltas to like flowers?

Patiently the DHC explained. If the children were made to scream at the sight of a rose, that was on the grounds of high economic policy. Not very long ago (a century or thereabouts), Gammas, Deltas, even Epsilons, had been conditioned to like flowers – flowers in particular and wild nature in general. The idea was to make them want to be going out at every opportunity, and so compel them to consume transport.

'And didn't they consume transport?' asked the student.

'Quite a lot,' the DHC replied. 'But nothing else.'

Primroses and landscapes, he pointed out, have one grave defect: they are gratuitous. A love of nature keeps no factories busy. It was decided to abolish the love of nature, at any rate, among the lower classes; to abolish the love of nature, but *not* the tendency to consume transport. For of course it was essential that they should keep on going to the country, even though they hated it. The problem was to find an economically sounder reason for consuming transport than a mere affection for primroses and landscapes. It was duly found.

'We condition the masses to hate the country,' concluded the Director. 'But simultaneously we condition them to love all country sports. At the same time, we see to it that all country sports shall entail the use of elaborate apparatus. So that they consume manufactured articles as well as transport. Hence those electric shocks.'

'I see,' said the student, and was silent, lost in admiration.

IV

(19)   There was a silence; then, clearing his throat, 'Once upon a time,' the Director began, 'while Our Ford was still on earth, there was a little boy called Reuben Rabinovitch. Reuben was the child of Polish-speaking parents.' The Director interrupted himself.

'You know what Polish is, I suppose?'

'A dead language.'

'Like French and German,' added another student, officiously showing off his learning.

He returned to Little Reuben – to Little Reuben in whose room, one evening, by an oversight, his father and mother ... happened to leave the radio turned on.

While the child was asleep, a programme broadcast from London suddenly started to come through; and the next morning, to the astonishment of his ... [parents] ..., Little Reuben woke up repeating word for word a long lecture by that curious old writer ('one of the very few whose works have been permitted to come down to us'), George Bernard Shaw, who was speaking, according to a well-authenticated tradition, about his own genius.

'The principle of sleep-teaching or hypnopaedia, had been discovered.' The DHC made an impressive pause.

The principle had been discovered; but many, many years were to elapse before the principle was usefully applied.

(20) 'The case of Little Reuben occurred only twenty-three years after Our Ford's first T-model was put on the market.' (Here the Director made a sign of the T on his stomach and all the students reverently followed suit.) Furiously the students scribbled, *Hypnopaedia, first used officially in A.F. 214. Why not before?*

'The early experimenters,' the DHC was saying, 'were on the wrong track. They thought that hypnopaedia could be made an instrument of intellectual education ... Whereas, if they'd only started on *moral* education,' said the Director, leading the way towards the door. The students followed him, desperately scribbling, as they walked and all the way up in the lift. 'Moral education, which ought never, in any circumstances, to be rational.'

'Silence, silence,' whispered a loud speaker as they stepped out at the fourteenth floor, and 'Silence, silence,' the trumpet mouths indefatigably repeated at intervals down every corridor. The students and even the Director rose automatically to the tips of their toes. They were Alphas, of course; but even Alphas have been well conditioned. 'Silence, silence.' All the air of the fourteenth floor was sibilant with the categorical imperative.

Fifty yards of tiptoeing brought them to a door which the Director cautiously opened. They stepped over the threshold into the twilight of a shuttered dormitory. Eighty cots stood in a row against the wall. They was a sound of light regular breathing and a continuous murmur, as of very faint voices remotely whispering.

A nurse rose as they entered and came to attention before the Director.

'What's the lesson this afternoon?' he asked.

'We had Elementary Sex for the first forty minutes,' she answered. 'But now it's switched over to Elementary Class Consciousness.'

The Director walked slowly down the long line of cots. Rosy and relaxed with sleep, eighty little boys and girls lay softly breathing. There was a whisper under every pillow. The DHC halted and, bending over one of the little beds, listened attentively.

'Elementary Class Consciousness, did you say? Let's have it repeated a little louder by the trumpet.'

At the end of the room a loud speaker projected from the wall. The Director walked up to it and pressed a switch.

'... all wear green,' said a soft but very distinct voice, beginning in the middle of a sentence, 'and Delta children wear khaki. Oh no, I don't want to play with Delta children. And Epsilons are still worse. They're too stupid to be able to read or write. Besides, they wear black, which is such a beastly colour. I'm *so* glad I'm a Beta.'

There was a pause and the voice began again.

'Alpha children wear grey. They work much harder than we do, because they're so frightfully clever. I'm really awfully glad I'm a Beta, because I don't work so hard. And then we are much better than the Gammas and the Deltas. Gammas are stupid. They all wear green, and Delta children wear khaki. Oh no, I don't want to play with Delta children. And Epsilons are still worse. They're too stupid to be able ...'

(21) The Director pushed back the switch. The voice was silent. Only its thin ghost continued to mutter from beneath the eighty pillows.

'They'll have that repeated forty or fifty times more before they wake; then again on Thursday, and again on Saturday. A hundred and twenty times three times a week for thirty months. After which they go on to a more advanced lesson.'

Roses and electric shocks, the khaki of Deltas and a whiff of asafoetida – wedded indissolubly before the child can speak. But wordless conditioning is crude and wholesale; cannot bring home the finer distinctions, cannot inculcate the more complex courses of behaviour. For that there must be words, but words without reason. In brief, hypnopaedia.

'The greatest moralizing and socializing force of all time.'

The students took it down in their books. Straight from the horse's mouth.

V

(22) It was a small factory of lighting-sets for helicopters, a branch of the Electrical Equipment Corporation. They were met on the roof itself (for that circular letter of recommendation from the Controller was magical in its effects) by the Chief Technician and the Human Element Manager. They walked downstairs into the factory.

'Each process,' explained the Human Element Manager, 'is carried out, as far as possible, by a single Bokanovsky group.'

(23) And, in effect, eighty-three almost noseless black brachycephalic Deltas were cold-pressing. The fifty-six four-spindle chucking and turning machines were being manipulated by fifty-six aquiline and ginger Gammas. One hundred and seven heat-conditioned Epsilon Senegalese were working in the foundry. Thirty-two Delta females, long-headed, sandy, with narrow pelvises, all within 20 millimetres of 1 metre

69 centimetres tall, were cutting screws. In the assembling room, the dynamos were being put together by two sets of Gamma-Plus dwarfs. The two low work tables faced one another; between them crawled the conveyor with its load of separate parts; forty-seven blond heads were confronted by forty-seven brown ones. Forty-seven snubs by forty-seven hooks; forty-seven receding by forty-seven prognathous. The completed mechanisms were inspected by eighteen identical curly auburn girls in Gamma green, packed in crates by thirty-four short-legged, left-handed male Delta-Minuses, and loaded into the waiting trucks and lorries by sixty-three blue-eyed, flaxen and freckled Epsilon Semi-Morons.

(24)   'O brave new world ...' By some malice of his memory the Savage found himself repeating Miranda's words. 'O brave new world that has such people in it.'

'And I assure you,' the Human Element Manager concluded, as they left the factory, 'we hardly ever have any trouble with our workers. We always find ...'

But the Savage had suddenly broken away from his companions and was violently retching behind a clump of laurels, as though the solid earth had been a helicopter in an air pocket.

12.4 REV: Question search

Objective

- To encourage students to revise the key facts and concepts associated with scientific management.

Introduction

The purpose of this test is to ensure that students read the chapter thoroughly, and are fully conversant with its content. On this occasion, students are provided with answers, and have to find the relevant questions. All the answers are to be found in *ORBIT3*, Chapter 12.

Procedure

Below are a list of 36 answers. Review the chapter, and write in the appropriate question alongside each of the answers provided.

Answer	Question
1. 1.85	
2. 5	
3. 12.5	
4. 18	
5. 20–50	
6. 92	
7. 2000	
8. 350	
9. Bethlehem	

10. Billancourt	
11. Bunker	
12. Midvale	
13. Philadelphia	
14. Watertown	
15. Winslow	
16. 1856	
17. 1898	
18. 1905	
19. 1911	
20. 1914	
21. Best-known-way-at-present	
22. Betterment-of-work	
23. Piecework	
24. Fatigue	
25. Field system	

26. Functional	
27. Mental revolution	
28. One-best-way	
29. Ergonomics	
30. Standardization	
31. Systematic soldiering	
32. Therbligs	
33. Rationalism	
34. Modern machine theory	
35. Farmer machines	
36. Systems	

Chapter 13
Bureaucracy and roles

13.1 LGA: Organizational characteristics

Objectives

- To allow students to assess the level of bureaucratization in an organization of their choice.
- To familiarize students with the characteristics of Max Weber's ideal type bureaucracy.

Introduction

While the concept of bureaucracy is easily understood by students, its concrete manifestation in organizational structure is less readily appreciated. The purpose of this exercise is to help students assess the degree to which a given organization possesses bureaucratic characteristics.

Procedure

Step 1 This instrument measures the degree to which five characteristics are optimally present in a particular organization's structure. Think of an organization with which you are familiar. This may be the university that you are studying at, your present or past firm, your church, social or sports club or trade union. Write in your focus organization in the space below:

Organization: _____

Step 2 The ten questions that follow ask you about certain conditions in the above named organization. Indicate, with a tick, which of the five responses most accurately describe the conditions in it. There are no right or wrong answers as you are only trying to be accurately descriptive of existing organizational conditions and characteristics.

	completely	mostly	partly	slightly	not at all
1. Work roles in this organization are highly specialized; each person has clear cut authority and responsibility.					
2. The formal hierarchy in this organization is formal to the point of being rigid and inflexible.					
3. In this organization people are selected and promoted on the basis of their demonstrated technical competence.					
4. It often seems that people in this organization are so concerned with conforming to rules and procedures, that this interferes with their psychological well-being.					
5. Everyone in this organization expects to be subject to the same set of rules and controls; there are no favourites.					
6. People in this organization are often so wrapped up in their own narrow specialities, that they can't see that we all have common interests. This causes unnecessary conflicts.					
7. The job titles and positions in this organization are arranged in a clear and logical hierarchy.					
8. Overall, this organization is composed of a managerial elite who got where they are through political wheeling-and-dealing.					
9. Managers in this organization see themselves on a clear career ladder and expect to make regular progress in their careers.					
10. Many of the rules in this organization have either become ends in themselves, with no logical function, or else have come to specify the minimum tolerable performance levels.					

Step 3   Insert the question numbers as supplied by your instructor. Then score your answers using this key:

For question numbers:	completely	mostly	partly	slightly	not at all		
_ _ _ _ _	5 pts.	4 pts.	3 pts.	2 pts.	1 pt.	=	_____
For question numbers:							
_ _ _ _ _	1 pt.	2 pts.	3 pts.	4 pts.	5 pts.	=	_____
						Total	_____

Step 4   Add up the points for all 10 questions to get your score. The higher the score, the more your focus organization manifests the characteristics of a true bureaucracy (see *ORBIT3*, Chapter 13). Similarly, a low score indicates an absence of bureaucratic features. For example:

Below 18   Serious problems. Either over-bureaucratic rigidity or under-bureaucratic chaos.

18–24   Low bureaucracy, indicating a cause for concern.

25–35   Average bureaucracy.

over 35   Indicates a 'strong' bureaucratic structure.

Your overall score above is composed of an analysis of five important characteristics of bureaucracy, each of which is measured by two questions:

Questions 1 and 6
Each office has a clearly defined sphere of competence resulting in work being specialized and each office holder having a specified amount of authority and responsibility.

Questions 2 and 7
There is a clear and logical hierarchy of authority and responsibility that everyone knows. Through a firmly ordered system of super- and subordination, the supervision of lower offices is carried out by higher ones.

Questions 3 and 8
Candidates are selected on the basis of their technical qualifications, and promoted on their demonstrated competence and performance.

Questions 4 and 9
People see their job as constituting their career, with all managers and professionals having a regular, fixed salary.

Questions 5 and 10
The management of the office follow rules and regulations which are more or less stable, more or less exhaustive, sensible, can be learned, and which are applied in the same way to everyone.

You can add up the scores for the five item pairs above in order to examine specific bureaucratic characteristics. The scores for each will range from 2 to 10 with:

Under 5   Suggests specific problems exist with respect to that characteristic.

5–7   Average.

Above 7   Effective bureaucratic characteristic.

Source: M. Sashkin and W.C. Morris, *Experiencing Management*, Addison Wesley, 1987, pp. 89–91. Used with permission.

13.2 SGA: Managerial assumptions and organization structure

Objective

• To demonstrate how managerial assumptions about human behaviour become formalised into organizational structures and operating systems.

Introduction

This activity provides students with an opportunity to consider the relationship between managerial assumptions and organizational structure. It allows them to explore the extent to which an organization's structure reflects its managers' assumptions about employees' behaviour and motivation. The presence or absence of rules, roles, procedures, controls and so on, as well as their nature, and the way they are implemented, tells employees a great deal about how the organization views them. In this activity, students will consider in depth one organization with which they are familiar.

Procedure

Step 1   Before the session, students complete the questionnaire *Assumptions about people* questionnaire in the workbook using the scoring frame.

Step 2   Students familiarize themselves with Douglas McGregor's Theory X and Theory Y. This is summarized in *ORBIT3*, Chapter 11.

Step 3   Based on their understanding of McGregor's ideas, they predict their personal balance between Theory X and Theory Y (50–50; 70–30; 25–75?).

Step 4   At the class session, they score their questionnaire using the key provided by their instructor.

Step 5   Each student's individual score reflects their personal assumptions about people. Managers' assumptions about other people and human nature become translated into an organization's structure.

Select one organization with which you are familiar. This may be a past or present company that you worked for, or a shop, school, club or your university, or some similar institution. Below is a detailed list of McGregor's Theory X and Theory Y assumptions. Identify aspects of your chosen organization, such as its job design, reward systems, procedures, practices, authority and responsibility allocation, division of labour, departmentalization, span-of-control, rules, hierarchy, and decide whether each embodies a Theory X or a Theory Y assumption. For example, if the company required all its employees to 'clock in and out' of work, then this might reflect Theory X assumptions 1 that, 'people are naturally lazy and prefer to do nothing'. A single firm many have a predominance of Theory X or Theory Y assumptions, or a mixture of both.

Step 6   In the class, in syndicates, and using McGregor's ten dimensions as a discussion framework, members should supply personal examples of structural elements which, in their view, reflect a Theory X or a Theory Y philosophy.

Assumptions about people questionnaire

This instrument is designed to help you to understand the assumptions that you make about people and human nature. There are ten pairs of statements. Assign 10 points across each pair of statements to indicate your relative belief in them (e.g. 10–0; 9–1; 5–5; 2–8, etc.).

Remember the points in each pair must total ten. Be honest with yourself, and resist the natural tendency to respond 'like you think you should'. This is not a test, and there are no right or wrong answers. The instrument is designed to be a stimulus for personal reflection and discussion.

1. (a) It's only human nature for people to do as little work as they can get away with.

   (b) When people avoid work, it's usually because their work has been deprived of its meaning.

2. (c) If employees have access to any information they want, they tend to have better attitudes and behave more responsibility.

   (d) If employees have access to more information than they need to do their immediate tasks, they will usually misuse it.

3. (e) One problem in asking for the ideas of employees is that their perspective is too limited for their suggestions to be of much practical value.

   (f) Asking employees for their ideas broadens their perspective and results in the development of useful suggestions.

4. (g) If people don't use much imagination and ingenuity on the job, it's probably because relatively few people have much of either.

   (h) Most people are imaginative and creative but may not show it because of limitations imposed by supervision and the job.

5. (i) People tend to raise their standards if they are accountable for their own behaviour and for correcting their own mistakes.

   (j) People tend to lower their standards if they are not punished for their misbehaviour and mistakes.

6. (k) It's better to give people both good and bad news because employees want the whole story, no matter how painful.

   (l) It's better to withhold unfavourable news about business because most employees really only want to hear the good news.

7. (m) Because a supervisor is entitled to more respect than those below him/her in the organization, it weakens their prestige to admit that a subordinate was right and that they were wrong.

   (n) Because people at all levels are entitled to equal respect, a supervisor's prestige is increased when s/he supports this principle by admitting that a subordinate was right and that they were wrong.

8. (o) If you give people enough money, they are less likely to be concerned with such intangibles as being given responsibility or recognition for the job.

(p) If you give people interesting and challenging work, they are less likely to complain about such things as pay and supplementary benefits.

9. (q) If people are allowed to set their own goals and standards of performance, they tend to set them higher than the boss would.

(r) If people are allowed to set their own goals and standards of performance, they tend to set them lower than the boss would.

10. (s) The more knowledge and freedom a person has regarding their job, the more controls are needed to keep them in line.

(t) The more knowledge and freedom a person has regarding their job, the fewer controls are needed to ensure satisfactory job performance.

Scoring frame

1. (a) ____ (b) ____ 10	6. (k) ____ (l) ____ 10
2. (c) ____ (d) ____ 10	7. (m) ____ (n) ____ 10
3. (e) ____ (f) ____ 10	8. (o) ____ (p) ____ 10
4. (g) ____ (h) ____ 10	9. (q) ____ (r) ____ 10
5. (i) ____ (j) ____ 10	10. (s) ____ (t) ____ 10

Theory X assumptions	Theory Y assumptions
1. People are naturally lazy; they prefer to do nothing.	1. People are naturally active; they set goals and enjoy striving.
2. People work mostly for money and status rewards.	2. People seek many satisfactions in work; pride in achievement; enjoyment of process; sense of contribution; pleasure in association; stimulation of new challenges; etc.
3. The main force keeping people productive in their work is fear of being demoted or fired.	3. The main force keeping people in their work is desire to achieve their personal and social goals.
4. People remain children grown larger; they are naturally dependent on leaders.	4. People normally mature beyond childhood; they aspire to independence, self-fulfilment, responsibility.
5. People expect and depend on direction from above; they do not want to think for themselves.	5. People close to the situation see and feel what is needed and are capable of self-direction.
6. People need to be told, shown and trained in proper methods of work.	6. People who understand and care about what they are doing can devise and improve their own methods of doing work.
7. People need supervisors who will watch them closely enough to be able to praise good work and reprimand errors.	7. People need a sense that they are respected as capable of assuming responsibility and self-correction.
8. People have little interest beyond their immediate, material concerns.	8. People seek to give meaning to their lives by identifying with nations, communities, churches, unions, companies, causes.
9. People need specific instruction on what to do and how to do it; larger policy issues are none of their business.	9. People need ever-increasing understanding; they need to grasp the meaning of the activities in which they are engaged; they have cognitive hunger for the universe
10. People appreciate being treated with courtesy.	10. People crave genuine respect from their fellows.
11. People are naturally compartmentalised; work demands are entirely different from leisure activities.	11. People are naturally integrated; when work and play are too sharply separated both deteriorate; 'The only reason a wise man can give for preferring leisure to work is the better quality of the work he can do during leisure'.

12. People naturally resist change; they prefer to stay in old ruts.	12. People naturally tire of monotonous routine and enjoy new experiences; to some degree, everyone is creative.
13. Jobs are primary and must be done; people are selected, trained and fitted to predefined jobs.	13. People are primarily seeking self-realization; jobs must be designed, modified and fitted to people.
14. People are formed by heredity, childhood and youth; as adults they remain static; old dogs don't learn new tricks.	14. People constantly grow; it is never too late to learn; they enjoy learning and increasing their understanding and capability.
15. People need to be 'inspired' (pep talked) or pushed or driven.	15. People need to be released and encouraged and assisted.

Procedure

Ask students to complete the *Assumptions about people* questionnaire before proceeding. Using your own notes, do a short input on Douglas McGregor's Theory X and Theory Y assumptions. These are covered briefly in *ORBIT3*, Chapter 11. Ask students to predict their personal balance between X and Y assumptions (50–50; 70–30; 255–7?), and present the scoring key below on an overhead transparency:

Scoring key:

Add the numbers associated with each set of letters as shown below:

(a) + (d) + (e) + (g) + (j) + (l) + (m) + (o) + (r) + (s)   =   _____ Theory X score

(b) + (c) + (f) + (h) + (i) + (k) + (n) + (p) + (q) + (t)   =   _____ Theory Y score

In the class, using a blackboard or flipchart, the instructor divides the class (as far as possible) into syndicates by similarity of organization: for example, electronics companies, shops, schools, churches, local and central government departments, etc. Using McGregor's ten sets of assumptions dimensions as a discussion framework, syndicate members supply examples of structural elements which reflect either Theory X or Theory Y management assumptions.

13.3 PREP: Role set analysis and role conflict

Objectives

- To examine role conflict in an organizational setting.
- To clarify your position in an organization.
- To establish what demands and expectations are made of you in your role.
- To identify possible and actual areas of conflict arising from your role.

Introduction

One source of conflict in organizations is that which arises from the different expectations that those in particular roles have of each other. This activity helps you to examine this. The activity is designed to be used by both undergraduates and experienced managers. The former may choose to consider their role as a student at the university. Significant members of their role-set might include fellow students, course instructors, personal tutors or advisors, employers, parents and boy- and girlfriends. The latter group of managers may choose to make an analysis of their work situation.

Procedure

Step 1   Before the class, use the blank space in your workbook, (see box below), and write in the title of a role that you occupy in an organization (e.g. student, nurse, operations manager).

Step 2   Around the box, enter, in circles, the titles of all the other people who make significant demands upon you, and have significant expectations of the role that you occupy (e.g. course instructor, nurse administrator, divisional manager).

Step 3   You will have reciprocal expectations of, and demands on, these people. You should not forget members of other organizations, if appropriate (e.g. student union officer, nursing equipment salesperson, customer).

Those with whom your links are particularly strong should be located nearer the box at the centre of the page. Weaker-linked individuals should be located more on the periphery. Five such individuals should be identified by their job title.

Using the sheet overleaf, list in column A the five members of your role-set who make the most demands upon you (i.e. those identified in the circles on your diagram). For each, in turn, complete the other three columns.

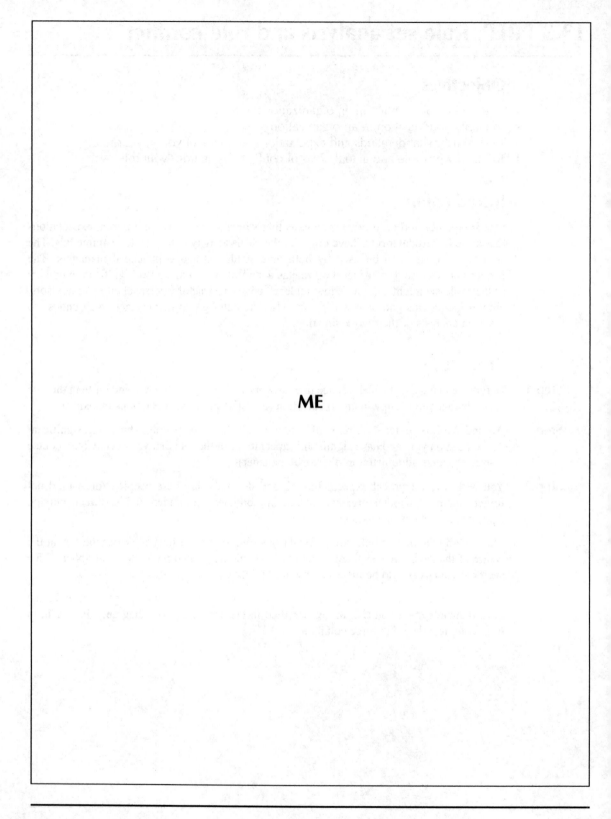

A	B	C	D
Role set member	Their demands/ expectations of me as	My demands/ expectations of them as	Possible conflict areas
1.			
2.			
3.			
4.			
5.			

Step 4   Now answer the following four questions:

1. Are you sure that you know what all the demands and expectations are that others have of you? Would these others agree with what you have written?

2. Would your expectations of them fit in with their perceptions? If asked, would they agree with what you have written?

3. Can you cite any specific examples of problems related to the conflict areas in column D? How have you tried to resolve these?

4. What conflicts do you experience between roles, e.g. being a student and an employee simultaneously?

Bring these notes with you to the next class.

Step 5   1. Discuss with other syndicate group members the chart showing your network. Use this to check that you have included all significant relationships.

2. Identify how your network differs from those of other members of your group. What are the reasons for this? What are the implications of this for the skills you need to develop?

3. Exchange information about the conflicts or difficulties shown up in column D. Suggest practical actions that might be taken to address two of these.

4. Prepare to report to the class as a whole on one specific example of a role conflict that you are experiencing and suggest how it might be resolved.

13.4 REV: Missing letters

Objective

- To assess your knowledge of the concepts, ideas and authors considered in Chapter 13 of *ORBIT3*.

Introduction

This test concerns the bureaucracy and roles. If you have read and understood the contents of Chapter 13, you should find this test straightforward.

Procedure

Write, in the box alongside, the one missing letter from each of the jumbled or anagrammed words. When the letters are read downwards, they spell out three more words closely related to this chapter.

Insert missing
letters here

	Missing letter	Anagram	Clue
1.		INSEN	Originator of the concept of 'adhocracy' as an alternative to bureaucracy.
2.		ITHOTYAR	Getting things done because order or requests are seen as legitimate.
3.		SAYRIG	He observed how bureaucracy impacted negatively on employees' psychological maturity and mental well-being.
4.		PROW	Using threats of force or sanctions to get things done.
5.		RACISM ITCH	A type of authority based on the belief that the leader possesses some heroic or religious virtue.
6.		EQSAJ	A supporter of those who felt it had not been implemented properly.
7.		ON IMAGINED SIK	The reliance on rules, tradition, precedence and standard procedures reduces or eliminates the need to do this.
8.		ZEROIC	A critic of bureaucracy who felt that it did not learn from its own mistakes.

9.		REGLY	He argued that organizational rules and roles are a better predictor of an employee's behaviour than their personality.
10.		VIPER PRIEST	An aspect of bureaucratic structure designed to ensure equal treatment of all.
11.		SIMPLETON AIR	A definition of role which stresses how it should be performed.
12.		LIFE SPONSOR	A form of bureaucracy used to organize doctors, engineers and lecturers.
13.		BOSRIB	He listed reasons to explain the on-going popularity of bureaucratic organizational structures.
14.		IS COST FUNNY	These inefficiencies of bureaucracy were studied by researchers in the 1950s.
15.		ALIENIST HOP	The mixture of feelings and emotions which exist between people.
16.		ANTRIAL	The type of principle upon which authority is based in a bureaucracy.
17.		IN FAT AIR ZOOM	Another term for bureaucracy.
18.		SLUR	Their purpose is to encourage co-ordination between and conformity among employees.
19.		SLOTREE	For a lecturer, the head of department, students, fellow lecturers and secretaries are part of their _____.

Chapter 14

Classical management theory

14.1 Large group activity: **Exodus 18: 13–26**
14.2 Small group activity: **Speedyprint Ltd**
14.3 Prepared task: **Sanders and Murgatroyd, Accountants**
14.4 Review: **Reorganizing the Allied Paint Company**

14.1 LGA: Exodus 18: 13–26

Objectives

- To introduce students to the purposes of organizational design.
- Give them practice in redesigning the structure of an organization.

Introduction

Throughout recorded history, whenever humankind has sought to achieve a major goal that has necessitated the contribution of many people, there has always been the need to apply the skills of management and organization. The construction of the Pyramids, starting in 2700 B.C., involved the application of project management skills at the very highest level. It is true that these skills were not written down in the form of 'principles of management' until the beginning of the twentieth century. However, they were both known about, were communicated orally, and have been applied for thousands of years.

This activity gives students the opportunity to become familiar with the idea of consciously designing an organization's structure and introduces them to some of the key concepts involved. Perhaps more importantly, however, it makes the point that activities, management and organization, were not *invented* a hundred years ago, but have existed as long as human beings have banded together to achieve goals which they could not attain as individuals.

Procedure

As briefed by your instructor, read the case, 'Exodus 18: 13–26' and then answer the nine questions that follow.

Exodus 18: 13–26

All through recorded history people have had to organize themselves so as to accomplish their objectives. Moses was faced with an organization that prevented him from achieving the more important goals that his Boss has set him. Luckily Jethro, Moses' father-in-law, gave him some sound advice.

13. And it came to pass on the morrow, that Moses sat to judge the people; and the people stood by Moses from the morning unto the evening.

14. And when Moses' father-in-law saw all that he did to the people, he said, What is this thing that thou doest to the people? Why sittest thou thyself alone, and all the people stand by thee from morning unto evening?

15. And Moses said unto his father-in-law, Because the people come unto me to enquire of God:

16. When they have a matter, they come unto me; and I judge between one and another, and I do make them know the statutes of God, and His laws.

17. And Moses' father-in-law said unto him, The thing that thou doest is not good.

18. Thou wilt surely wear away, both thou, and this people that is with thee: for this thing is too heavy for thee; thou are not able to perform it thyself alone.

19. Harken now unto my voice, I will give thee counsel, and God shall be with thee: Be sure for the people to God-ward, that thou mayest bring the causes unto God:

20. And thou shalt teach them ordinances and laws, and shalt shew them the way wherein they must walk, and the work that they must do.

21. Moreover thou shalt provide out of all the people able men, such as fear God, men of truth, hating covertness; and place such over them to be rulers of thousands, and rulers of hundreds, rulers of fifties and rulers of tens:

22. And let them judge the people at all seasons: and it shall be, that every great matter they shall bring unto thee, but every small matter they shall judge: so shall it be easier for thyself, and they shall bear the burden with thee.

23. If thou shalt do this thing, and God command thee so, then thou shalt be able to endure, and all this people shall also go to their place in peace.

24. So Moses harkened to the voice of his father-in-law, and did all that he had said.

25. And Moses chose able men out of all Israel, and made them heads over the people, rulers of thousands, rulers of hundreds, rulers of fifties and rulers of tens.

26. And they judged the people at all seasons: the hard cases they brought unto Moses, but every small matter they judged themselves.

Numbers 1:44 mentions that the 'heads over the people' were twelve, one from each tribe. The total number of men of sword-bearing age (women were not counted in the scheme of things, since the issue of women's rights was still far off) was slightly over 600,000.

Questions

1. Assuming each of the twelve tribes to be of the same size (although they weren't), draw an organizational chart of the Nation of Israel in the Wilderness. You need only complete a chart for one tribe as we are assuming the others to be identical in size and structure.

2. What was Moses' span-of-control before the reorganization and after it?

3. How many levels of hierarchy were there below Moses?

4. Which tasks did Moses delegate to his subordinate managers? Speculate as to why he delegated these particular tasks?

5. Did Moses's father-in-law, Jethro, occupy a line or a staff position when he gave his advice to Moses? Why?

6. Did Moses occupy a line or a staff position? Why?

7. Who had the largest and smallest span-of-control?

8. In total, how many managers did Moses create to take over the duties he had previously done himself?

9. What effect do you think this reorganization had on Moses' ability to do his primary task of planning and leading the Nation of Israel to the Promised Land?

Note

This activity is taken from R.M. Fulmer and T.T. Herbert, *Exploring the New Management: A Study Guide*, Macmillan Publishing Company, 1978, pp. 78–80. Used with permission.

14.2 SGA: Speedyprint Ltd

Objectives

- To contrast the formal and informal organizational structures in an organization.
- To examine the consequences when individuals have not been incorporated fully into the formal organization structure.

Introduction

At an intellectual level, the distinction between formal and informal organization is easily grasped by students. So too are the concepts of line and staff relationships, authority, accountability and responsibility. However, being asked to identify these in an organizational context, is perhaps more complex. This activity gives students the opportunity to examine these concepts and their application, in a company setting.

Procedure

Step 1   Read the case *Speedyprint Ltd* and, using your knowledge from the course and the textbook, individually answer the questions below. Bring these notes with you to the next class session. Your instructor may give you additional directions with respect to the preparation of this activity.

Step 2   In your groups, discuss the individual answers to the questions set.

Speedyprint Ltd

Trevor Horton inherited the managing directorship of Speedyprint eight years ago. The firm was established in the 1970s and was located in Flexborough, a town of 40,000 inhabitants. He and his family owned the company. He had been more-or-less forced into this job upon the death of his father, as he was the only son. Mr Horton's training and ambition was to be a musician. As a result he seemed to be more interested in his composing and playing than in the success of the family business. Most of his time was spent attending concerts and practising the piano.

Nevertheless, Mr Horton did take an interest in the firm to the extent that he frequently made personnel and work changes which he felt improved the immediate situation. These changes were made on the spur-of-the-moment, and he rarely analysed a situation carefully so as to anticipate the possible effects or repercussions of his decision on the entire workforce. Mr Horton's manner with employees was quite forceful. He indicated that he was the owner and boss, and accepted no arguments. Mr Horton was assisted in his management task by Steven Philips, who was the general manager.

The organizational chart shows Horton and Philips and also Dennis Pringle, who was the chief accountant and office manager. Mr Pringle had been with the firm for twenty years, ever since he had left school. Since joining, he had been given a varied range of responsibilities until he had been formally appointed to these two posts eight years ago. Pringle had an easygoing nature, supervised little, and only gave orders when specifically requested to.

Because of his nature, he assumed an ever-increasing number of duties without making a fuss.

Toni Barlow was in her mid-twenties and had been hired by Horton earlier in the year. Toni had worked in the accounts department of an engineering company, but had left when her husband was offered a more senior job by his company. Her appointment was opportunistic. Toni and her husband were attending a local rotary club dinner at which Horton was present. Horton was introduced to Toni's husband through a mutual friend, and the three of them got talking. Finding out that she was an accountant and taking an instant liking to her (he said that she reminded him of his sister), Horton offered Toni a job at Speedyprint.

Toni would have preferred to visit the firm and meet the employees with whom she would work before deciding on the offer. However, Horton's offer was attractive, and she was currently between jobs. Horton seemed to want an immediate decision so, after discussing it with her husband during the meal, Toni accepted before Horton left that evening. Once Toni had accepted, Horton told his friend, 'I haven't talked this over with my chief accountant, but I'm sure it will be O.K.'

Speedyprint Ltd (partial organizational chart)

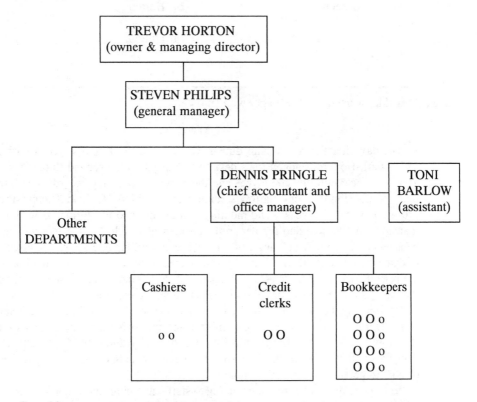

O = older women   o = younger women

The office staff at Speedyprint consisted of six young women and eleven older women. They all got on well with each other, met during the day and planned office parties and weekend coach trips. They often met after work, being members of the local church and leisure centre. The older office employees had been with the company virtually all their working lives. Indeed, some of them had been at Flexborough High School with Dennis Pringle, and had worked with him during the eight years he had been chief accountant and office manager. Because of their length of service, their 'chumminess' in the office, and the comparative freedom in their jobs, the office staff were satisfied to get somewhat less than the going local rate for the job.

The general office at Speedyprint was located on the first and second floors above the printing shop. The credit control department (three older women), cashiers (two younger girls), and Mr Pringle were on the first floor. The general accounts office (eight older women, and four younger girls), and Mr Horton and Mr Philips were located on the second floor.

Floor plan showing layout of offices

FLOOR 1
Credit control   Cashiers
O O O   o o   Mr Pringle

FLOOR 2
General accounts   Mr Horton
O O o
O O o   Mr Philips
O O o
                                           Toni

O = older women   o = younger women

The day after the rotary club dinner, Horton discussed Toni's arrival with most of the office staff. Horton arranged for a desk to be placed on the second floor. This would allow Toni to be near both the employees and the general accounting records which would be her main responsibility. Toni Barlow's main task would be to help Dennis Pringle in the preparation of daily, weekly and monthly accounting reports. Horton, as well as the general manager (Mr Philips) and the departmental managers, felt that the reports which they had been receiving from Pringle were of little use in controlling operations because they were out of date when they got them. Typically, they were received between one and four months after the period covered. Pringle acknowledged that these reports were issued late, but explained that he was too busy with day-to-day tasks to improve the situation.

On Toni's first day at the firm, she was taken on a tour of the printing works and the offices by Mr Horton, and was introduced to most of the employees including Dennis Pringle whom she would be assisting. Mr Horton introduced Toni to the office staff and to the general managers with the comment, 'Toni is going to help us out in the accounting office. Now we'll be able to get the reports out on time'.

Toni spent most of her first day talking to staff with whom she would be working. She also asked Mr Horton about the type of information that he and the general managers needed. The employees were very helpful and Toni looked forward to working with them in this friendly atmosphere. That evening, Toni and her husband were guests of Mr and Mrs Horton at a local restaurant as a 'welcome-to-the-firm' celebration. During the evening, Horton talked enthusiastically about music and what he was doing. Toni felt quite flattered when he said, 'I feel that I can confidently stay away from the office much more now knowing that the reports to our managers will be coming out on time'.

Toni spent most of the first week with Mr Pringle learning about the various accounting procedures. She found Pringle very cordial and willing to help whenever asked. Over the next few weeks the pair became quite friendly. As the months passed, the two with their wives, met for an evening of bridge. Toni respected Dennis Pringle's judgement and found him very obliging. Frequently, Pringle would say, 'Toni, you've really helped me out by taking the pressure of those reports off my shoulders. When Trevor isn't wrapped up in his music, he regularly grills me as to why they are so late'.

After a month, Toni became accustomed to the routine of her duties. She found herself working closely with most of the women in the two offices. All of them turned out to be involved, to some degree, in bookkeeping activities. Specifically, she was in daily contact with nine of the older women (eight on the second floor, and one on the first floor); and with three of the younger girl employees (two on the second floor and one on the first floor). Using the statistical and accounting data produced by these women, Toni prepared her financial reports for Mr Horton and the departmental managers.

Toni worked on her tasks with great commitment because she wanted to succeed at this job. Within two months, she was able to get reports onto the desks of Mr Horton, Mr Philips, and the departmental managers within a time which they found satisfactory. Toni was often called into senior departmental sales meetings to discuss the reports that she had prepared. Since Toni's desk was located on the second floor, it was convenient for Mr Horton or Mr Philips, to call her in a loud voice, with a comment such as, 'Toni, could you come in here and help us with these reports?'

Toni felt that she was doing a good job at Speedyprint. However, during the first six months she did have many minor problems. The three experiences described below were typical, and they are presented in the order in which they occurred.

(a) When requesting data from one of the older women, Toni was asked, 'What's the hurry? Dennis never pressured us to supply this information by a deadline. We gave it to him when we were ready'. In response, Toni explained how the reports would be used and the need for their promptness. It seemed to Toni that her explanation only encouraged the woman to delay giving her the information even longer.

(b) One of the younger girls in the second floor office came to Toni and complained that the credit clerks were making errors; in particular, on sales tickets, receiving invoices and packing slips. The girls frequently brought errors of this type to Toni's attention. As usual, she spoke tactfully and courteously to the clerks, and also to any other company employees who made errors. She pointed these out and explained how these affected the information that was needed. Some time later, Toni heard on the 'grapevine' that the employees whom she corrected had complained that she was trying to 'run the firm'.

(c) Mr Philips told Toni to instruct the girls in the first and second floor offices not to stay in the canteen so long in the mornings. It was the practice of all the girls to gather in the canteen at ten-thirty (Mr Pringle and Toni had coffee at their desks). Although a staggered coffee break would have made more sense, this practice had existed for a number of years without any objection from management. However, it seemed to Mr Philips that the girls frequently stayed longer than seemed reasonable. In response to Mr Philips' instructions, Toni said to the women in the offices, 'Mr Philips has asked me to ask you not to take such long coffee breaks in the morning'. She made this announcement to all the women as a group, on each floor, one afternoon as they were getting ready to go home.

Toni sometimes noticed resentment towards her amongst the older office women. She therefore tried to be especially nice to them. She attempted to be tactful and courteous in her requests for data, and to be helpful whenever they requested anything from her. Despite her efforts, through their actions, manner and words, the older women made Toni feel both uncomfortable and out of place.

One morning, about nine months after Toni joined, Mr Horton came into his office. Mr Horton had not been coming into the plant regularly for weeks because he was busy preparing for a recital. He said to Toni, 'I'd like you to do a couple of things for me as a kind of special project. First, revise our expenses code system. We need to expand our classification of expenses. The current one is out of date: it hasn't been changed for years. It'll mean staff having to memorize a new code, but I don't think they'll find it too difficult. And second, I want you to prepare a job analysis on each of the girls in this office. Mr Philips suggested that you do this. It's never been done before, so I think it will be useful to find out just what each of the girls is doing. Prepare one for the girls on the first floor too, will you? Take your time on these projects, just work them in with your regular duties. Oh, by the way, tell Dennis you're doing this for me'. Toni agreed that she would try to do this.

As Mr Horton left the office and Toni returned to her desk, she pondered how she would go about this new project.

1. (a) Prepare for contrast with the formal organizational chart, a chart that shows the informal organizational relationships that existed at Speedyprint Ltd.
    (b) Identify any significant differences between the two.
    (c) Has management encouraged these differences? How?

2. (a) What managerial and human relations errors were made in the process of hiring Toni Barlow and in introducing her into the organization?
    (b) Who made the errors?
    (c) What results did they have?

3. How did the following people affect Toni's successful performance of her duties?
    (a) Trevor Horton.
    (b Steven Philips.
    (c) Dennis Pringle.

4. List the problems that Toni faced during her first nine months at Speedyprint Ltd.
    (a) At what point did she face them?
    (b) Should she have been aware of each problem as it arose?
    (c) In what way, if any, should Toni have conducted herself differently?

5. Describe Toni Barlow's level and area of authority as perceived by:
    (a) Trevor Horton
    (b) Steven Philips
    (c) Dennis Pringle
    (d) Younger office women
    (e) Older office women
    (f) Toni Barlow

6. Did a satisfactory level of communication exist between the persons in this case? Explain.

7. How should Toni go about the project given to her at the end of the case? What particular problems does she now face?

8. Identify examples of change in this case. What are the effects of each? What is management's responsibility here?

14.3 PREP: Sanders and Murgatroyd, Accountants

Objectives

- To illustrate how different organizational perspectives can lead to differences in problem definition and solutions.
- To revise three major organizational perspectives.

Introduction

Organizational behaviour theory contains many different perspectives and approaches to problems which beset companies. Being predominantly based upon social science, many of the prescriptions offered compete with each other. To new students, especially those coming from science disciplines and backgrounds which offer, 'The one right answer', this may be both confusing and frustrating. Nevertheless this situation has to be confronted. In this activity, the same case study is analysed using three different perspectives. It stresses that every OB approach has both strengths and weaknesses, and that none is complete in itself.

Procedure

Individually, prepare the following assignment that Sanders and Murgatroyd's senior management has asked for:

1. An analysis of the reasons for the turnover of its trainee accountants.
2. A set of recommendations to solve the problem.

You are required to prepare three separate reports. These will analyse the problem and make recommendations from:

1. A scientific management perspective   (Taylor: *ORBIT3*, Chapter 12).
2. A human relations perspective   (Mayo: *ORBIT3*, Chapter 7).
3. A motivation perspective   (Herzberg: *ORBIT3*, Chapter 5).

Analyse the case as you think Frederick Taylor would, and then make recommendations based on his scientific management principles. Repeat the procedure for Elton Mayo, and finally for Frederick Herzberg. Re-read the textbook material before proceeding. *For each perspective*, your analysis should:

1. List the main principles of the perspective.
2. Identify those that are broken by the company.
3. Recommend the steps to be taken by the firm (in line with the perspective's principles).

Sanders and Murgatroyd, Accountants

1. Phil was one of 24 Trainee Accountants (TA) who worked for a large, international accounting firm. He had been with it for ten months every since he completed his B.Accountancy degree at university. He was pleased to get a job with this prestigious firm since it recruited only from the 10% of each year's graduating class. His academic

career had not been brilliant, but luckily his dad knew one of the senior partners in the firm. He said that it was a good, steady job. Phil was pleased that he had only to undergo an interview, and was spared the psychological and problem-solving tests that the other applicants were subjected to.

2.   On his first day, he was shown into a small office in which he was to work. He had hoped to share it with a fellow TA but apparently these people were scattered in similar small offices throughout the large building. Phil discovered his job responsibilities in an ad hoc manner as different senior auditors briefed him on what he was to do. He had expected an introductory course, or at least some sessions on the company since it had recruited two dozen graduates that year. He was interested in knowing about the firm, what it did, the different departments in which one could work and so on. His university friends with jobs at some large firms had called these induction courses. Anyway, no one invited him to attend an induction course here.

3.   In his post, Phil was responsible for gathering financial data and relevant information on each client to whom he was assigned. Having accumulated the information, he often he had to supplement it with visits and interviews with the client's staff. Phil roughed out an outline of the report, which laid out the factors of importance in the client's financial standing.

4.   Once he had got to grips with it, Phil found the job extremely tedious. It involved him wading through mountains of cost data, as well as tracing cost figures to determine if they were correctly allocated. Sometimes he would use the financial summaries provided by the clients, while at other times he referred to past data collected by F & C. Most of the time he did not bother to cross check the information because this practice was timeconsuming. However, when dealing with the accounts of certain clients, he did do this secondary analysis. Additionally, Phil had to ensure that all the categories of data were covered and appraised in his analysis. Once his research was completed, he passed it on to a Senior Auditor (SA) who wrote the final report based on Phil's work, correcting any minor errors. The SA then visited the client to give a verbal summary and to answer any questions. Meanwhile, Phil started another assignment.

5.   This occurred irrespective of the complexity of the report. In some 60% of cases, Phil found that the SA's final report differed very little from his own. The six senior auditors were divided into departments according to the type of organization they dealt with. When a job came in, they called upon a TA who was either between reports, or who was about to complete one. Sometimes finding one took a bit of time as the SA's secretaries had to ring around the TAs to find out who had finished what.

6.   Looking at Phil's job in a little more detail, it involved specifying what raw material the report required (financial data); searching for and locating the raw material; classifying and sorting it; analysing and abstracting trends and patterns; and writing the outline for submission to the SA. After the first three months he had managed to get the hang of the techniques to be used. Many of them were similar to those he had picked up at university, and therefore required no new learning. He had hoped to be sent on a training course to develop the skills he had, but none of the senior auditors had suggested any training.

7. At times he found his progress was slowed by the fact that about 20% of client records had not been computerised. When there was a query about an uncomputerized file, it took him a disproportionately long time to sort it out. In addition, the major computer installation in the company had occurred some four years ago during which time all the hardware and software had been updated. Since that time, technological improvements in computer power and developments in software had made the system dated and increasingly more difficult to use. It did not appear that any one manager had the remit to monitor developments in information technology and update the facilities as required.

8. Phil always looked forward to the lunchbreaks in the dining rooms since it gave him the opportunity to talk to the other TAs who were scattered throughout the building. Most of them did similar work to his. What he found most interesting was that some of them used different approaches to calculating things like return on investment and the value of inventory. Phil remembered how he had once received a sharp rebuke from a SA for one of his outline submissions concerning the way be accounted for depreciation. However, when he submitted a report to another SA (using the same technique), he found he did not complain. Perhaps the first SA had had a bad day !

9. He was often surprised by the different amounts of time that it took his colleagues to complete similar tasks. The male trainees often bragged about how long they took to complete a piece of work, and how little effort they managed to put into it. Many of the senior accountants seemed reluctant to discuss the performance of the TAs and their reports. The female TAs seemed more conscientious but were reluctant to reveal how many reports they had completed for fear of being jeered at.

10. After these lunch breaks, Phil came away feeling glad that the particular group of SAs for whom he prepared reports were happy to leave him to get on with it. In fact, he had very little to do with them other than receiving a briefing. He was once asked, by one of them, how he was getting on and whether he had any problems, That, however, had been an accidental meeting while both of them were waiting for the lift. He was thanked by the SA when submitting his report, but was rarely phoned up or seen again unless there was a problem.

11. The office itself was full of PCs and the latest electronic hardware. At his induction day, he had been told that customised firm software would ensure a speedy analysis of data in a standardised format. At the end of the day, he had applied for a place on the computing course, but was still waiting to go. In talking to some people who had been on the course, it appeared that they were expected to deliver outline reports at a higher rate. Perhaps course attendance was not such a good idea after all.

12. Phil's time was charged to the account of the client for whom he was working. Since it represented a cost to the firm, it was important that Phil was as productive in his job as possible, and carried out the work carefully since there were numerous opportunities for error and bad judgement.

13. However, despite not having seen him for a few weeks, one of the SAs noted that at their last briefing, Phil's enthusiasm seemed to have worn off, and his productivity (in terms of the speed of completed assignments) has reduced. Perhaps most seriously, the quality of his work has dropped off recently, and several errors (one of them quite

serious) had been discovered. However, this decline in performance was not restricted to Phil but had been noted amongst the other Junior Accountants who had been recruited at the start of the year. Reviewing last year's staff turnover figures, the head of administration discovered that the figure for trainee accountants was 50% above the average. Some had resigned, while others were dismissed for unsatisfactory work performance.

Note

This activity is based on an exercise, 'Analysing a problem through management links', in R.M. Fulmer and T.T. Herbert, *Exploring the New Management: A Study Guide with Cases, Readings, Incidents and Exercises*, Macmillan, New York, 1978, 2nd edition, pp. 29–30.

14.4 REV: Reorganizing the Allied Paint Company

Objective

- To apply the principles of classical structural design in order to identify potential organizational problems.

Procedure

Review the organizational chart of the Allied Paint Company that follows. The organization of the company has grown over the years without very much planning or reflection. There are now a number of problems. Examine the organizational chart in detail, focusing on the concerns that would be expressed by the classical management theorists in areas such as job titles, seniority of positions, unity of command and spans of control. Identify 15 problems and suggest possible solutions.

Allied Paint Company Organizational Chart

1. Problem
Solution
2. Problem
Solution
3. Problem
Solution

4. Problem

   Solution

5. Problem

   Solution

6. Problem

   Solution

7. Problem

   Solution

8. Problem

   Solution

9. Problem

    Solution

---

10. Problem

    Solution

---

11.   Problem

    Solution

---

12. Problem

    Solution

---

13. Problem

    Solution

14. Problem

    Solution

15. Problem

    Solution

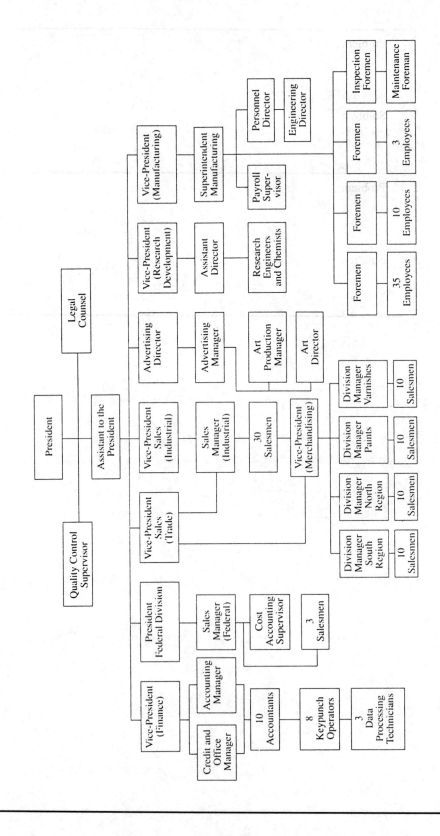

Chapter 15

Contingency approach

15.1 LGA: Identifying your preferred organizational structure

Objectives

- To allow students to distinguish between two very different types of organizational structure.
- To explore their preferences for working in one or the other.
- To reflect on the possible effects of different organizational structures on the motivation of the employees within them.

Introduction

The type of organization structure in which people work can greatly affect their motivation and productivity. Structure concerns the number of levels in the hierarchy, the span of control, the extent to which jobs are defined in detail, and the number and types of rules. Some people operate most effectively in very hierarchical organizations with narrow spans of control, where each job is defined in detail, and where ample rules exist to guide actions and avoid ambiguity. Other people would find such structural arrangements excessively stifling, and would prefer more autonomy to make their own decisions. This activity will introduce two different organizational forms, and help students to decide in which they prefer to work.

Procedure

Step 1 Individually, complete your *Organizational structure questionnaire*.

Step 2 Listen to your instructor's explanation of the different features of mechanistic and organic organizational structures.

Step 3 Score your questionnaire using the key in your workbook, and then read the score interpretations.

Step 4   With the person next to you, use your score interpretations, and understanding of the differences between the two organizational structures, to discuss the four questions below:

1. Which organizational structure do you prefer? Why?

2. What problems might result from a conflict between a new employee's expectations of a company's structure, and its actual structure?

3. Can you give an example of a 'pure' organic or mechanistic system? On what evidence would you label it as one or the other?

4. Which type of organizational structure would motivate today's workforce? Which personal needs might each structure best satisfy?

Organizational structure questionnaire

Think of the type of organization for which you would like to work. Then read the fifteen A and B statements below, and score each using the following scale:

If statement A is totally descriptive of your ideal organization, give yourself 5 points.

If statement A is more descriptive of your ideal organization than statement B, give yourself 4 points.

If statement A is slightly more descriptive of your ideal organization than statement B, give yourself 3 points.

If statement B is slightly more descriptive of your ideal organization than statement A, give yourself 2 points.

If statement B is much more descriptive of your ideal organization than statement A, give yourself 1 point.

If statement B is totally descriptive of your ideal organization, give yourself 0 points.

Write your points score for each of the fifteen questions in the space adjacent to the question number.

1. _____

A. Job descriptions should be detailed and complete so personnel know exactly what they are supposed to be doing.

B. Job descriptions are not really necessary. A general verbal description of the work to be done will get the personnel into the ballpark, and that should be enough.

2. _____

A. Organizational charts should be constructed for every unit and department as well as for the enterprise as a whole so that everyone knows where they fit in the total structure.

B. Organization charts are unnecessary. At best they merely serve to provide a general scheme of things, but since operators are in a continual state of flux, they really never reflect things as they truly are.

3. _____

A. Authority should be reflected in the position. For example, in every department or unit, personnel who are in higher-level positions should have authority over those in lower-level positions.

B. Authority should be a function of knowledge. Regardless of formal job descriptions and authority, the person who knows the most about the problem or solution should be the one who decides what should be done.

4. _____

A. Goal setting should be done from the top down, with managers setting objectives for their people and then communicating them to the personnel.

B. Goal setting should be a participative process, with managers and subordinates getting together to mutually set objectives for the latter.

5. _____

A. The general nature of the work should be routine and repetitive.

B. The general nature of the work should be non-routine and challenging.

6. _____

A. The focus of the planning process should be on the formulation and implementation of long-term goals.

B. The focus of the planning process should be on the formulation and implementation of short-term goals.

7. _____

A. The environment in which the organization operates should be a predictable one.

B. The environment in which the organization operates should contain a great deal of uncertainty.

8. _____

A. Interpersonal relations should be formal in nature.

B. Interpersonal relations should be informal in nature.

9. _____

A. Motivation to work should come basically in the form of extrinsic rewards e.g. increases in pay, promotions, company cars.

B. Motivation to work should come basically in the form of intrinsic rewards e.g. responsibility, recognition, sense of achievement.

10. _____

A. The technology in the industry should be stable and not subject to much change.

B. The technology in the industry should be dynamic and subject to much change.

11. _____

A. The general nature of the industry should be calm.

B. The general nature of the industry should be turbulent.

12. _____

A. Control procedures, tools and techniques should be basically impersonal in nature e.g. rules, regulations, procedure manuals.

B. Control procedures, tools and techniques should be basically interpersonal in nature e.g. personal requests, group pressure.

13. _____

A. The pervading values of the organization should be efficiency, predictability and security.

B. The pervading values of the organization should be effectiveness, adaptability and risk taking.

14. _____

A. The decision-making process should entail only standard, routine decisions.

B. The decision-making process should include many non-standard and non-routine decisions.

15. _____

A. The organizational emphasis should be on bottom-line performance.

B. The organizational emphasis should be on problem solving.

Scoring

Insert each of your 15 answers and total them.

1. ____	9. ____
2. ____	10. ____
3. ____	11. ____
4. ____	12. ____
5. ____	13. ____
6. ____	14. ____
7. ____	15. ____
8. ____	TOTAL _____

Interpretation

0–15   You would feel most comfortable working in an organization that is highly organic.

16–30   You would feel most comfortable working in an organization that is basically organic.

31–45   You would feel most comfortable working in an organization that is a blend of organic and mechanistic characteristics.

46–60   You would feel most comfortable working in an organization that is basically mechanistic.

61–75   You would feel most comfortable working in an organization that is highly mechanistic.

Note

The original source of this activity is unknown.

15.2 SGA: Thompson interdependence demonstration

Objectives

- To illustrate the concepts of pooled, sequential and reciprocal interdependence.
- To illustrate interdependence within groups, departments and organizations.
- To illustrate interdependence between groups, departments and organizations.
- To illustrate the reasons for spatial and hierarchical priorities based on the level of interdependence between units.

Introduction

James Thompson published an enduring classic of organizational theory in 1967, *Organizations in Action*. Despite its brevity – 192 pages – and the passage of a quarter of a century, the concepts, ideas, and insights revealed by Thompson continue to provide a fundamental contribution to organization theory in general, and to an understanding of contingency aspects of organizational structures. This activity allows students to understand Thompson's ideas experientially.

Procedure

Step 1   Two members of the class are selected to serve as the executive committee.

Step 2   The remaining students are divided into 6 groups of roughly equal size, and labelled A, B, C, D, E and F respectively.

Step 3   The six groups are located around the room as directed by the instructor.

Step 4   There will be six rounds and groups will be given work instructions by members of the executive committee.

Have a pack of scrap paper pieces with you. Inside the classroom, ensure that the six groups (A to F) are spread around, and are not seated in alphabetical order. Also check that you have a space or a corridor, out of earshot of the groups.

Round 1

Take the executive committee members into the corridor and give them the following instructions:

In Round 1, each person in each group is to write the time on a piece of paper every ten seconds. At the end of the round, each member of a group will pass his or her paper to a central collection point for that group. You are now to re-enter the room and give these instructions to each group, and tell the groups to begin. You will stop the round after exactly three minutes. These instructions, and those for the other five rounds, can be photocopied and given to the executive committee members.

Round 2

Take the executive committee members back into the hallway, and tell them to repeat in

Round 2, everything that they did in Round 1.

Round 3

Return to the hallway with the executive committee and give its members the following instructions:

In Round 3, each group member must write one time on a piece of paper every ten seconds, and pass it on to another group member every ten seconds. After all members of a group have written a time on a piece of paper, it must be passed to another group. Sheets of paper may be circulated only in the following sequence: A→B→C→D→E→F. Return to the room and give these instructions to the groups. Then have them begin. End Round 3 exactly three minutes after it begins.

Round 4

Take the executive committee members into the hallway and tell them to repeat in Round 4, everything that they did in Round 3, but that they are allowed to make any changes that they believe will improve the functioning of the organization if these do not violate the instructions given previously for Round 3.

At this point, the executive committee will normally either rearrange the groups so that they are arranged in alphabetical order or will re-label the groups to achieve the same effect.

Round 5

Return the executive committee members to the hallway and give them the following instructions:

In Round 5, do everything the same as in Rounds 3 and 4 except that the sheets of paper must circulate among groups in the following patterns:

a. A→E→A
b. B→D→B
c. C→F→C

Give these instructions to the groups and begin Round 5. End Round 5 after exactly three minutes.

Round 6

Return with the executive members to the hallway and tell them to repeat all the procedures for Round 5 in Round 6, except that they are allowed to make any changes that would improve the functioning of the organization if these do not violate the previously given Round 5 instructions.

The executive committee will normally decide to move groups (or re-label them) so that A and E are adjacent physically; B and D are, too; and so are C and F.

Following Round 6, the demonstration proper ends, and the time has come to debrief the class and discuss the exercise with everyone.

Source: Adapted from Bluedorn, A.C. (1993), 'The Thompson interdependence demonstration', *Journal of Management Education*, 17 (4), pp. 505–509.

15.3 PREP: Technology and organization structure

Objectives

- To examine Charles Perrow's theory of the relationship between technology and structure.
- To assess the degree of task variety and task analyzability in different departments within an organization.

Introduction

Every department in an organization has a production process that consists of a distinct technology. Here the term 'technology' is used in the second of Winner's conceptions as *technique*. Technique refers to the technical activities such as skills, methods, procedures and routines. Chapter 18 will remind us that the Greek word *techne* means art, craft or skill, and that these are related to particular organizational, human or departmental goals. For example, the Ford Motor Company has departments for engineering, research and development, personnel, advertising, quality control, and many others. Other firms have fewer departments, but each has its own unique technology.

Procedure

Your task is to interview four people. Any one from column C; one from column NR; a third from column R; and the fourth from column ET listed below. Through your personal contacts, or through your friends or relations, find a person who has the job shown. Conduct an interview by having them answer the 10 questions in the *Technology and organizational structure questionnaire*.

C	NR	R	ET
School teacher	Researcher doing basic (non-applied) research	Assembly line worker	Civil engineer
University or college lecturer		Salesperson	Solicitor
Plumber	Strategic planner	Auditor	Tax accountant
Electrician		Draughtsman	Market researcher
Performing artist (actors or musicians)		Bank clerk	General accountant
Computer software fixer		Supermarket shelf-stacker	General practitioner

Bring your interview data back to class, and compare it with that provided by the other class members. Focus your discussion on the following five questions:

1. To what extent was there a similarity of scores between interviews within each of the four categories of work (C, NR, R and ET)?

2. To what degree did the scores differ between the four categories of work?

3. Give examples of how established knowledge, steps-in-doing-things, and established-procedures-and-practices, were used to get the task done or the problem solved.

4. Explain how, in the absence of established knowledge, steps, procedures and practices, workers completed the task or solved the work problem.

5. Speculate on the effect that task variety and task analyzability can have on the way a department of a company is structured.

Technology and organizational structure questionnaire

Task variety

The following five questions relate to the normal, day-to-day pattern of work carried out by yourself and the people in your work unit. Please tick the appropriate response.

	Very few of them		Some of them			Most of them	
	1	2	3	4	5	6	7
1. How many of your work tasks are the same from day to day?							

This part asks you about the nature of your normal, day to day work activities. Please tick the appropriate response to each of the following three questions.

	To a small extent		To some extent			To a great extent	
	1	2	3	4	5	6	7
2. To what extent would you say that your work is routine?							
3. Most people in this work unit do the same job, in the same way, most of the time.							
4. Basically, unit members perform repetitive activities in doing their jobs.							

The next question asks you how much variety there is in your job. Tick the box that best answers the question.

	Very little		Moderate amount			Large amount	
	1	2	3	4	5	6	7
5. How much repetition is there in the duties that you perform as part of your job?							

Task analysability

The next set of questions relate to the normal, daily patterns of work carried out by yourself and the people in your work unit. Please tick the appropriate boxes.

	To a small extent		To some extent			To a great extent	
	1	2	3	4	5	6	7
1. To what extent is there a clearly known way of doing the major types of work that you normally encounter?							

These questions concern the nature of your normal, daily work activities.

	To a small extent		To some extent			To a great extent	
	1	2	3	4	5	6	7
2. To what extent is there a clearly defined body of knowledge that can guide you in doing your work?							
3. To what extent is there an understandable sequence of steps that can be followed in doing your work?							
4. In doing your work, to what extent can you actually rely on established procedures and practices?							

5. Ask your interviewee to describe how they perform their most typical work task. Make notes about (1) how they approach or define the task to be performed or problem to be solved, (2) whether they use established knowledge, steps and procedures, or devise their own.

Source: Activity reproduced, with amendments, from H.E. Baker, and S.K. Paulson, *Experiential Exercises in Organization Theory*, Prentice Hall, 1995, pp. 30–33. This is itself based on Withey, M., Daft, R.L. and Cooper, W.H., 1983, 'Measures of Perrow's work unit technology: An empirical assessment and a new scale', *Academy of Management Journal*, vol. 26, no. 1, pp. 45–63.

15.4 REV: Mix and match

Objective

- To assess student familiarity with the content of *ORBIT3* chapters on the contingency approach to organizational structuring.

Introduction

This test is based on Chapter 15 of the *ORBIT3* textbook. It considers authors and their concepts, concepts and their examples, and concepts and their sub-concepts.

Procedure

The two lists below consist of a total of 40 items (names, concepts, nouns and so on). Twenty of these are numbered in List A, while the remaining twenty are lettered in List B. On the basis of Chapter 15, correctly associate these two sets of twenty items. Where the same item appears in both lists, it should not be associated with itself. Insert the correct letter alongside the appropriate number in column 2.

Insert correct letter here

		List A		List B
1.		Joan Woodward	A.	paper system co-ordination device
2.		William Foote Whyte	B.	hierarchical referral
3.		strategic choice	C.	task variety and analyzability
4.		pooled task interdependence	D.	environmental complexity and dynamism
5.		environmental strategic choice	E.	airports
6.		routine technology	F.	relationships of interdependence
7.		Lawrence and Lorsch	G.	law of the situation
8.		Charles Perrow	H.	structural universalist
9.		reciprocal task interdependence	I.	American football
10.		Robert Duncan	J.	mediating technology
11.		Burns and Stalker	K.	telecommunications industry
12.		environmental dynamism	L.	enacted environment
13.		environmental determinants	M.	organic
15.		high differentiation	O.	integration and differentiation

16.		sequential task interdependence	P.	bank clerks
17.		Karl Weick	Q.	closed systems theory
18.		co-ordination mechanism	R.	John Child
19.		Mary Parker Follett	S.	technological complexity
20.		Max Weber	T.	Miles and Snow

PART IV

ORGANIZATIONAL CHANGE AND DEVELOPMENT

Organizational change

16.1 LGA: Your reaction to change

Objectives

- To establish how students would respond to different change situations.
- To identify factors that affect our reactions to change.

Introduction

Managing changes is an almost continuous activity of a manager – not the earthshaking kind of changes usually, but the small, day-to-day kind. But how these changes are handled can determine the quality of relationships which exist in a shop or office and can determine how the job gets done. Communication plays a large part in managing change effectively, as it does in every facet of working relationships. Before you can manage changes for others, however, you should first have an understanding of how you react to change.

When non-routine changes are proposed or announced, each person evaluates what the change will mean to them personally. Initially, and depending on several factors, the relatively healthy, 'normal' person may react to change in one or more of the following ways. He may feel that the change is destructive or threatening; he may not know how he feels about the change; he may be uncertain, but generally positive about the change; or he may feel very good about the change.

Procedure

Assume that you are the assistant branch manager of a bank, and that you have been there for two months. Here are five situations. You are to assign a value to each using the following scale:

–5	–4	–3	–2	–1	0	+1	+2	+3	+4	+5

Destructive	Threatening	Don't really know	Uncertain, but positive	Very good

Each of the items below should be considered *independently*. In the right-hand column, indicate your initial feelings about each situation.

Situation	Your assigned value from the scale (–5 → +5)
A You are offered a promotion to assistant manager of the investments department in the district office, where there is a sudden opening. You have no experience in this area and would have to be making important decisions without background experience.	
B The district office has approved a morale survey to be made in all local branches. It would be designed, administered, and used as a thesis by a graduate student at the local university. Results will be identified by branches, and the district office will see the results before they come to the branch.	
C Without explanation or warning, the branch manager brings in another assistant manager, Jill Blake, who is several years younger than you, and was a 'fast-track' graduate recruit to the bank. The only thing you know is what the branch manager told you: 'Clear out the next desk for her and split your duties with her so she can learn the branch operations'.	
D The clerks ask if they can take on more of the decision-making functions within the branch, without your approval. This would include writing and signing their own letters, handling inquiries from customers in person or by telephone, etc. This was tried in the branch you came from, with near-disastrous results. (One plaintiff based his case against you on the argument that the clerk was your agent.)	
E The branch manager, who has a good reputation as a 'developer', wants you to learn more about his duties. He proposes that you go with him to see important customers, attend important district meetings, take an active role in representing the bank to the community, etc. This will prepare you to take over the management of a branch.	

Source: A.A. Zoll, 'Managing Changes' in *Explorations in Management*, Addison Wesley, 1969. Used with permission.

16.2 SGA: Causes of resistance to change

Objectives

- To establish the possible causes of resistance to change in organizations.
- To identify approaches to overcoming resistance to change in organizations.

Introduction

Many managers regard resistance to change as one of the main barriers to organizational development and technological innovation. The expectation that change will be resisted thus influences the way in which changes are introduced in the first place. Resistance is often taken for granted. Solutions to organizational problems are naturally based on what we assume or know to be the cause of those problems. If our assumptions are correct, our knowledge sound, then our proposed solutions are more likely to be effective. We would like to invite you in this exercise to consider – and possibly to refine – your own personal assumptions about resistance to change and also about how it can be overcome or avoided. If we want to solve the problem of resistance to change, we need to know what causes it; we will therefore begin by looking at some actual instances of resistance to change and at the causes of that behaviour.

Procedure

Step 1   Working on your own, complete the *Resistance to change analysis sheet* which follows. Give particular attention to the *why?* question; what caused the resistance in this case? Remember that there may be more than one cause.

Step 2   Working in syndicates, each with three members, go round the group sharing the examples which you have each generated. Note similarities in and differences between the accounts. Note any *patterns* that seem to emerge from these accounts. As you listen to the other accounts, ask questions to ensure that you understand *why* the change was resisted in that example.

Step 3   The instructor issues a separate *Explanations for resistance* (1) sheet. Read the list and, for each of the examples of resistance to change represented in your syndicate group, *identify the reason or reasons* that apply. Note the item number or numbers of the explanations that apply in each example. This checklist may not cover all the reasons in the cases under discussion. Note any additional explanations you would want to add to the checklist.

Step 4   The instructor takes a 'popularity poll' by asking each person in turn simply to reveal the number or numbers of the explanations that apply to their examples of resistance to change. When the poll is complete, you will have a count against each of the ten items (and possibly for a few additional explanations as well).

Step 5   The instructor issues a separate *Explanations for resistance* (2) sheet. Comparing the results of your popularity poll with the *Resistance* (2) sheet, what conclusions can you reach about the causes of resistance to change, and thus about the most appropriate forms of solution to this problem?

Resistance to change analysis sheet

Think of a specific example of resistance to change. This could involve new organization structures, systems or working practices, or it could involve new technology, or it could involve a combination of such factors. Choose if you can a specific instance you have experienced personally. If that is not appropriate, there may be instances you can recall from the accounts of friends or relatives, or media accounts. Use the space on this page to make notes, initially for your own purpose, in response to the following questions:

What did the change or changes involve?

Who resisted?

Why did they resist?

What *form* did the resistance take?

How was the matter resolved?

Explanations for resistance (1)

Resistance to change in an organization can be caused by a number of factors. Identify which of the following *possible* explanations apply to the case or cases you have been considering. What follows is simply a *checklist of possibilities*; there may be explanations here with which you disagree, and there may be explanations that you feel have been missed out. Several of these items may apply to the explanation of resistance in one given setting. Check within your syndicate group that you are each clear about the explanation or explanations that apply in each case.

1. People have a natural resistance to all change.

2. Older people are more likely to resist change.

3. Users of new technology resist the introduction of equipment and systems that are poorly designed.

4. Users of new technology resist the introduction of equipment and systems that have poor ergonomic features, such as seating, and the positioning of controls and lighting.

5. Users of new technology resist the introduction of equipment and systems that are complicated and difficult to learn and use.

6. People resist changes that interfere with their established ways of working with others in the organization.

7. People resist changes that disturb the distribution of tasks and responsibilities across the organization.

8. People resist changes that interfere with their autonomy and decision making.

9. People resist changes that interfere with their access to information and discretion over how it is being used.

10. People resist changes that reduce their ability to influence and control other people and events in the organization.

Explanations for resistance (2)

There are four broad types of explanation:

1. People-focused
Here the fault, or blame, or cause of resistance lies with the individuals involved, their personalities, their attitudes, values, preferences, and so on.

2. Systems-focused
Here the fault lies with system designers and with equipment characteristics such as 'user friendliness', complexity, ergonomic features, access for maintenance, and so on.

3. Organization-focused
Here the cause of resistance lies with the perceived lack of 'fit' between the change and its organizational context. The key factor here concerns allocation of responsibility. New technology, for example, or a 'total quality management' package, typically involve new patterns of working, and changes to social interaction in the organization. This may cut across traditional cultures and established 'ways of doing things'. Can also affect real and presumed status differentials.

4. Politics-focused
Here the cause of resistance again lies with the interaction between changes and context. But the key factor under this heading is *distribution of power*. New ways of working alter the 'ownership' of information, alter patterns of access to information, and affect established patterns of decision making and the exercise of influence by individuals and groups.

On the checklist of possible options,

> items 1 and 2 are people-focused;
>
> items 3 to 5 are systems-focused;
>
> items 6 to 8 are organization-focused;
>
> items 9 and 10 are politics-focused.
>
> Item 8 could relate to either of the last two sets of explanations. This depends on why people are resisting interference with their autonomy.

Notes

This exercise and the classification of explanations is based on the following article: M.L. Markus, 1983, 'Power, politics and MIS implementation', *Communications of the ACM*, vol. 26, no. 6, pp. 430–44.

The practical implications for the change agent in what Markus calls, 'the political variant' are explored in: David Buchanan and David Boddy, *The Expertise of the Change Agent: Public Performance and Backstage Activity*, Prentice Hall International, Hemel Hempstead.

16.3 PREP: Managing change – good practice

Objectives

- To establish from experience guidelines for good management practice in the implementation of change.
- To develop understanding of the wide range of individual, organizational and managerial issues involved in implementing change effectively.

Introduction

We have all experienced change, in different forms and settings. We are frequently reminded by media commentary that increasingly rapid and complex change is a central facet of our modern lifestyles. What factors influence our reactions to change? Do we, as many will argue, have a 'natural' resistance to change? Or do we get bored with routine and seek fresh experiences from time to time? The argument that we would like to advance here is that our reactions to change and the outcomes of change depend to a large extent on how change is *managed*. How *should* change be managed, to avoid or overcome resistance, and to ensure that the implementation is smooth and effective? In this activity we would like to invite you to consider your own experiences of change, positive and negative, and to identify 'rules' for good management practice.

Procedure

Step 1 Working on your own, consider your own experiences of change in organizations. This should ideally concern recent personal experience. However, if you have so far avoided such an experience, perhaps you know what relatives and friends have experienced. Or perhaps you have a good understanding of change issues from media and other accounts.

Step 2 Make notes for your own use on what you would regard as characteristics of effective change management. What should management do to ensure smooth and effective change?

Step 3 Still working on your own, make notes on what you would advise management to *avoid* in attempting to implement change effectively.

Step 4 In the class, working in buzz-groups of three or four members, depending on your seating arrangements, compare notes and produce a master list of management 'best practice', and of things to avoid with respect to effective change implementation. Nominate a spokesperson to feedback your lists of 'dos' and 'don'ts' to your instructor.

Step 5 Feedback and discussion, according to your instructor's wishes.

16.4 REV: Join the halves

Objectives

- To assess understanding of the concepts introduced in Chapter 16 of *ORBIT3*.
- To assess understanding of the arguments introduced in Chapter 16 of *ORBIT3*.

Introduction

How closely did you read Chapter 16? How much of that chapter do you now recall? The following review may appear to imply that you need to recall the material word for word. That is not necessarily so. If you *understood* the concepts and arguments in the chapter, you will find the following review easy. Remember the last piece of fiction you read? You can probably describe the plot of the story, the main characters, what happened and how the story ended (in at least enough detail to spoil the surprise ending for someone who has not read it yet) without any memory whatsoever of any of the lines and sentences written by the author. Simple recall helps. Understanding, however, is more useful and makes fewer demands on memory.

Procedure

Step 1   Read through the two sets of incomplete sentences.

Step 2   Decide which items in Set B complete those in Set A. Insert them in the table on the right.

Step 3   Score your answers as your instructor requires.

Step 4   Congratulate yourself if you got 15 or more correct; go read the chapter again if you scored less than 10.

A1	
A2	
A3	
A4	
A5	
A6	
A7	
A8	
A9	
A10	
A11	
A12	
A13	
A14	
A15	
A16	
A17	
A18	
A19	
A20	

Sentence completion: Set A

A1   The concept of readiness for change holds that

A2   Both Gerard Egan and Tony Eccles can be said to take a

A3   It has been argued that the rational linear model of organizational change implementation underplays

A4   Elizabeth Kubler-Ross' life cycle model can be applied to change; it consists of

A5   Four common causes of resistance to change identified by Arthur Bedeian were

A6   People resist change because it

A7   Authors have recognised the tension between organizations flexible enough structurally to respond to external challenges, and

A8   What distinguishes Business Process Re-engineering (BPR) from earlier change strategies is

A9   The argument that organizational change is a strategic imperative holds that

A10   A field experiment conducted by Coch and French found that

A11   Dunphy and Stace argue that the participative management approach to change implementation is only appropriate if

A12   Andrew Pettigrew's organizational change model emphasises that

A13   It is argued that, increasing, change agents require

A14   Gleiter and Little argue that for organizational change to occur

A15   Ahituv and Neumann's life cycle model draws upon

A16   W.F. Ogburn argued that

A17   The participative management approach to change implementation stresses

A18   Many different authors have drawn the contrast between organizations that have structures which are stable, orderly predictable, rigid and relatively effective in the past, and

A19   There is a contrast between a processional perspective on organizational change which recognises complexity and provides theoretical depth for researchers and

A20   Bott and Hill identified the personal qualities needed by people implementing change which

Sentence completion: Set B

B1   change models which are partial, but which offer convenient change guidelines for managers.

B2   the untidy, unpredictable nature of strategic change.

B3   involves new situations, problems and challenges, which create ambiguity and uncertainty, and this is experienced as painful and frustrating by them.

B4   organizations have to modify their design and functioning in order to respond to unpredictable changes in their environment.

B5   openness, honesty and support of employees when change is implemented.

B6   if certain organizational conditions exist, resistance to change will be localised and less significant, thereby making change easier to implement.

B7   five stages of life – denial, anger, bargaining, depression and acceptance.

B8   the first practical steps need to be known; the status quo must be unacceptable; and a desirable future vision must exist.

B9   those organizations whose structures are flexible, adaptive and responsive, and are more likely to be successful in the future.

B10   its 'clean sheet, fresh start' approach, and its emphasis on the process that delivers an output to the customer.

B11   the way people are treated and involved in change influences whether they resist or accept it.

B12   project management methods' ten activities – beginning with preliminary analysis and ending with project termination.

B13   the *process* of change, *content* of change, and the *inner* and *outer contexts* of change, must all be considered.

B14   technology increases the number of innovations which in turn increases the speed of social change.

B15   the change is minor, time is available, and the key interest groups favour change.

B16   they then clustered into setting direction, fostering relationships, and stabilizing beliefs.

B17   political approach towards the implementation of organizational change.

B18   yet stable enough internally to provide a comfortable and secure working environment for their employees.

B19   less technical expertise in the content of change and more in the management of the change process.

B 20 parochial self-interest, non-understanding, contradictory assessments, and low tolerance of change.

Organizational development

17.1 LGA: What's the cause? What's the solution?

Objectives

- To demonstrate different perceptions of causes concerning the same behavioural event.
- To assess the range of causal explanations that tend to be offered.
- To stress the importance of matching the appropriate solution to the problem cause.

Introduction

We know that people can perceive the same behavioural event or situation differently. In the case of a company crisis or problem, how one attributes cause can determine, or at least influence, the choice of solution. In such circumstances, two reactions are common. First, people often jump to conclusions about causes without having first analyzed the situation. Second, the conclusions that they jump to about the causes tend to be narrow in their scope. This activity is designed to illustrate the second point.

Procedure

Step 1   Read the following 15-word case study in the box below:

> An elderly woman in a nursing home is found dead; she has apparently committed suicide.

Step 2   In the space below, write down four alternative hypotheses or possible explanations for this tragic event.

1. _____

2. _____

3. _____ ☐

4. _____ ☐

Be prepared to offer some of your explanations to your instructor, who will chart them up on the board.

Procedure

1. Ask volunteers to shout out their explanations (one per person) and write these up on the board as space and time allows. Keep going until a number of unusual ones have been suggested.

2. Introduce the 'levels of explanation' framework by projecting an overhead foil of the table below:

> **Levels of Explanation**
> I   = individual
> IP = interpersonal
> G   = group
> IG = inter-group
> O   = organizational
> IO = inter-organizational
> S   = societal
> IN = international
> GL = global

3. Describe each of these seven levels of explanation (see table overleaf) and look for an example of each among the students' contributions shown on the board. Code each with the appropriate letters, e.g. IP.

4. Ask students to code their own alternative hypotheses in the boxes provided in Step 2 in their workbooks.

Source: This activity was developed by Professor Jack Denfield Wood, IMD, Lausanne, Switzerland. Used with permission.

17.2 SGA: Force field analysis

Objectives

- To develop understanding of the technique of force field analysis.
- To develop the ability to translate such an analysis into a practical action plan.

Introduction

If you have completed the activities in this and the previous section, you will be fully aware of the multi-variate, multi-dimensional, multi-faceted nature of organizational change. Put more crudely, there are an awful lot of factors to take into account! Organizational development (OD) consultants who are engaged in planning and implementing change, find it to be a complex, untidy, messy business. This is particularly so when the factors affecting the change are in conflict, with some dimensions favourable, and some not. In such circumstances, it is helpful to find and to use methods that bring order to chaos, and that bring systematic structure to complex and contradictory information. One such 'ordering and systematizing' technique used in OD is *force field analysis*, developed by the social psychologist Kurt Lewin in the 1960s and now widely cited and used. In this activity, we plan to:

- introduce the technique;
- ask you to conduct an analysis of the force field related to a specific change;
- work that analysis through to a practical action plan; and to
- present that action plan for critical appraisal.

The need for clarity of objectives is frequently mentioned as an element in the effective implementation of change. If you do not know the destination, it is difficult to determine the direction of travel. Before we begin this exercise, therefore, we would like to ask you to reflect on a specific organizational change that you would like to introduce. This proposed change should have a number of criteria. It should be relevant to your current experience and be visible to you. It should be specified in precise terms, either with respect to events, behaviours or outcomes or some combination of these factors. It should be realistic, in terms of practical implementation, time scale, and resource implications.

Organizational changes that could meet these criteria could include the introduction of a new committee structure for the local students' union, the introduction of revised organizational behaviour course examination and feedback procedures, the introduction of improved student evaluation of teaching performance mechanisms, the implementation of a new scheme of social and sports club membership and fee charges, and so on. There will be specific local issues of relevance to you and to fellow students; choose a *target situation* that is of some immediate relevance and significance, and one that would be interesting to work on for this assignment.

Procedure

Step 1 Identify an appropriate *target situation* for this assignment, using the criteria set out in the *Introduction*. Your target situation should be capable of precise and unambiguous definition, and should not be stated in vague and generalized terms.

Step 2   Conduct a *force field analysis* using the guidance sheet which follows, identifying and rating as instructed the driving and the resisting forces.

Step 3   Write a short and realistic assessment of how the forces balance, and of the probability of success should you proceed with the proposal.

Step 4   Produce a practical action plan in accordance with the advice and instruction set out on the *Components of an action plan* sheet.

Step 5   Produce a realistic assessment of your action plan against the criteria identified, and up to three additional criteria that you find relevant.

Step 6   Submit your force field analysis, your action plan, and your action plan assessment in accordance with the directions of your Instructor.

Force field analysis

Main steps:

1.   Define your target situation in terms of events, outcomes or behaviours.

2.   Identify all the driving forces you can think of.

3.   Identify all the resisting forces you can think of.

4.   Drivers and resistors can include people (key individuals and groups), aspects of the context, and arguments for which there is support and evidence. Do not be surprised if some drivers appear in a modified form as resistors, and vice versa.

5.   Rate each of the driving and resisting forces in terms of *strength*: high, medium or low.

6.   Give the *strength* ratings numerical values – 5 for high, 3 for medium, and 1 for low; you can now calculate totals for the driving and resisting forces to help you assess the balance.

7.   Rate each of the driving and resisting forces in terms of how *easily influenced* they are: high, medium, low (this is independent of the *strength* of each force).

Hint: identify the *strong* forces that are *easily influenced*. These are the ones on which you may wish to concentrate when formulating a practical action plan. However, these are not necessarily the only factors to be considered at that stage.

The target situation is: _____

Components of an action plan

To translate your force field analysis into a practical action plan designed to achieve the target situation, you need to consider the following items:

* definition of the problem or issue to be resolved
* specification of the target situation, outcomes, and results

- practical actions: first steps
                    next steps
                    what next
                    what then
- any preconditions for the above?
- any options or contingencies to mention, should things go wrong?
- specified milestones and deadlines
- specific responsibilities: who's going to do all this?
- timing of events.

Put your proposed action plan into the form of a summary report. In deciding on action to increase driving forces, introduce new driving forces, and to reduce or eliminate resisting forces, consider in particular the advice offered in Chapter 16 in *ORBIT3* with respect to 'rules for overcoming resistance', 'techniques for blocking interference', 'effective project definition', and 'causes of resistance'. There may be other research-based ideas you can incorporate too.

Force field analysis

Driving forces	Resisting forces

Action plan assessment

Having produced a practical action plan to achieve your desired target situation, how should you evaluate the plan? Once again, there are perhaps a large number of dimensions on which such a plan can be assessed, and it would be helpful if we could structure or systematize this assessment.

One commonly applied technique is *cost benefit analysis*. This can be a sophisticated evaluation methodology, but it can also be applied with effect in a simplified form. Try this approach:

- List the main *costs* of your proposed action plan. These costs can be financial, material, and psychological (money, resources, time, frustration, and so on).

- Rate each cost, subjectively, in terms of its *strength* – high cost, medium cost, low cost.

- List the main *benefits* of your proposed action plan.

- Rate the strength of each benefit.

- You do not need to attach numbers to the strength ratings to get a reasonably good feel as to whether one set of outcomes outweighs the other, or whether the costs and benefits balance each other out. If the benefits outweigh the costs, or if the costs and benefits evenly balance, would you wish to give up – or would you try to find additional benefits and new ways to reduce the costs?

- Indicate how you would amend your action plan (if at all) in the light of your cost-benefit analysis.

There are other criteria on which you can assess your action plan. These should include:

impact   will this action make a significant difference to the organization and its performance?

can-do   will this action plan really work in practice?

appeal   will this action plan 'strike a chord' and attract the attention of those who will contribute to its success?

timing (1)   is this the right time to be doing something like this?

timing (2)   are the stages of the action plan timed in an appropriate and realistic way?

Optional   Identify up to three additional criteria on which you feel it appropriate to assess your action plan.

17.3 PREP: Campus organizational assessment

Objectives

- To apply the popular organizational development (OD) technique of organizational assessment.
- To practise collecting and interpreting organizational data.

Introduction

One of the first steps in organization development is doing an organizational assessment to evaluate the strengths and weaknesses of the organization. You and your team have been hired as a consulting group by the university to assess the strengths and weaknesses of the university. You are to collect data from your group members in these five areas:

1. Academics and scholarly environment
2. Quality of teaching on campus
3. Campus social relationships
4. Student events on campus
5. Management by the university administration

After you have gathered the data, list the strengths and weaknesses that you have identified. What interventions/changes would you recommend, in each of the five areas, to overcome the weaknesses and build on the strengths? These recommendations must be very specific so the university administration could implement them tomorrow without any more explanation. Avoid saying things like 'Teachers need to lecture better'. Be specific by saying things such as 'We found 10% of the teachers didn't talk loud enough in class' or '50% of teachers stray off the subject too frequently'. Each team should then present its diagnosis to the class.

Procedure

Before coming to class, interview six of your fellow students using the *Campus profile questionnaire*. Aggregate their responses, and note their views about the strengths and weaknesses.

Identify the organization's strengths and weaknesses, and summarize these in the *Campus assessment sheet*. Recommend interventions which would rectify the weaknesses and build on the strengths.

Be ready to input your data to the group discussion later.

Campus profile questionnaire

Not true   1   2   3   4   5   Very true

I Academic

1 2 3 4 5   1. There is a wide range of courses to choose from.
1 2 3 4 5   2. Course standards are too low.
1 2 3 4 5   3. The library is adequate.
1 2 3 4 5   4. Textbooks are helpful.

II Teachers

1 2 3 4 5   1. Teachers here are committed to quality instruction.
1 2 3 4 5   2. We have high-quality teaching staff.
1 2 3 4 5   3. Teachers have a good balance between theory and practice.

III Social relationships

1 2 3 4 5   1. Students are friendly to one another.
1 2 3 4 5   2. It is difficult to make friends.
1 2 3 4 5   3. Instructors get involved in student activities.
1 2 3 4 5   4. Too much energy goes into drinking and socializing.

IV Student events

1 2 3 4 5   1. There are ample activities on campus.
1 2 3 4 5   2. Student activities are boring.
1 2 3 4 5   3. The administration places a high value on student activities.
1 2 3 4 5   4. Too much emphasis is placed on sport.
1 2 3 4 5   5. We need more social activities.

V Management/Administration

1 2 3 4 5   1. Decision making is shared at all levels of the organization.
1 2 3 4 5   2. There is unity and cohesiveness among departments and units.
1 2 3 4 5   3. Too many departmental clashes hamper the organization's effectiveness.
1 2 3 4 5   4. Students have a say in many decisions.
1 2 3 4 5   5. The budgeting process seems fair.
1 2 3 4 5   6. Recruiting and staffing are handled thoughtfully, with student needs in mind.

Campus assessment sheet

	Strength in	Weakness in	Recommended intervention
Academic			
Teaching			
Social relationships			
Student events			
Organizational Management			

Source: D. Marcic, *Organizational Behaviour: Experiences and Cases*, West Publishing Company, Minneapolis St. Paul, 1989, pp. 326–9.

17.4 REV: Anagrams

Objective

- To review organizational development (OD) philosophy, theory and techniques considered in *ORBIT3*, Chapter 17.

Introduction

Organizational development is considered by many to be a social philosophy concerning the most appropriate way in which to implement change within organizations. In this context, it has its own set of values and beliefs. It uses social science research and theory developed by leading researchers, and is most often manifested in the tools used by OD practitioners. The aim of this activity is to familiarize you with the main elements that constitute organizational development.

Instructions

The clues shown in the middle column of the table below relate to an aspect of organization development – a concept, term, label, theory, author, researcher or similar. The number at the end of each one indicates the number of words in the answer. The answer is provided, in an anagrammed form, in the first column of the table. Unscramble it, and insert it in the space in the third column. All the answers can be found in Chapter 17 of the *ORBIT* textbook.

Anagram	Clue	Answer
1. Tim	Home of the group dynamics centre (1)	
2. Is song aid	An early stage of OD performed by the organizational doctor (1)	
3. Character noise	The feedback model of OD (2)	
4. Roman rigor rationing	A technique that reflects well on the company (2)	
5. Nuke twirl	His FFA and T established him as a founding father of OD (2)	
6. Insecure beginners gossip sneer	Modern structural technique (3)	
7. Bicentennial typed paid	OD claims to help firm to develop this to resolve their own problems (2)	
8. Debut mailing	Belbin developed this technique (2)	
9. Total succession porn	Edgar's deliberation meeting (2)	
10. Intonate rim	End stage of OD. Performed by Arnie? (1)	

Anagram	Clue	Answer
11. Golden Palm Inn	One-shot, problem-solving OD approach (2)	
12. Nestle mystic	The patient (2)	
13. Tennis over tin	Term for OD techniques (1)	
14. Religion on to tea	Used for reconciling individual differences (2)	
15. In brawn sneer	Emphasized 'truth, trust, love and collaboration' (2)	
16. Meat	The new building block of organizations (1)	
17. Beefy ducks rave	Polling views, discussing results, finding solutions (2)	
18. Coat airlift	A non group leader (1)	
19. I am in Amontillado graze	OD rejects this notion of company/employee incompatibility (2)	
20. Salty cat	Non-expert OD consultant (1)	

Corporate culture

18.1 LGA: Assessing cultural strength

Objectives

- To introduce students to the concept of corporate (or organizational) culture.
- To summarize the work of Terrence Deal and Allan Kennedy on corporate culture.
- To allow them to assess the 'strength' of the culture of an organization with which they are familiar.

Introduction

Corporate culture has colloquially been defined as 'the way we do things around here'. More specifically, writers have seen corporate culture as being the fabric of an organization's most important, shared values, beliefs and norms. By learning a company's culture, new recruits also learn how to behave appropriately in their new firm. For many students, Deal and Kennedy's book, *Corporate Cultures: The Rites and Rituals of Corporate Life*, representing an introduction to this concept. These authors argue that organizations differ in terms of the strength of their cultures. This activity allows you to assess how strong or weak the culture is of an organization with which you are familiar.

Procedure

Step 1   Select an organization as directed by your instructor.

Step 2   Complete the *Cultural strength questionnaire*.

Step 3   Familiarize yourself with the four dimensions of corporate culture as described by Deal and Kennedy.

Step 4   Score the questionnaire and interpret it as directed by your instructor.

Corporate strength questionnaire

Statement	SA	A	N	D	SD
1. New recruits are carefully made aware of how things are done in this organization.	5	4	3	2	1
2. When an organization member performs excellently, they are recognized at formal ceremonies (e.g. Top Salesperson Award; Student of the Year Prize Giving).	5	4	3	2	1
3. Well established traditions are a feature of this organization (e.g. Fresher's Week, strategy 'Away Days', Employees' Family Fun Day).	5	4	3	2	1
4. As a newcomer, it isn't long before someone tells you a story about the organization in the 'old days'.	5	4	3	2	1
5. Employee can easily recognize the organization's basic beliefs which are reflected in many of its practices, procedures and programmes.	5	4	3	2	1
6. The memories of the organization's great heroes (e.g. founders, chief executives, professors) are kept alive for current members.	5	4	3	2	1
7. Members of this organization have distinctive ways of communicating and relating to one another (e.g. use of surnames; extensive emailing).	5	4	3	2	1
8. The organization has a procedure for matching new recruits with established staff to help the former become integrated.	5	4	3	2	1
9. The organization has a single ideal that symbolises to all its members what it stands for (e.g. quality, learning, customer care).	5	4	3	2	1
10. The success of some organization members is communicated to, and serves as a model for, the others.	5	4	3	2	1
11. Organizational ceremonies are taken seriously by senior staff who always attend them (e.g. graduations, long service award presentations).	5	4	3	2	1
12. The organization's grapevine regularly carries information about significant events that affect all employees.	5	4	3	2	1

Corporate strength questionnaire explanation

The questionnaire rates your perception of the strength of your chosen organization's culture along the four dimensions identified by Deal and Kennedy – values; heroes and heroines; traditions and rituals; and finally, the cultural network.

Values

Organizations with a strong value system give direction and purpose to their members. Churches, religious associations and cults are prime examples of this. Espoused values such as fairness, the importance of education, loyalty, or quality show that the company stands for something, and gives it a 'reason to be'. A corporate value system develops over a number of years.

Heroes and Heroines

These provide company employees with role models to aspire to and emulate. Organizational heroes and heroines are often company founders (e.g. Bill Hewlett and Dave Packard; Anita Roddick), successful chief executive officers (John Harvey-Jones, Lee Iaccoca), and entrepreneurs or innovators (Bill Gates, Ray Kroc). They may be ordinary employees who accomplish extra-ordinary things, and embody the corporate culture's ethic of success. Alive or dead, these people motivate staff by personifying the company which is, after all, an abstraction.

Traditions and Rituals

These are the means through which the culture's values are communicated to employees on a daily basis. They include meetings, ceremonies, and taken-for-granted rituals. Strong cultures look for opportunities to celebrate, reward and symbolize rites of passage, promotions and achievements which conform to and reinforce basic corporate values. Traditions and rituals are rarely written down. Nevertheless, they show members which behaviours are permitted and which are discouraged in the organization.

Cultural Network

The informal communication network is the vehicle for transmitting culture. *Storytellers* tell newcomers how they should behave in order to succeed in the company; priests are the guardians of the culture's values, speak in parables, and know the company's history; whispers and gossips spread news, embellish stories and created heroes and heroines; and cabals are small groups of people who organize themselves to advance up the organization. These communication roles are a feature of all companies. In a strong culture, they support and communicate important corporate values to all organizational levels.

Corporate strength questionnaire scoring and interpretation

Add the scores for the following sets of questions:

A. _____   B. _____

1. ____   2. ____

5. ____   6. ____

9. ____   10. ____

    Total _____   Total _____

C. _____   D. _____

  3. _____   4. _____

  7. _____   8. _____

11. _____   12. _____

              Total _____   Total _____

Grand total _____

	Values	Heroes & heroines	Traditions and rituals	Cultural network	Grand Total cultural strength
Very strong	13–15	12–15	12–15	13–15	47–60
Strong	11–13	10–11	10–11	11–12	41–46
Medium	9–10	6–9	7–9	9–10	33–40
Weak	7–8	4–5	5–6	8–9	26–32
Very weak	3–6	3–4	3–4	3–7	12–25

Add up your scores for each of the four dimensions, and then add these together to get a grand total. Refer to the chart above to get an idea of the cultural strength of the organization that you have considered.

Procedure

Deal and Kennedy's book, *Corporate Culture: The Rites and Rituals of Corporate Life*, (1982) is a common way in which new students are first introduced to the concept of corporate culture. Beyond the problem of defining the concept itself, described in *ORBIT3*, Chapter 18, there are many conceptual, theoretical and empirical problems with Deal and Kennedy's formulation. For example, the idea that a large company can have a single, all embracing culture; that this culture can be neatly categorized as 'bet-your-company'; that corporate cultures can be described as 'weak' or 'strong'; and perhaps most controversial, the claim that strong corporate cultures are associated with superior economic performance. However, one has to start somewhere when introducing the concept of corporate culture, and this is as good a place as any.

Decide if you want the students to consider an organization of their own choice, one with which they are familiar, or whether you want them all to answer the questionnaire with one organization in mind. If the latter, the choice will be limited to their university, business school, student union or similar institution. Ensure that everyone has completed the questionnaire before proceeding.

Briefly describe Deal and Kennedy's four dimensions of culture (Values, Heroes and Heroines, Traditions and Rules, and Cultural Network) since this is not included in the *ORBIT3* chapter. Ask them to score their questionnaire, indicating which questions relate to which dimensions (A = Values; B = Heroes and Heroines; C = Traditions and Rules; D =

which dimensions (A = Values; B = Heroes and Heroines; C = Traditions and Rules; D = Cultural Network). Finally, invite them to interpret their score using the table provided. How 'strong' was the culture of their selected organization?

Note

Activity based on material from T.E. Deal and A.A. Kennedy, *Corporate Culture: The Rites and Rituals of Corporate Life*, Addison Wesley, 1982.

18.2 SGA: Processing people

Objectives

- To distinguish different socialization strategies, define them, state their purpose, and identify anticipated circumstances.
- To apply the strategies to their own experiences of being socialized as organization (or role) newcomers.
- To compare the frequency, kinds, and consequences of different combinations of strategies.
- To design alternative socialization strategies for specific training programmes.

Introduction

The goals and values of an organization can be translated in concrete behavioural strategies which are then taught to its new members. There are a range of different socialization experiences through which new organizational members become oriented within the organization. Van Maanen (1978) distinguished fourteen such strategies, and these are summarized below. This activity is designed to increase your awareness of these.

Name of strategy	Definition
1. Collective	Puts newcomer through a common set of experiences as part of a group.
2. Individual	Processes recruits singly and in isolation from each other.
3. Formal	Segregates newcomers from regular organizational members.
4. Informal	Treats newcomers as not differentiated from other members.
5. Sequential steps	Requires entrant to move through a series of discrete and identifiable steps to achieve a defined role.
6. Non-sequential steps	Accomplishes achievement of a defined role in one transitional stage.
7. Tournament	Separate clusters of recruits into different programmes on the basis of presumed differences.
8. Contest	Avoids sharp distinctions between clusters of recruits.
9. Fixed	Gives the recruit complete knowledge of time required to complete passage.
10. Variable	Offers a timetable which does not fix the length of socialization.

11. Serial	Provides experienced members as role models for newcomers about to assume similar positions to follow.
12. Disjunctive	Has no role models available since newcomers do not follow in the footsteps of recent predecessors.
13. Investiture	Ratifies and documents the usefulness of personal characteristics of new recruits.
14. Divestiture	Seeks to deny and strip away recruits' personal characteristics.

Procedure

Step 1 Think about your own socialization experiences. These may have occurred on training courses; orientation sessions when starting a new job; apprenticeships; or any other experiences in which either you were 'learning the ropes' from others, or you were 'teaching others the ropes'.

Step 2 Write down in detail two such scenarios:
1. A situation in which you were being socialized.
2. A situation in which you were socializing another person.

Step 3 Form into pairs, analyze your own scenarios and then the other person's. Reach a consensus on which Van Maanen's socializing strategies were being used in each scenario.

Step 4 The instructor tallies the strategies described in the scenarios on the blackboard, producing totals for each of the fourteen types.

Note

Source of activity: Gordon, J.R. and Bartunek, J.M., 'Teaching Organizational Socialization Strategies', *EXCHANGE: The Organizational Behaviour Teaching Journal*, Vol. 5, No. 3, pp. 37–40. Reading: Van Maanen, J., 'People Processing: Strategies of Organizational Socialization.' *Organizational Dynamics*, 1978, 7(1), 19–36.

18.3 PREP: Organizational culture and socialization

Objectives

- To introduce students to the concept of corporate (or organizational) culture and how it is communicated to new employees through the process of organizational socialization.
- To identify specific organizational socialization strategies, describe their purpose, and suggest their probable consequences.
- To sensitize students to the subtle messages given and received during initial organizational and role experiences.

Introduction

If the organizational structure is to accomplish the controlled performance of collective goals, then the behaviour of its employees has, in some way, to be made predictable and in line with those goals. One way of doing this is to define peoples' jobs, limit their authority, establish reporting relationships and specify rules. That, in essence, is what organizational structure attempts to do. Such external and highly visible controls may be perceived as oppressive and burdensome by employees. For this reason, corporations attempt to instil the culture (values, beliefs and attitudes) which they want their employees to possess. These types of controls, because they are internal, less visible and operated by the staff members themselves are often more effective. The process by which corporate culture is internalized by new employees is called *organizational socialization*.

Organizational socialization is defined as the manner in which the experiences of people learning the ropes in a new organizational position, status or role are structured for them by others within the organization. Such structuring seeks to communicate the corporation's values, beliefs and attitudes into new recruits. Once instilled, this *corporate culture* helps them to interpret their company world in a standardized and predictable way, and publicly accept it despite any reservations. During the socialization process, the individual goes through what anthropologists call a *rite de passage* as he or she moves from 'outsider', to 'new body', to 'low man' (in the training group) before finally emerging as a 'fully fledged member'. These transitions are achieved by the processes of anticipation, initiation and assimilation.

Procedure

Students read the abridged section from Michael Lewis's book, *Liar's Poker*, and prepare individual answers to the questions below. These should be supported by evidence cited from the numbered paragraphs.

Anticipatory step of the socialization process

During this phase, three important things happen. Review the case, and give examples of each of these.

1. What values, beliefs and behaviours are required by the neophyte to enable them to

survive and prosper in Salomon Brothers? How were they learned?

2. How were the graduate trainees 'sold' the organization, and encouraged to see themselves as members of an elite who had to pay the 'price of admission' which only a few could pay?

3. With what were the graduate trainees' old reference groups, roles and states replaced?

Initiation step of the socialization process

In this step, the 'new boy or girl' becomes the 'low man or woman'. The initiates form themselves into a training group in which the process of role acquisition begins, in an effort to acquire a vast amount of technical information which generates anxiety. This is compounded by a fear of failure and of the possibility of rejection. The 'bosses' become the focus of a love-hate relationship. To survive, the group creates informal structures, status relationships and values. It takes over the job of indoctrinating other initiates. Give examples of these.

4. What informal training group structures were there?

5. How was social status assigned to members by the training group?

Assimilation step of the socialization process

In this step, the neophyte is taken into the work environment, and away from the relative safety of the training group, in order to be introduced to the complexities and dilemmas of the organization. He or she is introduced to the world of work families, each of which has their own territory, mandate, values and norms. These all operate but are hazy and difficult in the first instance to pick up.

6. Describe some of the processes of assimilation described in the case.

7. At which point in the case did Lewis feel that he was becoming absorbed into the Salomon Brothers apparatus?

Note

The case is taken from Michael Lewis's, *Liar's Poker*, Hodder and Stoughton, 1989. Pages 42–89 have been abridged. Used with permission.

I

(1) The one hundred and twenty-seven unlikely members of the class of 1985 were one of a series of human waves to wash over what was then the world's most profitable floor. At the time, we were the largest training class in Salomon's history, and the class after us was nearly twice as large again...

(2) We were a paradox. We had been hired to deal in a market, to be more shrewd than the next guy, to be, in short, traders. Ask any astute trader and he'll tell you that his best work cuts against the conventional wisdom. Good traders tend to do the unexpected. We, as a group, were painfully predictable. By coming to Salomon Brothers, we were doing what every sane money-hungry person would do. If we were unable to buck

convention in our lives, would we be likely to buck convention in the market? After all, the job market is a *market*.

(3) We were as civil to the big man addressing the class as we had been to anyone, which wasn't saying much. He was the speaker for the entire afternoon. That meant he was trapped for three hours in the ten-yard trench in front of the room with a long table, a podium and a blackboard. The man paced back and forth in the channel like a coach on the sidelines, sometimes staring at the floor, other times menacingly at us. We sat in rows of interconnected school chairs – twenty-two rows of white male trainees, in white shirts, punctuated by the occasional female in a blue blazer, two blacks, and a cluster of Japanese. The dull New England clam-chowder colour of the training room walls and floor set the mood of the room. One wall had long narrow slits for windows with a sweeping view of New York Harbour and the Statue of Liberty, but you had to be sitting right beside them to be able to see anything, and even then you were not supposed to soak in the view.

(4) It was all in all, more like a prison than any office. The room was hot and stuffy. The seat cushions were in an unpleasant Astroturf green; the seat of your trousers stuck both to it and to you as you rose at the end of each day. Having swallowed a large and greasy cheeseburger at lunch, and having only a mild sociological interest in the speaker, I was overcome with drowsiness. We were only one week into our five-month training programme, and I was already exhausted. I sank into my chair.

(5) The speaker was a leading bond salesman at Salomon. On the table in the front of the room was a telephone which rang whenever the bond market went berserk. As the big man walked, he held his arms tight to his body to hide the half-moons of sweat growing under his armpits. Effort or nerves? Probably nerves. You couldn't blame him. He was airing his heartfelt beliefs, and in so doing, making himself more venerable than any speaker yet. I was in the minority in finding him a bit tedious. He was doing well with the crowd. People in the back row listened. All around the room, trainees put down their New York Times crossword puzzles. The man was telling us how to survive. 'You've got to think of Salomon Brothers as like a jungle', he said. Except it didn't come out that way. It came out: 'Ya gotta tink of Salomon Bruddahs as like a jungle'.

(6) 'The trading floor is a jungle', he went on, 'and the guy you end up working for is your jungle leader. Whether you succeed here on not depends on knowing how to survive in the jungle. You've got to learn from your boss. He's key. Imagine if I take two people and put them in the middle of the jungle and I give one person a jungle guide and the other person nothing. Inside the jungle there's a lot of bad shit going down. Outside of the jungle there's a TV that's got the NCAA finals on and a huge fridge full of Bud ...'

(7) The speaker had found the secret of managing the Salomon Brothers' class of 1985: win the hearts and minds of the back row. The back row, from about the third day of the classes on, teetered on the brink of chaos. Even when they felt merely ambivalent about a speaker, back-row people slept or chucked paper wads at the wimps in the front row. But if the back-row people for some reason didn't care for a speaker, all hell broke loose. Not now. Primitive revelation swept through the back row of the classroom at the sound of the jungle drums; it was as if a hunting party of Cro-Magnon men had stumbled upon a new tool. The guys in the back row were leaning forward in their seats for the first time all day. Oooooooo! Aaaahhhhh!

(8) With the back row neutralised, the speaker effectively controlled the entire audience, for the people sitting in the front row were on automatic pilot. They were the same as front row people all over the world, only more so. Most graduates of Harvard Business School sat in the front row. One of them greeted each new speaker by drawing an organization chart. The chart resembled a Christmas tree, with John Gutfreund on the top and us at the bottom. In between were lots of little boxes like ornaments. His way of controlling the situation was to identify the rank of the speaker, visualise his position in the hierarchy, and confine him to his proper box.

(9) They were odd, these charts, and more like black magic than business. Rank wasn't terribly important on the trading floor. Organizational structure at Salomon Brothers was something of a joke. Making money was mostly what mattered. But the front row was less confident than the back that the firm was a meritocracy of money lenders. They were hedging their bets – just in case Salomon Brothers after all bore some relation to the businesses they had learned about at school.

(10) '... a huge fridge of Bud', said the speaker a second time. 'And chances are good that the guy with the jungle guide is gonna be the first one through the jungle to the TV and the beer. Not to say that the other guy won't eventually get there too. But (here he stopped pacing and even gave the audience a little sly look), he'll be *reeeaaal* thirsty and there's not going to be any beer left when he arrives'.

(11) This was the punch line. Beer. The guys in the back row liked it. They fell all over each other slapping palms, and looked as silly as white men in suits when they pretend to be black soul brothers. They were relieved as much as excited. When not listening to this sort of speech, we faced a much smaller man with a row of Bic fine points in a plastic case in his breast pocket – otherwise known as a nerd pack – explaining to us how to convert a semi-annual bond yield to an annual bond yield. The guys in the back row didn't like that. 'Fuck the fuckin' bond maths, man', they said. 'Tell us about the jungle.'

(12) That the back row was more like the post-game shower room than a repository for the future leadership of Wall Street's most profitable investment bank troubled and puzzled the more thoughtful executives who appeared before the training class. As much time and effort had gone into recruiting the back row as the front, and the class, in theory, should have been uniformly attentive and well behaved, like an army. The curious feature about the breakdown in discipline was that it was random, uncorrelated with anything outside itself, and therefore uncontrollable. Although most of the graduates from Harvard Business School sat in the front, a few sat in the back. And right beside them were graduates from Yale, Stanford and Pennsylvania. The back had its share of expensively educated people. It had at least its fair share of brains. So why were these people behaving like this?

(13) And why Salomon let it happen, I still don't understand. The firm's management created the training programme, filled it to the brim, then walked away. In the ensuing anarchy, the bad drove out the good, the big drove out the small, and the brawn drove out the brains. There was a single trait common to denizens of the back row, though I doubt it ever occurred to anyone: they sensed that they needed to shed whatever refinements of personality and intellect they had brought with them to Salomon Brothers. This wasn't a conscious act, more a reflex. They were the victims of the myth,

especially popular at Salomon Brothers, that the trader is a savage, and a great trader a great savage. This wasn't exactly correct. The trading floor held evidence to that effect. But it also held evidence to the contrary. People believed whatever they wanted to.

(14) There was another cause of hooliganism. Life as a Salomon trainee was like being beaten up every day by the neighbourhood bully. Eventually you grew mean and surly. The odds of making it into the Salomon training programme, in spite of my fluky good luck, had been six to one against. You beat the odds and you felt you deserved some relief. There wasn't any. The firm never took you aside and rubbed you on the back to let you know that everything was going to be fine. Just the opposite: the firm built a system around the belief that trainees should wriggle and squirm. The winners of the Salomon Brothers interviewing process were pitted against one another in the classroom. In short, the baddest of the bad were competing for jobs.

(15) Jobs were doled out at the end of the programme on a blackboard beside the trading floor. Contrary to what we had expected when we arrived, we were not assured of employment. 'Look to your left and look to your right', more than one speaker said, 'In a year, one of those people will be out on the street'. Across the top of the job-placement blackboard appeared the name of each department on the trading floor: municipal bonds, corporate bonds, government bonds, etc. Along the side of the board was each office in the firm: Atlanta, Dallas, New York, etc. The thought that he might land somewhere awful in the matrix – or nowhere at all – drove the trainee to despair. He lost all perspective on the relative merits of the jobs. He did not count himself lucky just to be at Salomon Brothers; anyone who thought that way would not have got in in the first place. The Salomon trainee saw only the extremes of failure and success. Selling municipal bonds in Atlanta was unthinkably wretched: Trading mortgages in New York was mouth-wateringly good.

(16) I considered myself an exception of course. I was accused by some of being a front-row person because I liked to sit next to the man from the Harvard Business School and watch him draw the organization charts. I wondered if he would succeed (he didn't). Also, I asked too many questions. It was assumed that I did this to ingratiate myself with the speakers, like a front-row person. This was untrue. But try telling that to the back row. I lamely compensated for my curiosity by hurling a few paper wads at important traders. And my stock rose dramatically in the back row when I was thrown out of class for reading the newspaper while a trader spoke. But I was never an intimate of those in the back row.

(17) Of all exceptions, the Japanese were the greatest. The Japanese undermined any analysis of the classroom culture. All six of them sat in the front row and slept. Their heads rocked back and forth, and on occasion fell over to one side, so that their cheeks ran parallel to the floor. So it was hard to argue that they were listening with their eyes shut, as Japanese businessmen are inclined to do. The most charitable explanation for their apathy was that they could not understand English. They kept to themselves, however, and you could never be sure of either their language skills or their motives. Their leader was a man called Yoshi. Each morning and afternoon, the back-row boys made bets on how many minutes it would take Yoshi to fall asleep. They liked to think that Yoshi was a calculating troublemaker. Yoshi was their hero. A small cheer would go up in the back row when Yoshi crashed, partly because someone had just won a pile of money, but also in appreciation of any man with the balls to fall asleep in the front row.

(18) Still, in the end, the Japanese were reduced to nothing more than a bizarre distraction. The back row set the tone of the class because it acted throughout as one, indivisible, incredibly noisy unit. The back-row people moved in herds, for safety and for comfort, from the training class in the morning and early afternoon, to the trading floor at the end of the day, to the Surf Club at night, and back to the training programme the next morning. They were united by their likes as well as their dislikes. They rewarded the speakers of whom they approved by standing and doing The Wave across the back of the class.

(19) And they approved wholeheartedly of the man at the front of the room now. The speaker paused, as if lost in thought, which was unlikely. 'You know', he finally said, 'you think you're hot shit, but when you start out on the trading floor, you're going to be at the bottom'. Was it really necessary? He was playing so well by telling the hooligans what they liked to hear; being a winner at Salomon meant being a He-man in a jungle. Now he risked retaliation by telling the hooligans what they didn't like to hear: in the jungle, their native talents didn't mean a thing. I checked around for spitballs and paper wads. Nothing. The speaker had built sufficient momentum to survive his mistake. Heads in the back row nodded right along. It is possible that they assumed the speaker intended the remark for the front row.

(20) In any case, on this point, the speaker was surely wrong. A trainee didn't have to stay on the bottom for more than a couple of months. Bond traders and salesmen age like dogs. Each year on the trading floor counts for seven in any other corporation. At the end of his first year, a trader or salesman had stature. Who cared for tenure? The whole beauty of the trading floor was its complete disregard for tenure.

(21) A new employee, once he reached the trading floor, was handed a pair of telephones. He went on line almost immediately. If you could make millions of dollars come out of those phones, he became the most revered of all species: a Big Swinging Dick. After the sale of a big block of bonds and the deposit of a few hundred thousand dollars into the Salomon till, a managing director called whoever was responsible to confirm his identity: 'Hey, you Big Swinging Dick way to be'. To this day, the phrase brings to my mind the image of the elephant's trunk swaying from side to side. Swish. Swash. Nothing in the jungle got in the way of the Big Swinging Dick.

(22) That was the prize we coveted. Perhaps the phrase didn't stick in everyone's mind the way it did in mine; the name was less important than the ambition, which was common to us all. And, of course, no one actually said, 'When I get out on to the trading floor I'm gonna be a Big Swinging Dick'. It was more of a private thing. But everyone wanted to be a Big Swinging Dick, even the women, Big Swinging Dickettes. Christ, even the front row people hoped to be Big Swinging Dicks, once they had learned what it meant. Their problem, as far as the back row was concerned, was that they didn't know how to act the part. Big Swinging Dicks showed more grace under pressure than the front row people did.

(23) A hand shot up (typically) in the front row. It belonged to a woman. She sat high in her regular seat, right in front of the speaker. The speaker had momentum. The back row were coming out of their chairs to honour him with The Wave. The speaker didn't want to stop now, especially for a front row person. He looked pained, but he could hardly ignore a hand in his face. He called her name, Sally Findlay. 'I was just wondering',

said Findlay, 'if you could tell us what you think has been the key to your success'. This was too much. Had she asked a dry technical question, she might have pulled it off. But even the speaker started to smile ... he knew he could abuse the front row as much as he wanted. His grin spoke volumes to the back row. It said, 'Hey, I remember what these brown-nosers were like when I went through the training programme, and I remember how much I despised the speakers who let them kiss butt, so I'm going to let this woman hang out and dry for a minute, heh, heh, heh'. The back row broke out in its loudest laughter yet. Someone cruelly mimicked Findlay in a high pitched voice, 'Yes, *do* tell us why you're *sooooo* successful'. Someone else shouted, 'Down Boy' as if scolding an overheated poodle. A third man cupped his hands together around his mouth and hollered, *'Equities in Dallas'*.

(24) Poor Sally. There were many bad places your name could land on the job-placement board in 1985, but the absolute worst was in the slot marked Equities in Dallas. We could not imagine anything less successful in our small world than any equity salesman in Dallas; the equity department was powerless in our firm, and Dallas was, well, a long way from New York. Thus, Equities in Dallas, became training programme shorthand for 'just bury the lowest form of human scum where it will never be seen again'. Bury Sally, they shouted from the back row. The speaker didn't bother with an answer. He raced to a close before the mob he had incited became uncontrollable. 'You spend a lot of time asking yourself questions: 'Are munis right for me? Are goveys right for me? Are corporates right for me? You spend a lot of time thinking about that. And you should. But think about this. *It might be more important to choose a jungle guide than to choose your product*. Thank you'.

II

(25) The powers of Salomon Brothers relied on the training programme to make us more like them. What did it mean to be more like them? For most of its life, Salomon had been a scrappy, bond-trading house, distinguished mainly by its ability and willingness to take big risks. Salomon had to accept risk to make money because it had no list of fee-paying corporate clients, unlike say, the genteel Gentiles of Morgan Stanley. The image Salomon had projected to the public was of a firm of clannish Jews, social nonentities, shrewd but honest, sinking its nose more deeply into the bond markets than any other firm cared to. This was a caricature of course, but it roughly captured the flavour of the place as it once was. Now, Salomon wanted to change.

(26) Despite the nouveau fluctuation in our corporate identity, the corporate training programme was, without a doubt, the finest start to a career on Wall Street. Upon completion, a trainee could take his experience, and cash it in for twice the salary on any other Wall Street trading floor. He had achieved, by the standards of Wall Street, technical mastery of his subject. It was an education in itself to see how quickly one became an 'expert' on Wall Street.

(27) But the materials were the least significant aspect of our training. The relevant bits, the ones I would recall two years later, were the war stories, the passing on of the oral tradition of Salomon Brothers. Over three months, leading salesmen, traders and financiers shared their experiences with the class. They trafficked in unrefined street wisdom – how money travels around the world (any way it wants); how a trader feels and behaves (any way he wants); and how to smooze a customer. After three months in

the class, trainees circulated wearily around the trading floor for two months more. Then they went to work. All the while there was a hidden agenda: to Salomonize the trainee. The trainee was made to understand, first, that inside Salomon Brothers he was, as a trader once described us, lower than whale shit on the bottom of the ocean floor and second, that lying under the whale shit at Salomon Brothers was like rolling in clover compared to not being at Salomon at all.

(28) In the short term, the brainwashing nearly worked. (In the long term it didn't. For people to accept the yoke, they must believe they have no choice. As we shall see, we newcomers had both an exalted sense of our market value, and no permanent loyalties.) A few investment banks had training programmes, but with the possible exception of Goldman Sachs, none was so replete with firm propaganda. A woman from the New York Times who interviewed us three months into our programme was so impressed by the universality in attitudes towards the firm, that she called her subsequent article, 'The Boot Camp for Top MBAs'.

III

(29) Each day after class, around three or four or five o'clock, we were pressured to move from the training class on the 23rd floor, to the trading floor on the 41st. You could get away with not going for a few days, but if not seen on the floor occasionally, you were forgotten. Forgotten at Salomon meant unemployed. Getting hired was a positive act. A manager had to request you for his unit ... you cruised the trading floor to find a manager who would take you under his wing, a mentor, commonly referred to as a rabbi. You also went to the trading floor to learn. Your first impulse was to step into the fray, select a likely teacher, and present yourself for instruction. Unfortunately this wasn't so easy. First, a trainee by definition had nothing of merit to say. And second, the trading floor was a minefield of large men on short fuses just waiting to explode, if you so much as breathed in their direction. You didn't just walk up and say hello. Actually, that's not fair. Many, many traders are instinctively polite, and if you said hello, they'd just ignore you. But if you happened to step on a mine, then the conversation went something like this:

(30) Me: Hello

Trader: What fucking rock did you crawl out from under? Hey Joe, hey Bob, check out this guy's suspenders.

Me (reddening):   I just wanted to ask you a couple of questions.

Joe: Who the fuck does he think he is?

Trader: Joe, let's give this guy a little test! When interest rates go up, which way do bond prices go?

Me: Down.

Trader: Terrific. You get an A. Now I gotta work.

Me: When would you have some time ...

Trader: What the fuck do you think this is, a charity? I'm busy.

Me: Can I help in any way?

| Trader: | Get me a burger. With ketchup. |

(31) So I watched my step. There were a million little rules to obey. I knew none of them. Salesmen, traders and managers swarmed over the floor, and at first I couldn't tell them apart. Sure, I knew the basic differences. Salesmen talked to investors, traders made bets, and managers smoked cigars. But other than that I was lost. Most of the men were at two phones at once. Most of the men stared at small green screens full of numbers. They'd shout into one phone, then into the other, then at someone across the row of trading desks, then back into the phones and scream 'Fuck!'. Thirty seconds was considered a long attention span. As a trainee, a pleb, a young man lying under all that whale shit, I did what every trainee did: sidled up to some busy person without saying a word and became the Invisible Man.

(32) That it was perfectly humiliating was, of course, precisely the point. Sometimes I'd wait for an hour before my existence was formally acknowledged, other times a few minutes. Even that seemed like for ever. Who is watching me in my current debased condition? I'd wonder. Will I ever recover from such total neglect? Will someone please notice that the Invisible Man has arrived. The contrast between me standing motionless, and the traders frenetic movements made the scene particularly unbearable. It underlined my uselessness. But once I'd sidled up, it was difficult to leave without being officially recognized. To leave was to admit defeat in this particular ritual of making myself known.

(33) Anyway, there wasn't really any place else to go. The trading room was about a third the length of a football field and was lined with connected desks. Traders sitting elbow to elbow formed a human chain. Between the rows of desks there was not enough space for two people to pass each other, without first turning sideways. Even if you shed your red suspenders and adopted protective colouration, you were easily identifiable as a trainee. Trainees were impossibly out of step with the rhythm of the place. The movements of the trading floor respond to the movements of the markets as if roped together. The entire Salomon Brothers trading floor might be poised for a number at eight thirty a.m., gripped by suspense and a great deal of hope, ready to leap and shout, to buy or sell billions of dollars-worth of bonds, to make or lose millions of dollars for the firm, when a trainee arrives, suspecting nothing and says, 'Excuse me, I'm going to the cafeteria, does anybody want anything?' Trainees, in short, were idiots.

(34) To avoid being squashed on my visits to the floor, I tried to keep still, preferably in some corner. Except for Gutfreund, whom I knew from magazine pictures, and thought of more as a celebrity than a businessman, the faces were foreign to me. That made it hard to know whom to avoid. Many of them looked the same, in that most were white, most were male, and all wore the same all-cotton buttoned-down shirts (one of our Japanese once told me he couldn't for the life of him tell them apart). The 41st floor of Salomon New York was Power Central, holding not just the current senior management of the firm, but its future management as well. You had to go by their strut to distinguish between who should be approached and who avoided.

(35) Did I grow more comfortable on the trading floor over time? I suppose. But even when I established myself with the firm, I got the creepy crawlies each time I walked out on to 41. I could see certain developments in myself however. One day, I was playing out the Invisible Man, feeling the warmth of the whale shit and thinking that no one in life

was lower than I. On to the floor rushed a member of the corporate finance department wearing his jacket like a badge of dishonour. Nobody wore a jacket on the floor. It must of been his first trip down from his glass-box office, and he looked one way and then the other in the midst of the bedlam. Somebody bumped into him and sharply told him to watch his step. Watch his step? But he was just standing there. You could see him thinking that the gaze of the whole world was on him. And he started to panic, like an actor who has forgotten his lines. He probably forgot why he'd come in the first place. And he left. Then I thought a nasty thought. But it showed I was coming along. What a wimp I thought. He doesn't have a fucking clue.

IV

(36) Four weeks had passed. The class had acquired a sense of its rights. The first inalienable right of a trainee was to dawdle and amuse himself before he settled into his chair for the morning. Cafeteria bagels and coffee were munched and swallowed throughout the room. People read the New York Post and laid bets on whatever game was to be played that evening. The New York Times crossword puzzle had been Xeroxed a hundred and twenty seven times and distributed. Someone had telephoned one of New York's sleazy porno recordings and linked the receiver to a loudspeaker on the table in front of the classroom. Sex talk filled the air. I was, as was my habit at this hour, biting into a knish.

(37) Susan James walked in to interrupt *The Revenge of the Nerds II*. James played a strange role. She was something between a baby-sitter, and an organizer of the programme. Quit fooling around you guys', she pleaded, like a camp counsellor before parents' day. 'Jim Massey is going to be here in a minute'. Massey, we all thought, was John Gutfreund's hatchet man. He had what some people might consider an image problem: he never smiled. Ostensibly, Massey had come to answer questions we might have about the firm. Thus the bugle was sounded before the chairman's keeper of the corporate culture arrived to answer our questions. He had a short jaw-line, lean and sharp enough to cut cake, and short cropped hair. He wore a grey suit with, unlike other board members, no pocket hankie. He had an economy of style and, like a gifted athlete, an economy of movement, as if he were conserving his energy for a meaningful explosion.

(38) He gave a short talk, the point of which was to stress how singular and laudable was the culture of Salomon Brothers. Yes, we knew it was the best trading firm in the world. Yes, we also knew Salomon stressed teamwork (who doesn't?). Yes, we realized that the quickest way to be fired was to appear in the press boasting about how much money we made (Salomon was modest and discreet). Perhaps we had heard the fate of the Salomon man in Los Angeles who appeared in *Newsweek*, lounging beside a swimming-pool and boasting about his good fortune? Yes, he had been sacked. Yes, we knew Salomon's 3 billion dollars in capital made it the most powerful force in the financial markets. Yes, we knew that no matter what we had achieved in our small lives, we weren't fit to get a cup of coffee for the men on the trading floor. Yes, we knew not to concern ourselves too much but rather let the firm (Massey) decide where on the trading floor we would be placed at the end of the trading programme.

V

(39) As the training neared its conclusion, the back-room game of Liar's Poker grew. Bond trading had captured the imaginations of more than half the men in the class. Instead of

saying buy and sell like normal human beings, they said 'bid' and 'offer'. Bonds, bonds and more bonds. Anyone who did not want to trade them for a living wanted to sell them. This group now included several women who had initially hoped to trade. At Salomon Brothers, men traded. Women sold. No one ever questioned the Salomon ordering of the sexes. But the immediate prohibition of women in trading was clear to all; it kept women further from power.

(40) More different types of people succeeded on the trading floor than I initially supposed. Some of the men who spoke to us were truly awful human beings. They sacked others to promote themselves. They harassed women. They didn't have customers. They had victims. Others were naturally extremely admirable. They inspired those around them. They treated their customers almost fairly. They were kind to trainees. The point is not that a Big Swinging Dick is intrinsically evil. The point is that it didn't matter one bit whether he was good or evil, as long as he continued to swing that big bat of his. Bad guys did not suffer their comeuppance in Act V on the 41st floor (though whether they succeeded *because* they were bad people, or because there was something about the business that naturally favoured them over the virtuous are separate questions). Goodness was not taken account of on the trading floor. It was neither rewarded nor punished. It just was. Or it wasn't.

(41) Because the 41st floor was the chosen home of the firm's most ambitious people, and because there were no rules governing the pursuit of profit and glory, the men who worked there, including the more bloodthirsty, had a hunted look about them. The place was governed by the simple understanding that the unbridled pursuit of perceived self-interest was healthy. Eat or be eaten. The men of the 41 worked with one eye cast over their shoulders to see whether someone was trying to do them in, for there was no telling what manner of man had levered himself to the rung below and was now hungry for your job. The range of acceptable conduct within Salomon Brothers was wide indeed. It said something about the ability of the free market-place to mould people's behaviour into a socially acceptable pattern. For this was capitalism at its most raw, and it was self-destructive.

(42) As a Salomon Brothers trainee, of course, you didn't worry too much about ethics. You were just trying to stay alive. You felt flattered to be on the same team as the people who kicked everyone's ass all the time. Like a kid mysteriously befriended by the playground bully, you tended to overlook the flaws of the bond people in exchange for their protection. I sat wide-eyed when these people came to speak to us, and observed a behavioural smorgasbord the likes of which I have never before encountered except in fiction. As a student, you had to start from the premise that each of these characters was immensely successful, then try to figure out why.

(43) The training programme wasn't a survival course, but sometimes a person came through who put the horrors of 41 into perspective. For me it was a young bond salesman, just a year out of the training programme and at work on 41, named Richard O'Grady. He began by telling us how he had come to Salomon. He had been one of the firm's lawyers. The firm's lawyers, when they see how good traders had it, often ended up as traders themselves. The firm had actually invited O'Grady to apply. He interviewed on a Friday afternoon. His first meeting was with a managing director named Lee Kimmell. When O'Grady walked into Kimmell's office, Kimmell was reading his resume. He looked up from the resume and said, 'Amherst, Phi Beta Kappa, star athlete,

Harvard Law School, you must get laid a lot'. O'Grady laughed (what else do you do?). 'What's so funny?' asked Kimmell. 'The thought that I get laid a lot' said O'Grady. That's not funny', said Kimmell, a viciousness coming into his voice. 'How much do you get laid?'. 'That's none of your business', said O'Grady. Kimmell slammed his fist on the desk. 'Don't give me that crap. If I want to know you tell me. Understand?'.

(44) Somehow O'Grady squirmed through the interview and others, until, at the end of the day, he found himself facing the same man who had given me my job, Leo Corbett. 'So Dick', said Corbett, 'what would you say if I offered you a job?' 'Well', said O'Grady, 'I'd like to work at Salomon, but I'd also like to go home and think it over for a day or two'. 'You sound more like a lawyer than a trader', said Corbett. 'Leo, I'm not making a trade; I'm making an investment', said O'Grady. 'I don't want to hear any of that Harvard Law School clever bullshit', said Corbett. 'I'm beginning to think you would be a real mistake ... I'm going to walk out of here and come back in ten minutes and when I come back I want an answer'.

(45) O'Grady's first reaction, he said, was that he had just made a catastrophic error of judgement. Then he thought about it like a human being. Salomon had invited *him* to interview. Where did these butt-heads get off issuing ultimatums? O'Grady worked himself into an Irish rage. Corbett was gone far longer than he had promised, making O'Grady even angrier. 'Well ...?', said Corbett upon his return. 'Well I wouldn't work here for all the money in the world', said O'Grady. 'I have never met more assholes in my entire life. Take your job and stick it up your ass'. 'Now I am finally beginning to hear something I like', said Corbett. 'That's the first smart thing you've said all day'. O'Grady stormed out of Salomon Brothers and took a job with another Wall Street firm.

(46) But that was only the beginning of the story which O'Grady said resumed a year after he had told Leo Corbett where to stick his job offer. Salomon called him again. They had apologised for the way they had behaved. They had been smart to do so because O'Grady became not only an excellent bond salesman, but also a rare and much-needed example of goodness on the training floor. The surprise was not that Salomon called him, but that O'Grady had agreed to listen. O'Grady took a job with Salomon Brothers.

(47) And now he was about to tell us what we all wanted to know. 'So you want to know how to deal with assholes, don't you?', he said. Trainees sort of nodded their heads. O'Grady said he had discovered the secret earlier than most. When he was just starting out, he said, he had an experience which had taught him a lesson. He had been a flunkey for a senior bond salesman named Penn King, a tall blond Big Swinging Dick if ever there was one. One day, King told him to find prices on four bonds for a very large customer, Morgan Guaranty. O'Grady therefore asked the relevant trader for prices. When the trader saw him, however, he said, 'What the fuck do *you* want'? Just a few prices, said O'Grady. 'I'm busy', said the trader. Oh well, thought O'Grady, I'll see if I can find the prices on the Quotron machine.

(48) As O'Grady fiddled with the keyboard of the Quotron – it resembles a personal computer – Penn King demanded the prices for his customer. 'I told you to get the prices godammit', he said. So O'Grady raced back to ask the trader again. 'Fuck it' said the trader, 'here, read it off the sheets', and handed O'Grady a sheet listing bond prices. O'Grady returned to his desk only to find that while there were plenty of prices on the sheet, they weren't the prices he needed. 'Where are the goddam prices?' asked Penn.

O'Grady explained what had transpired between himself and the trader to that point. 'Then this is what you do, you hear me?' said a completely pissed-off Penn King. 'You go over to that *asshole* and you say, 'Look *asshole*, since you were so *fucking* helpful the first time I asked, maybe you could give me the goddam prices for Morgan Guaranty'.

(49) So O'Grady went back to the trader. He figured he could edit the request, you know, take out the part about the asshole and being fuckin' helpful. He had this sanitized version in his mind; 'Look I'm really sorry to be such a pain in the neck,' he was beginning to say, 'but Morgan Guaranty is one of our biggest customers and we need your help ...'. But when he reached the trader, the trader rose to his feet and screamed, 'What the fuck are you doing back here? I told you: *I ... am ... busy*'. 'Look *asshole*', said O'Grady, forgetting the sanitized version, 'since you were so *fucking* helpful the first time I asked, maybe you would be so kind to give me the goddam prices *now*'. The trader fell back in his chair. Since O'Grady was about twice the size of the trader, he could threaten force. He stood over the trader and stared for about a minute. '*Asshole*', he shouted again, for effect.

(50) All of a sudden, the trader looked spooked. '*Pennnnn*'! he half-screamed, half-whined across the floor to O'Grady's boss. 'What the fuck is it with this guy?' Penn gave an innocent little shrug as if to say, he didn't have the faintest idea. O'Grady walked back to his seat to a standing ovation from three or four other bond salesmen who had watched the scene develop, and a big grin from Penn. Sure enough, not two minutes later, *the trader came to him with the prices*. 'And after that', said O'Grady to a spellbound training programme, 'he didn't fuck with me again'.

18.4 REV: Word search

Objective

- To review the corporate culture controversy, approaches and elements considered in *ORBIT3*, Chapter 18.

Introduction

When it first came to prominence during the 1980s, corporate culture was considered by many to be a passing management fad. Since that time, however, it has established itself not only as an explanatory concept within the field of organization behaviour, but also as a distinct perspective along with the human, structural and political views. An understanding of the terminological aspects of the concept of corporate culture is therefore fundamental. This review activity asks you not only to locate the key terms and labels associated with corporate culture, but also to illustrate some of them from your own experience, and of those people around you.

Instructions

The grid below contains 28 terms, concepts, labels, and perspectives mentioned in *ORBIT3*, Chapter 18. These are placed horizontally, backwards, vertically and diagonally. See how many you can locate. Then, select any five, and give an example of each from either an organization that you are familiar with, or by interviewing a friend, colleague or relation. Insert the answers and examples in the spaces below.

Corporate culture grid

C	C	O	N	S	I	S	T	E	N	C	Y	M	K	Y	V	S
H	O	C	W	O	I	D	S	A	G	A	S	R	N	U	N	L
L	O	U	A	R	I	L	I	S	Y	M	B	O	L	I	C	O
A	C	A	R	F	M	T	L	A	O	P	I	N	I	O	N	B
N	E	O	F	S	T	C	A	F	E	T	R	A	M	D	S	M
G	R	L	Q	O	E	R	N	T	A	F	V	H	G	F	T	Y
U	E	O	Y	C	L	S	O	Z	N	A	L	G	I	O	O	S
A	M	W	S	I	O	K	I	H	R	E	P	N	D	U	R	L
G	O	P	V	L	H	L	T	I	P	O	M	S	A	N	I	A
E	N	E	F	A	A	E	A	A	L	A	T	G	R	D	E	U
Y	I	R	C	I	L	B	R	W	L	E	T	I	A	E	S	T
Q	A	S	C	X	L	U	G	O	C	E	G	E	P	R	C	I
H	L	O	B	E	L	I	E	F	S	H	S	E	M	S	F	R
C	S	N	A	T	T	I	T	U	D	E	Y	O	N	K	G	I
N	O	I	T	A	I	T	N	E	R	E	F	F	I	D	E	T
T	E	C	N	A	T	S	I	D	R	E	W	O	P	J	S	E
Z	H	S	S	P	X	Z	M	Y	T	H	S	V	P	X	E	S

1. Spot the terms

1.	11.	21.
2.	12.	22.
3.	13.	23.
4.	14.	24.
5.	15.	25.
6.	16.	26.
7.	17.	27.
8.	18.	28.
9.	19.	
10.	20.	

2. Give an example

Term	Example
1.	
2.	
3.	
4.	
5.	

Technology as a trigger of change

19.1 LGA: Old McDonald's farm

Objectives

- To introduce students to sociotechnical systems theory.
- To give them practice in integrating social with technical systems in an organization.

Introduction

Sociotechnical Systems (STS) is a term which was originated by the research group at the Tavistock Institute in London. The concept of the sociotechnical system is based on the simple fact that any production system requires both a technology (machinery, plant layout, raw materials – and a work-relationship structure that links the human operators both to the technology and to each other. The technology makes demands and places limits on the type of work structure that is possible, while the work structure itself has social and psychological properties that generate their own unique requirements with regard to the task to be done.

To recap the two key concepts, the term, *social system*, in this context refers to the relationship between people who interact with each other in a given environment for the basic purpose of achieving an agreed-upon task or goal. The term, *technical or technological* system, consists of the tools, techniques and methods of doing work that are employed for task performance. So technology includes not only tangibles like machinery and tools, but also intangibles like ideas, procedures and methods of production.

Procedure

Step 1   Read the case *Old McDonald's farm*, and individually, write notes on the two questions that follow it.

Step 2   Use your individual notes as a basis for a discussion with a fellow student or students, as directed by your instructor.

Step 3   Review your decisions in the light of your instructor's comments and the sociotechnical systems principles listed.

Old McDonald's farm

Below you will see an illustration of Old McDonald's farm. On this farm, he had no pigs, cows or chickens. On this farm, he had only corn, planted in long rows that grew all year round. McDonald had a perfect environment for growing corn. The soil was rich and the climate was perfect, twelve months out of the year.

McDonald's rows of corn were so long that at one end of the row the soil was being prepared for planting, while the next section of the row was being planted, the next section was growing, and the next was being harvested. McDonald had four of these long rows.

	Soil Prep.	Planting	Growing	Harvesting
Row A				
Row B				
Row C				
Row D				
Row E				
Row F				

McDonald was a progressive and scientific farmer. He was concerned about both productivity and quality. He had an industrial engineer study the amount of effort required to complete the work in each function on each row. He found that two employees were required per section, on each row, fully employed in that function all year round. Therefore, he employed eight workers in each row. For the purpose of this case, assume that this is true.

Initially, Mr McDonald had only four rows, A, B, C and D, and a total of 32 people. But recently he decided to expand, adding two more rows, E and F. This had added 16 more workers. Now he had 48 employees. Until this time, he had only one supervisor responsible for directing the work of all the 32 employees on the original four rows. Then he decided that there was too much work for one supervisor, and he added a second.

Mr McDonald now had to decide whether to reorganize the work of his supervisors and employees. He spoke to his two supervisors, Mr Jones and Mr Smith, and discovered that each had a different idea of what should be done.

Mr Jones insisted that the only intelligent way to organize was round the technical knowledge, using the functional approach. He argued that he should take responsibility for the employees who work in the first two sections, soil preparation and planting, on all the six rows. In his view, his colleague Mr Smith, whom he acknowledged had greater expertise in growing and harvesting, would take responsibility for all employees in the last two sections. They would each have an equal number of employees.

Mr Smith had an entirely different idea. He argued that while there was some specialized knowledge needed, it was more important for all the employees to take responsibility for the entire growing cycle. This way they could move down the row, seeing the progress of the corn. He thus argued for organizing them into teams by row.

Mr McDonald has hired you as a consultant to help him build the best possible organization. You are now to design the basic organization from the bottom up. Answer the following questions:

1. How will you organize employees on Mr McDonald's farm and how will you assign responsibility to Smith and Jones? You are free to make any assignment you like, as long as you don't change the assumptions of the case (e.g. the numbers of employees required for each task).

2. Which organizational behaviour theories or research encountered in the course so far support your decision? Why is your decision better than alternatives?

Sociotechnical systems principles

There are nine principles:

1. Compatibility
The way that the system is designed (its process) must be compatible with its objective. If the objective is to design an organization which continuously adapts to its environment, the process of its design must involve the participation of its members in an on-going way.

2. Minimal critical specification
Organizations should provide the minimum of detailed specification about how tasks should be performed, and by whom. Instead, they should specify outcomes (how many, to what standard, why, when), allowing members to creatively meet such objectives.

3. Proximity of control
Variances or unplanned events which affect specified outcomes should be controlled as close to their point of origin as possible. For example, if a machine breaks down, it should be its operator who repairs it.

4. Information flow
An adjunct of the above, the principle holds that the system should provide information initially to those best able to act upon it. For example, the ovensman in a biscuit factory who controls the speed of progress of the biscuits on a belt through the ovens should receive real time information about biscuit weight and texture, allowing him to adjust their speed as necessary, so as to meet output requirements.

5. Broad tasks and multi-skilling
Organizations will adapt more easily to changing environmental conditions if the tasks to be performed are widely defined, and those who perform them are trained to perform a variety of different tasks.

6. Boundary location
Structuring an organization on the basis of technology (e.g. milling section, lathe section, assembly section) make it easy to control for the manager, but not particularly efficient. By creating boundaries based not on technology but on time reduces waiting times and delays. Group technology and just-in-time are examples of time boundaries. Since operations occur in sequence, the technologies required are grouped together in small, responsive clusters.

7. Support congruence
In STS, *support* is defined to include pay systems, selection, training, conflict resolution, work measurement, performance evaluation, time keeping, leave allocation, promotion and hiring and firing. Indeed, everything that supports task performance. The principle advocates consistency between these different elements, and the organization's design and general

philosophy. For example, a team-based approach to work accompanied by an individually-focused incentive pay scheme would be inconsistent.

8. Design and human values

STS is committed to improving the quality of working life of employees by making jobs reasonably demanding, and providing workers with opportunities for learning, decision-making and recognition. Additionally, they should meet workers' needs to relate their work life to their social life.

9. Continuous evaluation

This principle holds that organizational design involves a simultaneous consideration of social and technical systems in an on-going way. The evaluation and review of the adopted design therefore continues indefinitely.

Source: Dorothy Marcic, *Organizational Behaviour: Experiences and Cases*, West Publishing Company, Minneapolis/St. Paul, 4th edition, pp. 283–6. Itself based on Karen Brown, 'Integrating Sociotechnical Systems into the Organizational Behaviour Curriculum: Discussion and Class Exercise', *OBTR*, Vol. XII (1), 1987–88, pp. 35–48.

19.2 SGA: Stakeholder analysis

Objectives

- To develop understanding of the potential impact of technology change in organizations.
- To highlight the distinction between material technology and social technology.

Introduction

A *stakeholder* is someone who is likely to be affected by a change in technology, whether they regard the change as beneficial or damaging to them. One way to explore and predict the implications of technology change is through the procedure of *stakeholder analysis*. This exercise demonstrates what a *stakeholder analysis* involves. Such an analysis can also be used to shape the nature and direction of technology change, by anticipating problems and suggesting action to avoid them. A case exercise is provided as a basis for this analysis. You may, however, also like to consider conducting a *stakeholder analysis* with respect to technology change current in your institution. This can raise the question of 'what counts as technology change?'. Chapter 11 in *ORBIT3* discusses the definitional problems in this field and draws a distinction between *material technology* on the one hand and *social technology* on the other. This can also be expressed as a distinction between apparatus and organizational arrangements. In conducting a stakeholder analysis, it is usually necessary to consider not only the technology or apparatus, but also how it will be used in the context of particular organizational arrangements.

Stakeholder analysis is based first on a stakeholder map. Let us assume that somebody has at last developed an effective computer-based learning methodology for teachers and students of organizational behaviour. Much easier to programme and use than previous cumbersome approaches, the technology is still expensive and specialized, but offers the promise of reducing formal lecturing and allowing increased self instruction by students at their own pace. A stakeholder map would look something like this:

OB instructors   students

other lecturers   secretaries

computer-based
learning

library staff   computing services

You may like to add other stakeholders to this map for yourself (what about the publishers of conventional textbooks?). It should then be possible to identify for each stakeholder what benefits and disadvantages they might see in the proposed change. From this, we can then anticipate their respective perceptions and behaviours in relation to the proposed changes.

Potential problems can then also be anticipated, and action identified to address those problems.

Let us now apply such an analysis to a specific case.

Procedure

Step 1   Read the following *Maintenance planning case*.

Step 2   Produce a stakeholder map.

Step 3   Complete the analysis table that follows the case description, identifying how they can expect to benefit from the change, how they can expect to be disadvantaged by the change, their anticipated behaviour, possible coalitions, and action suggested by this analysis.

Step 4   Report findings in accordance with your Instructor's wishes.

Maintenance planning case

Consider yourself part of the management team for a large manufacturing company. You are committed to improving the efficiency of plant maintenance and you have come up with the following proposal.

At present, each of the 14 separate manufacturing plants on your site have their own maintenance crews, including skilled and unskilled personnel, team supervisors and support equipment. However, a system has been designed which you know will improve efficiency and reduce the costs of maintenance work. It will depend on the manufacturing supervisor responsible for each production plant entering maintenance requests through the computer terminal in his office. These maintenance requests will then be electronically mailed to a central computer which will allocate a priority to each request relative to other requests in the system at that time. Routine tasks, day to day workshop jobs and emergency work can be put in to the system and scheduled along with regular maintenance requests. The computer system will also keep a record of all the skills acquired by each individual maintenance engineer.

When considering each maintenance request, the system will use three items of information to calculate the time and staff required to schedule and to complete the work. This includes information about the work requested, the availability of maintenance engineering personnel, and the skills possessed by each engineer. This will ensure that the right staff are sent to each maintenance job. When allocating work and determining priorities, the system can also schedule activities to occur during plant shutdowns or at other appropriate periods to reduce interruptions to manufacturing output.

This new system will therefore centralize maintenance management and the issuing of maintenance work instructions in one engineering department site . Records will also be kept of the actual times taken for jobs, so that these can be compared with the time forecasts for the work. The costs of staff and equipment time, consumables and stocks of spares and other items will also be monitored by the system.

Stakeholder analysis

Stakeholder	Benefits	Disadvantages	Reactions

Can you expect any coalitions or partnerships between stakeholders either to support or to challenge the system?

What ideas for action does this analysis suggest? Are there ways of minimizing the implications for the 'losers'? How could 'losers' be turned into 'winners'?

Note

This case is drawn from the Diagnostics Module in *The Technical Change Audit: Action for Results*, by David Boddy and David Buchanan, Manpower Services Commission, Sheffield, 1987, p. 32.

19.3 PREP: McDonaldization

Objectives

- To consider the implications of one particular trend in the development of a particular configuration of material and social technology.
- To develop an understanding of how social and technological trends of this kind can be subverted.

Introduction

In his book *The McDonaldization of Society* (1993) George Ritzer argues that the process of 'McDonaldization' is affecting many areas of our social and organizational lives, and that this trend is undesirable. He has no particular complaint against McDonald's hamburger restaurants; he merely uses this fast food chain as an illustration of the wider process which is the real focus of his attention. His argument is that the process of McDonaldization is spreading and that, while it yields a number of benefits, the costs and risks are in Ritzer's view considerable. In this exercise, you are introduced to the four central dimensions McDonaldization that Ritzer identifies. You are then invited to consider the benefits of this trend, the costs and risks attached to this trend, and finally (using some of Ritzer's ideas as a basis) to consider whether and how such a social trend can be subverted by individual action.

Procedure

Step 1   Before your session, read the following brief on McDonaldization and make preliminary notes in response to the five questions posed.

Step 2   Once in class, working in syndicates of three to five members, share and compare your individual responses, nominate a spokesperson, and prepare a group consensus report in response to the three discussion questions.

Step 3   With the whole group back together, present your syndicate findings for comparison with the findings of the other syndicates.

Step 4   Following this session, you may find it interesting to track down for yourself and read a copy of George Ritzer's book.

McDonaldization

Everybody knows McDonald's. They are all over America. They are all over Britain. There is a McDonald's on the Champs Elysee in Paris. There is a McDonald's in Lisbon in Portugal and in Gothenburg in Sweden. There is a McDonald's in Moscow. The company has come to symbolize many aspects of popular modern culture. The McDonald's large yellow 'M' logo is one of the most widely recognized company symbols in the world (along with Holiday Inn and Coca Cola). In his book *The McDonaldization of Society*, George Ritzer argues that the McDonald's approach has four central dimensions:

1. *Efficiency*

with respect to the speed with which you are transformed from being hungry to being fed, including the drive-through option

2. *Calculability*

with respect to high value meals for discounted prices – quarter pounders, Big Macs, large fries, all ordered, delivered and consumed with a minimum waste of time

3. *Predictability*

the Big Mac in New York is the same as the Big Mac in Paris is the same as the Big Mac in Birmingham – no surprises, but nothing special either

4. *Control*

the staff who work in McDonald's are trained to perform a limited range of tasks in a precisely detailed way, and customers are similarly constrained by queues, limited menu options, and by the expectation that they eat and leave.

In addition to the simplified jobs that McDonalds' employees perform, their work is also limited by the sophisticated technology of fast food preparation which gives them little or no discretion in how they prepare and deliver food to customers. Hamburger grilling instructions are precise and detailed, covering the exact positioning of burgers on the grill, cooking times, and the sequence in which burgers are to be turned. Drinks dispensers, french-fry machines, programmed cash registers – all limit the time required to carry out a task and leave little or no room for discretion, creativity or innovation on the part of the employee. Such discretion and creativity would of course subvert the aims of efficiency, calculability, predictability and control.

Analysis questions

1. What are the benefits of this approach – to the company, to the customer, to society as a whole?

2. What are the disadvantages of this approach?

3. What examples of McDonaldization can you identify in sectors other than fast foods (for example, to what extent is further and higher education susceptible to McDonaldization)?

4. George Ritzer offers a number of suggestions for coping with McDonaldization. These include the avoidance of daily routine, self-help rather than the use of 'instant repair' chains, using small, local, independent traders and services rather than large companies, returning all 'junk mail', trying to establish meaningful communications with fast food counter staff, avoiding classes which are assessed using short answer examinations and computer-graded tests, and so on. Identify five other subversion strategies for yourself.

5. What is your realistic assessment of the impact of these subversion strategies? Can we really make a difference, individually and/or collectively? Is it worth the effort?

Note

This exercise is based on the book, *The McDonaldization of Society: An Investigation into the Changing Character of Contemporary Social Life*, by George Ritzer, Pine Forge Press, Thousand Oaks, 1993.

19.4 REV: Who said that?

Objectives

- To test students' memory of key ideas from Chapter 19 in *ORBIT3* concerning the definition and understanding of the place of technology in organizational behaviour.
- To encourage the habit of remembering accurately the authorship of ideas, as a memory aid and also as good study practice.

Introduction

Whose argument is that? Who defined that concept in that way? What did so-and-so have to say about that issue? Chapter 19 draws on the work of a relatively small number of authors who have been concerned with aspects of technology and behaviour in organizations. It is a matter of common courtesy to be able to attribute ideas and arguments accurately to their originators. In terms of one's learning ability, it is often important to remember what an author said or argued in case you come across that author again and find them building on or perhaps contradicting what they said previously. In terms of personal memory, the idea, concept or argument is often more easily recalled when one can also recall the source – and particularly where recall of the source brings back into conscious awareness related ideas from the same author or the chapter in the book where it appeared.

Procedure

Step 1 Ensure that you are familiar with the material in Chapter 19 in *ORBIT3*. Then put the book aside. You should not refer to it for the purposes of completing this review.

Step 2 Read the following list of statements, definitions, ideas and arguments. Then refer to the author list that follows. Place the relevant author letter beside each statement, depending on your understanding and memory of the source.

Step 3 Have your review scored as directed by your instructor. Feel pleased or sorry as appropriate!

Ideas list

	Author letter	Ideas list
1.		A recognition of the complexity of factory operations and the costs of high tech have led to the vision of the automated factory being replaced by the notion of an effective partnership between man and machine.
2.		Technology not only automates a process, transforming its activities, events and objects, but also infomates them, increasing their visibility.
3.		'Technology' used to be a term with a very precise meaning but today it can refer to apparatus, technique, or to organization.

4.		Effective technology complements rather than replaces the existing skills, knowledge and capabilities of workers.
5.		Mass production technology can produce a pattern of psychological reactions that can damage the mental health of employees.
6.		The technology of the organization is the collection of plant, machines, tools and recipes available for the execution of the production task.
7.		Working in groups is most likely to provide a meaningful work experience, and technology does not determine the form that work organization takes.
8.		Technological innovation opens up opportunities for organizing work in new ways, and can increase the cognitive and social skills demanded of employees.
9.		Certain forms of technology can cause work alienation whose components include powerlessness, meaninglessness, isolation and self-estrangement.
10.		Material technology is that which can be seen, touched and heard; social technology involves the structure of co-ordination, control, motivation and reward.
11.		New technology creates imperatives which increase the importance of 'intellective' skills.
12.		An organization's social and technical systems interact and are interdependent.
13.		An irony of automation is that the more advanced a system becomes, the more essential it is to have an operator input.
14.		Advances in technology reduce the worker's level of skill and discretion of the job, while increasing management's control.
15.		Technology can inhibit the formation of work groups, and prevent workers meeting their social needs.

Author list	
A. K.W. Bamforth	N. David Preece
B. Robert Blauner	O. Eric Miller
C. David Boddy and David Buchanan	P. A.K. Rice
D. Harry Braverman	Q. Tavistock Institute of Human Relations
E. Stuart Clegg and David Dunkerley	R. Eric Trist
F. Louis Davis and James Taylor	S. A.N. Turner and P.R. Lawrence
G. Fred Emery	T. Charles Walker and Robert Guest

H. Tom Forester	U. Toby Wall
I. Alan Fox	V. Richard Walton and Gerald Susman
J. Melvin Kranzberg	W. Langdon Winner
K. Herbst	X. James Womack, Dan Jones and Daniel Roos
L. Arthur Kornhauser	Y. Joan Woodward
M. Ian McLoughlin and Jon Clark	Z. Shoshana Zuboff

PART V

MANAGEMENT IN THE ORGANIZATION

Chapter 20

Leadership and management style

20.1 **Large group activity: Apia Harbour incident**
20.2 **Small group activity: Choose your leadership style**
20.3 **Prepared task: The shelf-fillers**
20.4 **Review: Fill in the blanks**

20.1 LGA: Apia Harbour incident

Objectives

- To identify the characteristics of incompetent leaders.
- To consider explanations of leadership behaviour.
- To consider the attributes of competent leaders.

Introduction

What makes a good leader? One way in which to approach this issue is to look at poor leadership, and that is what you are invited to do in this activity. The incident report which follows reports an actual event, and is not fictitious. The behaviour reported is both extraordinary and tragic. How can such behaviour – so obviously inappropriate at the time and with hindsight – be explained? One set of explanations lies in the personal attributes of leaders – their skills, knowledge and personalities. It is, however, necessary to look beyond personality and to look at the context in which leaders operate. The context reported in this particular incident is also unusual.

Procedure

Step 1 Read the *Apia Harbour incident*, on your own, without discussing it with colleagues.

Step 2 Make personal notes in response to the four questions following the case, again without discussing these issues with colleagues.

Step 3 Now compare your thinking and your notes with colleagues in buzz-groups of two to four members (depending on your seating arrangements).

Step 4 Share your thinking with your instructor, according to his or her wishes.

Apia Harbour incident

The place is Samoa and the date 1889. Seven warships – three American, three German and one British – are lying at anchor in the harbour of Apia. They are there as a naval and military presence to watch over the interests of their various governments in the political upheavals that are taking place ashore. Accordingly they anchor in what has been described as one of the most dangerous anchorages in the world, for to call Apia a harbour at all is at best an unfortunate euphemism. Largely occupied by coral reefs, this saucer-shaped indentation lies wide open to the north, whence the great Pacific rollers come sweeping in. In fair weather, Apia provides an uneasy resting-place for no more than four medium-sized ships. For seven large ships and numerous smaller craft, under adverse conditions, it is a death-trap.

This was the situation in which the seven men-of-war witnessed the first bleak portents of an approaching typhoon. Even to a landsman a rapidly darkening sky and falling glass, squally gusts of wind, and then a lull, would bode ill. For seven naval captains the signs were unmistakable. They knew they were in a region of the world peculiarly subject to typhoons, which, in a matter of minutes, could lash the sea into a furious hell of boiling water. They knew that such storms generate winds travelling at upwards of a hundred knots, gusts that could snap masts like carrots, reduce deck-fittings to matchwood and throw ships on to their beam ends. They knew that it was the worst month of the year and they also knew that only three years before every ship in Apia had been sunk by such a storm. In short, their stored information coupled with present input pointed to only one decision: to get up and get out. And, as if this was not enough, the urgency of weighing anchor and putting to sea was respectfully suggested by subordinate officers.

But the captains of the warships were also naval officers and so they denied the undeniable and stayed where they were. Their behaviour has been described as 'an error of judgement that will for ever remain a paradox in human psychology'.

When the typhoon struck, its effects were tragic and inevitable. Without sea room, their anchors dragging under the pressure of mountainous seas, their hulls and rigging crushed by the fury of the wind, three of the warships collided before being swept on to the jagged reefs of coral. Another sank in deep water; two more were wrecked upon the beach. Of all the ships in the harbour the only survivor was a British corvette, which, thanks to its powerful engines and superb seamanship, squeaked through to the open sea.

Apia Harbour incident: analysis

1. Using this incident as a guide, and drawing on your own experience, draw up a list of *rules for incompetent leaders* – rules which would help senior organizational figures to make sure that blunders like this happened more often.

2. What aspects of the *situation* or *context* in which the captains found themselves could explain their error of judgement?

3. We are not told much in this incident report about the naval captains as individuals. However, from the available evidence what can we guess about the *personality traits* of those captains?

4. You are a seaman on board one of the warships in Apia Harbour in 1889. Identify the five main *leadership qualities* of the person you would most like to be the captain of the vessel on which you serve.

Note

This activity is based on an incident reported in Norman F. Dixon's *On The Psychology of Military Incompetence*, Futura Publications, London, 1976, pp. 34–5. For a fascinating (but not flattering) assessment of the behaviour of one individual military leader, see Denis Winter's *Haig's Command: A Reassessment*, Penguin Books, London, 1991.

20.2 SGA: Choose your leadership style

Objectives

- To illustrate the use of different leadership styles.
- To demonstrate the issues that arise from the advice that leaders change their style to suit the circumstances.

Introduction

Situational leadership is an approach to determining the most effective style of influencing which takes into account the amounts of direction and support the leader gives, and the readiness of followers to perform a particular task. Paul Hersey and Ken Blanchard identify four leadership styles:

Telling   in which the leader gives direct instructions and supervises performance closely

Selling   in which the leader takes care to explain decisions and gives subordinates an opportunity to check their understanding

Participating   in which the leader shares ideas and involves subordinates in decision making

Delegating   in which the leader gives responsibility for decision making and implementation to subordinates

These styles thus vary in the attention given to task behaviour or guidance on the one hand, and relationships behaviour or support on the other. As with other similar approaches to leadership, Hersey and Blanchard argue that the leader must adapt the style to fit the context. One of the main elements in the context, they argue, is the readiness or willingness of subordinates to carry out the task in hand.

To use this approach effectively, the leader has to change style according to the situation, participating with some subordinates, for example, and perhaps telling others. But most of us don't change the way in which we interact with other people. We each have our own 'comfort zone' or preferred ways of behaving, and we do not typically make conscious choices about how to speak to this person, how to speak with that other person. So, what is involved in making conscious choices about behavioural style and potentially moving outside our comfort zone? This exercise offers an opportunity to experience those choices and the outcomes.

Procedure

Step 1   Familiarize yourself with the situational leadership approach of Hersey and Blanchard as explained in Chapter 20 of *ORBIT3*. Make sure that you know what each of the four styles means in terms of your behaviour as a leader.

Step 2   Divide into groups of three, and label each other A, B and C at random. We are going to set up a series of three interviews; on each run of the series, one person will take the role of the superior, one will take the role of the subordinate, and the third will act as observer. The series looks like this:

	run		
role	**1**	**2**	**3**
superior	A	B	C
subordinate	B	C	A
observer	C	A	B

Step 3 Allocate and read the briefs for run 1. Give the superior and subordinate time to 'think themselves' into the role they are being invited to play, and give the superior in particular an opportunity to decide how they are going to tackle the interview.

Step 4 Run the first interview for about five to seven minutes, and give the observer five minutes to provide feedback. Each interview run should take from 10 to 15 minutes; remember that between each run, each of the participants needs a little time to familiarize themselves with their new role.

Step 5 Repeat the process for run 2; five to seven minutes for the interview and five minutes for observer feedback.

Step 6 Repeat the process finally for run 3.

Step 7 Return to plenary session, and debrief. Egos and self-esteem are most effectively preserved by asking one or more superiors first to give their account and assessment of the conversations; this enables them to 'give away' the main self-criticisms before anyone else in the group can deliver these blows. Then ask the respective subordinates how they felt they have been treated and how they responded to the style used on them. Finally ask the observers for overall assessments and specific comments on the conduct of the meetings. Key learning points can be captured on OHP or whiteboard or flipchart.

Choose your style

Run 1: Superior's briefing (A)

You are Pat Lowry, the office supervisor. One of your clerks, Bill Taylor, seems to spend a lot of time on the job socializing, talking with the secretaries and regularly coming back late from lunch. As a result, a lot of the clerical work does not get done on time, and you can see the work of others being disrupted. You have asked Bill to come and see you because you want to see what can be done about this.

How are you going to handle this conversation? In particular, what *style* are you going to use: telling, selling, participating or delegating? You could choose a style (or styles) that you feel would be appropriate in a situation like this, or you could on the other hand choose a style that you feel you would not normally use – to see how it feels to behave in that way.

When you have decided on your style or styles, decide how you are going to open the conversation, how you are going to progress it, what questions you might ask and in what sequence, what responses you expect to get, and how you hope to end the conversation. When you have completed your preparation, write the name of your chosen style on a scrap piece of paper and hand it to your observer. There is a knock on your door and your subordinate comes in.

Run 2: Superior's briefing (B)

You are Chris Peacock, the manager of the sales department. One of your staff, Peter Albrow, has started coming to work late over the past couple of months. He can arrive anything between 10 and 30 minutes after the normal starting time. This is annoying other people on the staff, as well as yourself, and you have asked him to come and see you about it so that you can try to persuade him to come in on time.

How are you going to handle this conversation? In particular, what *style* are you going to use: telling, selling, participating or delegating? You could choose a style (or styles) that you feel would be appropriate in a situation like this, or you could on the other hand choose a style that you feel you would not normally use – to see how it feels to behave in that way.

When you have decided on your style or styles, decide how you are going to open the conversation, how you are going to progress it, what questions you might ask and in what sequence, what responses you expect to get, and how you hope to end the conversation. When you have completed your preparation, write the name of your chosen style on a scrap piece of paper and hand it to your observer. There is a knock on your door and your subordinate comes in.

Run 3: Superior's briefing (C)

You are Les Johnson, head of the computing department. Peter Long, one of your subordinates, has special computing skills and is at present deeply involved in a major project. Something urgent has come up, an exciting software development programme for a major customer, and you have asked him to come and see you, to give him this extra work on top of his existing work load which cannot be passed on to anybody else.

How are you going to handle this conversation? In particular, what *style* are you going to use: telling, selling, participating or delegating? You could choose a style (or styles) that you feel would be appropriate in a situation like this, or you could on the other hand choose a style that you feel you would not normally use – to see how it feels to behave in that way.

When you have decided on your style or styles, decide how you are going to open the conversation, how you are going to progress it, what questions you might ask and in what sequence, what responses you expect to get, and how you hope to end the conversation. When you have completed your preparation, write the name of your chosen style on a scrap piece of paper and hand it to your observer. There is a knock on your door and your subordinate comes in.

Run 1: Subordinate's briefing (B)

You are Bill Taylor, a clerk in the general office. Your job is pretty mundane and routine, and you don't see it as much of a challenge. Nevertheless, you enjoy the job. The people you work with are nice, and you enjoy talking to them as you go round to collect the mail and other paperwork. Sometimes you all go to the pub for lunch, and are sometimes late in getting back. Your boss, Pat Lowry, has asked you to come for a talk today. You are not sure what it is about, but you suspect that it might have something to do with these long lunches.

You knock on the door and enter.

Run 2: Subordinate's briefing (C)

You are Peter Albrow, and you have worked in the sales department for some time. You have recently moved to a new apartment which is further away from the office. If you miss the bus-train connection, which has a reputation for being unreliable, you can be late for work. This has happened a few times recently. Your boss, Chris Peacock, has asked to see you today. You are not sure what it is about, but you suspect that it might be about your timekeeping.

You knock on the door and enter.

Run 3: Subordinate's briefing (A)

You are Peter Long and you work in the computing department. At present, you are up to your eyes in a major programming project, which is interesting and requires skills that nobody else in the department has. Your boss, Les Johnson, has set up a meeting with you today. You are not sure what this meeting is about, but you think that it might mean more (unwelcome) work for you.

You knock on the door and enter.

Observer's briefing: Run 1 (C), Run 2 (A), Run 3 (B)

You are about to observe a meeting between a manager and his or her subordinate. The meeting has been called because the manager has a specific issue to discuss with the subordinate, perhaps to reach a decision or to resolve a problem. Before the meeting starts, the manager will let you know what style he or she has decided to adopt in the meeting.

Your first task is to make sure that the meeting does not run beyond the seven minutes maximum, or whatever other limit your Instructor sets for this exercise.

Your second task is to make brief personal notes during the meeting on how the manager handles the conversation and how the subordinate is responding. Points to note might include:

- the way in which the meeting began;
- how the manager introduced the topic;
- how the manager controlled the conversation;
- the way in which the subordinate responded;
- problems that arise and how they are dealt with;
- how conflicts or disagreements are handled;
- how the issues are resolved;
- how the conversation is closed.

Your final task is to give the manager feedback after the meeting, for about five minutes, before moving on to the next stage of the exercise. Your feedback should cover:

- At least one weakness in the manager's approach, one aspect of the style or a behaviour that you felt could have been avoided or handled better;

- At least one strength in the manager's approach, one aspect of the style or a behaviour that you felt worked well and could be repeated in future;

- General observations about the conduct of the meeting and the subordinate's response.

20.3 PREP: The shelf-fillers

Objectives

- To demonstrate the application of concepts from Chapter 20 in *ORBIT3* concerning leadership and management style to a specific organizational setting.
- To offer students experience of peer assessment of assigned work.

Introduction

The area of leadership and management style is rich with theories and concepts. These are topics that have attracted a lot of academic and management attention and changes in thinking and understanding in this area are still taking place. However, can these concepts and theories be applied to practical organizational settings? That is the question that we wish to raise in this exercise. Also in this exercise we would like to suggest that, instead of your Instructor assessing, commenting on and grading your preparation, you exchange your work with somebody else in your class or group and grade each other's submissions.

Procedure

Step 1   Working out of class time, read *The shelf-fillers* organizational description which follows.

Step 2   Still working out of class time, make brief and precise notes in response to the questions which follow the case description.

Step 3   Bring your responses with you to class as instructed and exchange your work in groups of three; A gives their material to B who gives their material to C who gives their material to A. (You may be left with one pair who simply exchange between them.)

Step 4   Assess, and grade the work that you have received, checking the answers against your own understanding, and by referring back to the textbook (if you really feel that you must). Give the work a percentage grade, out of 100, and write a brief comment explaining what you see as the main strengths and weaknesses in the work.

Step 5   Return the work to the author in your group of three. Identify, discuss and seek to resolve any disagreements or disputes among the members of your group. Adjust your grades if necessary. If you are unable to reach agreement, consult your instructor.

Step 6   Discuss with your Instructor any general points arising from this exercise, either about the leadership style issues which have arisen, or about the peer assessment and grading approach.

The shelf-fillers

Malcolm worked on the backshift at Sainsway Supermarket in Ashlock (7.00 pm until 10.30 pm). He was one of twenty of the store's employees who worked these hours. The store manager often had to plead with staff to work overtime but, as this was not compulsory, he rarely got any volunteers.

The shelf-filling job cannot be described as creative or as a route to self-actualization or

The shelf-filling job cannot be described as creative or as a route to self-actualization or as a means of self-expression. Having said that, a section of shelving, stocked correctly, can look very impressive. The monotonous simplicity of the job means that only minimal skill is required and that skill is easy to pick up. Indeed, the less active your mind, the more likely you are to enjoy the job.

Boredom can lead to inefficient working and can reduce productivity. The store manager believed that productivity was reduced when the shelf-fillers spent time talking to each other. So he prohibited them from talking to each other. The boredom also encouraged staff to stick rigidly to their contracted working hours. Although staff were supposed to take a fifteen minute tea-break after four hours on shift, they were rarely allowed to have this. Apart from the store manager, Ashlock Sainsway had a grocery manager, a backshift manager, a shopfloor manager and a warehouse manager. You were either a 'chief' or an 'indian'. There were no intermediate levels. The managers distanced themselves from the 'common' workers and were rarely seen on the shop floor after they had given their orders. The organization structure looked like this:

Store Manager

| Warehouse | Grocery | Backshift | Shopfloor |
| Manager | Manager | Manager | Manager |

Shopfloor workers

Managers continually shouted at and harassed staff in an effort to make them work faster. Management would introduce new ideas, but no sooner had staff been told to do a job one way, they were told by somebody else to do it differently. On the whole, the store manager's comments to staff tended to be negative, critical and derogatory. The staff reciprocated by holding managers in contempt. One week, three visiting inspectors came from head office to check on the store. As they sauntered around, one of them stopped behind Malcolm who was stacking a bottom shelf, put his hand on his shoulder and said, 'Well done, son, keep up the good work.' So unused to praise, Malcolm nearly fainted from shock.

The wage rates on offer were not high enough to encourage workers to work late, especially since overtime was paid at the normal hourly rate. A frequent cause of resentment among the backshift staff was the receipt of a smaller paycheque than they were entitled to. It was common knowledge that even if you did work overtime, you were unlikely to get the full benefit. It was thought that the store manager deleted hours from the record of overtime. This made his figures look better in the eyes of head office, and it saved the company money. The staff were moved around the different display sections, and were constantly reallocated to different parts of the store. About the only thing that remained constant were the hours worked.

One afternoon, the store received a large delivery. When asked, only five of the twenty workers were willing to work overtime. Malcolm was one of them. Because of the lack of volunteers, the small team of five did not finish the task of shelf-filling and rubbish compacting until six o'clock the next morning. The store manager complained that the trouble with young people today was that they had no loyalty or commitment to their employer.

Ashlock Sainsway questions

1. Problem solving is often simplified if we can distinguish causes from symptoms. However, establishing that distinction is not always straightforward. Identify three main symptoms of the problem facing management in the Ashlock Sainsway store, and three main causes.

2. If you were able to get the managers in this store to complete Edwin Fleishman's Leadership Behaviour Description Questionnaire, how would you expect them to rate on the two dimensions? Give specific examples of store management behaviour that support your conclusion.

3. John French and Bertram Raven identify five main bases of power. On which base or bases do the managers in Ashlock Sainsway exercise power? Which bases would you recommend they use in addition to or instead of those currently in use?

4. Rensis Likert, University of Michigan, identified four 'leadership systems' or leadership styles. In Likert's terminology, which leadership system is in use in this store? Cite specific management behaviours to support your answer.

5. In terms of Fred Fiedler's theory of leadership behaviour, in which 'condition' are the store managers operating? What are the implications of this analysis for the store managers?

6. The most effective style in a *situational leadership* approach depends on subordinate readiness or maturity. How would you rate the readiness or maturity of subordinates in the Ashlock Sainsway? What are the implications of this rating for management?

20.4 REV: Fill in the blanks

Objectives

- To test students' memory of key ideas from Chapter 20, *ORBIT3,* concerning leadership theories, their dimensions and their authors.
- To encourage the habit of remembering accurately the authorship of ideas, as a memory aid and also as good study practice.

Introduction

Leadership is probably the single most studied topic in the field of organizational behaviour and management. Numerous research studies exist. Most tell you about leadership, somewhat fewer say precisely how one should lead. Many theories of leadership use different labels to refer to the same ideas. A useful starting point for the student is therefore to understand the historical development of the subject of leadership; gain familiarity with the names of the key theories and their authors; and understand how different leadership theories can be grouped together on the basis of common features.

Procedure

This activity invites you to read the chapter on leadership thoroughly, and then fill in the blank spaces in each sentence. Some sentences have more than one gap, and for full marks, both inserts have to be correct. A list of possible inserts is not provided, but all the answers can be found in the chapter.

Sentences

1. In _____'s research, leaders rated their co-workers on _____ dimensions.

2. A task which has _____ goals, various success criteria, several correct solutions, and many ways of achieving acceptable outcomes, is called _____.

3. Leadership behaviours that focus on the task-in-hand and the achievement of goals are referred to as _____ _____.

4. A _____ process in which one individual influences the behaviour of others without the use of threat or violence is called _____.

5. Hersey and Blanchard developed a leadership theory which takes into account the _____ and _____ of subordinates to perform a given task.

6. _____ is a behaviour style that flexibly combines male and _____ attributes.

7. For Fiedler, a leader's _____ with their followers, task structure and _____ _____ were important elements in choice of style.

8. A leadership behaviour that stresses relationships, and shows sensitivity to the social _____ of workers is called _____ .

9. The successful exercise of power is not only dependent on the properties of leaders, but also upon the _____ of followers.

10. The _____ approach to leadership research sought to identify and measure the characteristics of effective leaders.

11. _____ power is based on the conviction of followers that the leader has personality traits and abilities that can and should be _____ .

12. The _____ _____ theory of leadership holds that people are born with leadership _____ which will emerge in whatever situation they find themselves.

13. _____ is often defined as deciding what should be done and getting other people to do it.

14. A _____ score is obtained from a questionnaire which indicates which type of person a particular leader can not work effectively with.

15. _____ is defined by some as the creation of a vision about a desired future state which, it is hoped, will be shared by all the members of an organization.

16. Likert's _____ _____ management style emphasizes paternalism, motivation through rewards, and participative problem-solving.

17. _____ believed that direction, team-building capability and creativity are the characteristics required of the strategic leader.

18. International managers require the superordinate value orientation of _____ which involves personal flexibility, and adjustment to the demands of different cultures.

19. Leadership theories which consider the human and organizational context to be an important variable when deciding which style of management to adopt are labelled _____ .

20. The leadership theory which holds that a leader's main job is to smooth the way for the achievement of desired objectives was developed by _____ _____ and is called the _____ _____ theory.

Chapter 21
Managing conflict

21.1 LGA: My conflict resolution approach

Objectives

- To introduce students to the different ways in which conflict can be resolved.
- To allow students to identify which conflict resolution approach they typically use.

Introduction

Individuals all possess particular ways of resolving conflicts in which they become involved. This activity seeks to raise students' awareness of which conflict resolution approach they typically use, and which others are available.

Procedure

Step 1   Individually complete the *conflict resolution approaches* questionnaire.

Step 2   Score the questionnaire as directed by your instructor.

Step 3   Compare your scores with the two people sitting on either side of you.

Conflict resolution approaches questionnaire

Consider work or non-work situations in which you find that your wishes differ from those of another person. How do you usually respond to such situations? Below is a list of statements describing possible behavioural responses. For each one, indicate on a 5-point scale (5 = always, through to 1= never), the degree to which this is characteristic of your own behaviour in a conflict situation.

Statement	Always 5	Frequently 4	Occasionally 3	Rarely 2	Never 1
1. I try to show the other party the logic and benefits of my position.					
2. I endeavour to satisfy all the needs that I and the other party have.					
3. I give up some of my requirements if they give up theirs.					
4. I believe that some differences are not worth worrying about.					
5. I avoid hurting the other person's feelings.					
6. I seek to convince the other person of the merits of my position.					
7. I strive to get all concerns and issues out on the table, immediately.					
8. I propose a middle ground between us.					
9. I postpone a decision until I have had some time to think it over.					
10. I sacrifice my own wishes for those of the other person.					
11. I am determined when pursuing my goals.					
12. I seek the other person's help in working out a solution.					
13. I try to find a fair combination of gains and losses for both of us.					
14. I refrain from taking positions which would create controversy.					
15. I soothe the other person's feelings in order to preserve our relationship.					
16. I assert my wishes.					
17. I address all the concerns that I and the other party have.					
18. I adjust to the other's requirements, if they adjust to mine.					
19. I do what is required to avoid useless tensions.					
20. I focus on the things upon which we agree rather than disagree.					
21. I press to get my points accepted.					

Statement	Always 5	Frequently 4	Occasionally 3	Rarely 2	Never 1
22. I tell the other person my ideas, and ask them for theirs.					
23. I try to find a compromise solution.					
24. I avoid creating unpleasantness for myself.					
25. When approaching negotiations, I am concerned with the other party's needs.					
26. I make a strong effort to get my way.					
27. I use direct discussion to work through our difficulties.					
28. I will give up some of my positions if they concede some of theirs					
29. I let others take the initiative for solving the problem.					
30. I let the other person maintain their views, if it makes them happy.					

Scoring

Insert the number opposite each of your 30 responses in the grid below. Total up the numbers in each column. Insert the name of each of the five conflict resolution styles at the top of each column, when directed by your instructor.

Conflict resolution approaches

	I	II	III	IV	V
Insert approach name here →					
	1.	2.	3.	4.	5.
	6.	7.	8.	9.	10.
	11.	12.	13.	14.	15.
	16.	17.	18.	19.	20.
	21.	22.	23.	24.	25.
	26.	27.	28.	29.	30.
Total					

Note

This activity is based on Kenneth Thomas, 'Conflict and conflict management' in M. Dunnette (ed.), *The Handbook of Industrial and Social Psychology*, Rand McNally, Chicago, 1976.

21.2 SGA: Prisoner's dilemma

Objectives

- To demonstrate the effects of inter-group conflict and competition.
- To explore trust and betrayal between group members.
- To assess the merits of, and obstacles to, a collaborative approach to intra-group and inter-group relations.

Introduction

Organizational conflict arises from the differences in goals created by the process of departmentalization; differences in employee backgrounds; and the scarcity and importance of limited resources. This activity demonstrates this in an impactful way.

Procedure

Step 1   Form teams
The instructor divides the class into two teams, each consisting of no more than eight members. One is designated the Blue Team and the other the Red Team.

Step 2   Seat teams
The two teams are seated well away from each other, so that they cannot eavesdrop on their discussion.

Step 3   Communication rules
Both teams are instructed not to communicate with the other in any way, verbally or non-verbally, except when directed to do so by the instructor.

Step 4   Tally sheet
Team members are referred to the *Prisoner's dilemma tally sheet* in their workbooks.

Step 5   Round 1
Round 1 is begun. The instructor announces to each of the teams that they will have 3 minutes to make a team decision and tells them not to write down their decision until the time is up.

Step 6   Scoring
The choices of each team are announced for Round 1. The scoring for that round is agreed upon and is entered on the scorecard section of the tally sheet.

Step 7   Rounds 2 and 3
These rounds are conducted in the same way as Round 1.

Step 8   Round 4
Round 4 is announced as a special round in which the payoff points are doubled. One or two representatives of each team confer with their opposite numbers for 3 minutes. They return to their own teams which, as before, have 3 minutes to make their decision. When recording their scores for this round, they should remember that payoff points are doubled for *this round only*.

Step 9   Rounds 5 to 8
These rounds are conducted in the same way as the first three rounds.

Step 10   Round 9
Round 9 is announced as a special round in which the payoff points are 'squared' (multiplied by themselves; for example, a score of 4 would be 4 x 4 = 16). The minus sign should be retained (e.g. –3 x –3 = –9). Team representatives meet each other for 3 minutes; then the teams discuss for 5 minutes. At the instructor's signal, the teams write their choices, which are then announced.

Step 11   Round 10
This round is handled exactly as round 9. Payoff points are squared.

Step 12   Discussion
The entire group meets to discuss what happened. The points total for each team is announced, and the sum for the two teams is calculated, and compared to the maximum positive or negative outcomes (+126 or –126)

Source: Reprinted from J. William Pfeiffer and John E. Jones (Eds.), *A Handbook of Structured Experiences for Human Relations Training*, Vol. III, San Diego, CA: University Associates, Inc., 1974. Used with permission.

Prisoner's dilemma tally sheet

For ten successive rounds, the Red Team will choose either an A or a B and the Blue Team will choose either an X or a Y. The score each team receives in a round is determined by the pattern made by the choices of both teams, according to the schedule below.

Payoff schedule

AX –   Both teams win 3 points

AY –   Red Team loses 6 points
Blue Team wins 6 points

BX –   Red Team wins 6 points
Blue Team loses 6 points

BY –   Both teams lose 3 points

Scorecard

		Choice		Cumulative Points	
Round	Minutes	Red Team	Blue Team	Red Team	Blue Team
1.	3				
2.	3				
3.	3				
4.	3 (reps) 3 (teams)				
5.	3				
6.	3				
7.	3				
8.	3				
9.	3 (reps) 3 (teams)				
10.	3 (reps) 3 (teams)				

A Payoff points are doubled for this round.
B Payoff points are squared for this round. Retain the minus sign.

Source: Reprinted from J. William Pfeiffer and John E. Jones (Eds), *A Handbook of Structured Experiences for Human RelationsTraining*, Vol. III, San Diego, CA: University Associates, Inc., 1974. Used with permission.

21.3 PREP: Strikebreaker

Objectives

- To understand the criteria that third parties use when they intervene in an effort to resolve others' conflict.
- To practise mediation skills as a mechanism for resolving conflict between others.

Introduction

In addition to being involved in their own conflicts, managers are often called upon to intervene and to settle conflicts between other people. *ORBIT3*, Chapter 21, briefly describes the conflict resolution process called mediation. This activity allows students to explore how third parties may enter conflicts for the purpose of resolving them, and to experience the mediation intervention approach at first hand.

Procedure

Before the class the instructor will indicate whether activity A or B will be conducted.

Activity A: Case discussion

Step 1   Before the class, students familiarize themselves with Isaac Isamov's short story, *Strikebreaker*.

Step 2   They write notes in response to the two questions below:

1. Assuming that you were Stephen Lamorak, what would you do in this situation regarding the conflict between Ragusnik and the Council?
2. What would be your primary objectives by intervening in this way?

Step 3   The instructor discusses the case with the entire class.

Step 4   The instructor summarises the case discussion, and presents a framework for understanding how participants analyzed the case and decided how to intervene.

Step 5   The instructor leads a discussion addressing some of the student questions below.

1. How much agreement was there among students in the class, as to how Lamorak ought to approach the problem? How did this compare with your own preferred approach?

2. Which style of conflict resolution approach do you use most frequently? Which do you use least frequently? Are there are approaches not listed here?

3. Which one of the four criteria of efficiency, effectiveness, participant satisfaction and fairness, are typically most important to you when you intervene in someone else's dispute? Which are most important to you when someone intervenes in a discussion that you are having? Are these different? If so, what implications does this have?

4. Do you use different styles in different situations? If so, what kinds of situational factors affect which style you use?

Activity B: Role play

Step 1   Before the class, students familiarize themselves with Isaac Isamov's short story, *Strikebreaker*, and read the *Mediation guide*.

Step 2   5 minutes
In the class, students are divided into threes or fours (the latter if an observer is to be used). One person plays the role of Lamorak who will mediate the issue. The other two parties will play the roles of Ragusnik and Blei.

Step 3   10 minutes
Students re-read the *Mediation guide*.

Step 4   15 minutes
Each role player reminds themselves of the key aspects of their role, as described in the case story. Each person should:

1. Empathize with the role, and see the world as their assigned character sees it, and behave accordingly.

2. Not add facts that are not in the case story.

3. Stay in role. Do not jump out to comment on the process.

4. Try to make it realistic.

The third person playing the role of Lamorak will try to defuse the conflict and seek a resolution. Do not make it unnecessarily difficult for them. 'Play along' to observe how third-party dispute resolution can work. On the other hand, you are not required to settle if you believe that your character's needs are not truly being met by the proposed agreement.

Step 5   20–30 minutes
Lamorak will lead each small group in an effort to resolve the problem. When each party has achieved a resolution, write it down so that you can report it to the class later.

Step 6   20–30 minutes
At the plenary session, be prepared to report the outcome of your mediation session to the class, and highlight the particular problems that occurred with the mediation session in your small group.

Plenary session questions

1. What were some of the different settlements arrived at by the different groups?

2. How did your group's specific settlement emerge? How much influence did Lamorak have in shaping the final settlement? How much influence did Ragusnik and Blei have?

3. Was the mediation process fair? Was the achieved outcome fair? What made it fair or unfair?

4. What tactics did Lamorak as mediator use that were most effective? Least effective?

5. When would it be most useful to use mediation in an organization? When would it be least useful?

6. What are some of the major problems and obstacles to using mediation as a manager?

Mediation guide

The Steps

Step 1: Stabilize the setting
Step 2: Help the parties communicate
Step 3: Help the parties negotiate
Step 4: Clarify the agreement

Step 1: Stabilize the setting

Parties often bring strong feelings of anger and frustration into mediation. These can prevent them from talking productively about their dispute. You, as a mediator, will seek to secure their trust in both yourself and the mediation process. Stabilize the setting by being polite, showing that you are in control, and showing that you are neutral. This step helps the parties feel safe and comfortable, so that they can air their feelings, and speak freely about their complaints.

1. Greet the parties.
2. Indicate where each of them is to sit.
3. Identify yourself and each party, by name.
4. Offer water, paper and pencil, and patience.
5. State the purpose of mediation.
6. Confirm your neutrality.
7. Get their commitment to proceed.
8. Get their commitment to one party only speaking at a time.
9. Get their commitment to speak directly to you.
10. Use calming techniques as needed.

Step 2: Help the parties communicate

Once the setting is stable and the parties seem to trust you and the mediation process, begin to build trust between them. Both parties must make statements about what has happened so far. Each will use these statements to air their negative feelings. They may express anger, make accusations, or show frustration in other ways. With your help, this mutual ventilation lets each side hear the other's story, perhaps for the first time. It can help calm their emotions, and build the basis for trust between them.

1. Explain the rationale for who speaks first.

2. Reassure them that both will speak without interruption, for as long as is needed.

3. Ask the first speaker to tell you what has happened.
   a) Take notes
   b) Respond actively, respond and echo what is said.
   c) Calm the parties as needed.
   d) Clarify, with open or closed questions, or with restatements.
   e) Focus the narration on the issues in the dispute.
   f) Summarise, eliminating all disparaging references.
   g) Check to ensure that you understand the story.
   h) Thank this party for speaking, and the other for listening quietly.

4. Ask the second speaker to tell *you* what has happened.
   a) Take notes.
   b) Respond actively, respond and echo what is said.
   c) Calm the parties as needed.
   d) Clarify, with open or closed questions, or with restatements.
   e) Focus the narration on the issues in the dispute.
   f) Summarise, eliminating all disparaging references.
   g) Check to ensure that you understand the story.
   h) Thank this party for speaking, and the other for listening quietly.

5. Ask each party, in turn, to help clarify the major issues to be resolved.

6. Inquire about basic issues, probing to see if something that has so far not surfaced may be at the root of the complaints.

7. Define the probe, by re-stating and summarizing it in terms of parties' interests rather than positions.

8. Conduct private meetings, if needed, explaining what will happen during and after the private meetings.

9. Summarise areas of agreement and disagreement.

10. Help the parties set priorities on the issues and demands.

Step 3: Help the parties negotiate

Co-operation is needed for negotiations that lead to agreement. Co-operation requires a stable setting, to control disruptions, and exchanges of information, to develop mutual trust. With these conditions in place, the parties may be willing to co-operate, but still feel driven to compete. You can press for co-operative initiatives by patiently helping them to explore alternative solutions, and by directing attention at their progress.

1. Ask each party to list alternative possibilities for a settlement.
2. Re-state and summarize each alternative.
3. Check with each party on the workability of each alternative.
4. Re-state whether the alternative is workable.
5. In an impasse, suggest the general form of alternatives.
6. If the impasse continues, suggest a break or second mediation session.
7. Encourage the parties to select the alternative that appears most workable.
8. Increase their understanding by rephrasing the alternative.
9. Help them place a course of action to implement the alternative.

Step 4: Clarify the agreement

Mediation should change each party's attitude towards the other. When both have shown their commitment through a joint declaration of agreement, each will support the agreement more strongly. For a settlement to last, all the components of each party's attitude to the other – their thinking, feeling and acting – has to change. Now they will not only *act* differently towards each other, but will also *feel* differently (more positive), and will *think* about their relationship in a new way.

1. Summarize the agreement terms.
2. Re-check with each party their understanding of the agreement.
3. Ask whether any other issues need to be addressed.
4. Help them to specify the terms of their agreement.
5. Restate each person's role in their agreement.
6. Recheck with each party *when* they are to do certain things, *where*, and *how*.
7. Explain the process of follow-up.
8. Establish the time for follow-up with each party,
9. Emphasize that the agreement is theirs, not yours.
10. Congratulate the parties on their reasonableness and on the workability of their solution.

Steps in a mediation process

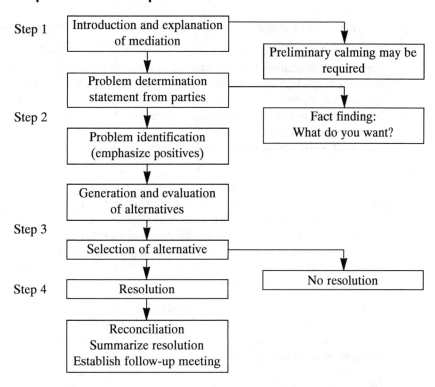

Note

This activity is based on 'Third party conflict resolution' in R.J. Lewicki, D.D., Bowen, D.T. Hall and F.S. Hall, *Experiences in Management and Organizational Behaviour*, John Wiley, 3/e, pp. 107–14. The short story was written by Isaac Asimov in 1957. It appears in *The Best Science Fiction of Isaac Asimov*, Grafton Books, London, 1987, pp. 258–71. Both used with permission.

Strikebreaker

I

(1)   Elvis Blei rubbed his plump hands and said, 'Self-containment is the word.' He smiled uneasily as he helped Steven Lamorak of Earth to alight. There was uneasiness all over his smooth face with its small wide-set eyes.

Lamorak puffed smoke appreciatively and crossed his lanky legs.

His hair was powdered with grey and he had a large and powerful jawbone. 'Home grown?' he asked, staring critically at the cigarette. He tried to hide his own disturbance at the other's tension.

'Quite', said Blei.

'I wonder', said Lamorak, 'that you have room on your small world for such luxuries'.

(Lamorak thought of his first view of Elsevere from the spaceship visiplate. It was a jagged, airless planetoid, some hundred miles in diameter – just a dust-grey, rough-hewn rock, glimmering dully in the light of its sun, 200,000,000 miles distant. It was the only object more than a mile in diameter that circled that sun, and now men had burrowed into that miniature world and constructed a society in it. And he himself, as a sociologist, had come to study the world and see how humanity had made itself fit into that queerly specialized niche.)

(2)   Blei's polite fixed smile expanded a hair. He said, 'We are not a small world, Dr Lamorak; you judge us by two-dimensional standards. The surface area of Elsevere is only three quarters that of the State of New York, but that's irrelevant. Remember, we can occupy, if we wish, the entire interior of Elsevere. A sphere of 50 miles radius has a volume well over half a million cubic miles. If all Elsevere were occupied by levels 50 feet apart, the total surface area within the planetoid would be 56,000,000 square miles, and that is equal to the total land area of Earth. And none of these square miles, Doctor, would be unproductive'.

Lamorak said, 'Good Lord', and stared blankly for a moment. 'Yes, of course, you're right. Strange I never thought of it that way. But then Elsevere is the only thoroughly exploited asteroid world in the Galaxy; the rest of us simply can't get away from thinking of two-dimensional surfaces, as you pointed out. Well, I'm more than ever glad that your Council has been so co-operative as to give me a free hand in this investigation of mine'.

Blei nodded convulsively at that.

Lamorak frowned slightly and thought: he acts for all the world as though he wished I had not come. Something's wrong.

(3)   Blei said, 'Of course, you understand that we are actually much smaller than we could be; only minor portions of Elsevere have as yet been hollowed out and occupied. Nor are we particularly anxious to expand, except very slowly. To a certain extent we are limited by the capacity of our pseudo-gravity engines and solar energy converters'.

'I understand. But tell me Councillor Blei – as a matter of personal curiosity, and not because it is of prime importance to my project – could I view some of your farming and herding levels first? I am fascinated by the thought of fields of wheat and herds of cattle inside a planetoid.'

'You'll find the cattle small by your standards, Doctor, and we don't have much wheat. We grow yeast to a much greater extent. But there will be some wheat to show you. Some cotton and rice, too. Even fruit trees.'

'Wonderful. As you say, self-containment. You recirculate everything, I imagine.'

Lamorak's sharp eyes did not miss the fact that this last remark twinged Blei. The Elseverian's eyes narrowed to slits that held his expression.

He said, 'We must recirculate, yes. Air, water, food, minerals – everything that is used up – must be restored to its original state; waste products are reconverted to raw materials. All that is needed is energy, and we have enough of that. We don't manage with one hundred per cent efficiency; of course, there is a certain seepage. We import a small amount of water each year; and if our needs grow, we may have to import some coal and oxygen'.

Lamorak said, 'When can we start our tour, Councillor Blei?'

Blei's smile lost some of its tangible warmth. 'As soon as we can, Doctor. There are some routine matter that must be arranged'.

Lamorak nodded, and having finished his cigarette, stubbed it out. Routine matters? There was none of this hesitancy during the preliminary correspondence. Elsevere had seemed proud that its unique asteroid existence had attracted the attention of the Galaxy.

(4) He said, 'I realize I would be a disturbing influence in a tightly-knit society', and watched grimly as Blei leaped at the explanation and made it his own.

'Yes', he said, 'we feel marked off from the rest of the Galaxy. We have our own customs. Each individual Elseverian fits into a comfortable niche. The appearance of a stranger without fixed caste is unsettling'.

'The caste system does involve a certain inflexibility.'

'Granted', said Blei quickly; 'but there is also a certain self-assurance. We have firm rules of intermarriage and rigid inheritance of occupation. Each man, woman and child knows his place, accepts it, and is accepted in it; we have virtually no neurosis or mental illness'.

'And there are no misfits?' asked Lamorak.

Blei shaped his mouth as though to say no, then clamped it suddenly shut, biting the word into silence; a frown deepened on his forehead. He said, at length, 'I will arrange for the tour, Doctor. Meanwhile, I imagine you would welcome a chance to freshen up and to sleep'.

They rose together and left the room, Blei politely motioning the Earthman to precede him out of the door.

II

(5)   Lamorak felt oppressed by the vague feeling of crisis that had pervaded his discussion with Blei.

The newspaper reinforced that feeling. He read it carefully before getting into bed, with what was at first merely clinical interest. It was an eight-page tabloid of synthetic paper. One quarter of its items consisted of 'personals': births, marriages, deaths, record quotas, expanding habitable volume (not area! three dimensions!). The remainder included scholarly essays, educational material and fiction. Of news, in the sense to which Lamorak was accustomed, there was virtually nothing.

One item only could be so considered and that was chilling in its incompleteness.

It said, under a small headline: DEMANDS UNCHANGED: *There has been no change in his attitude of yesterday. The Chief Councillor, after a second interview, announced that his demands remain completely unreasonable and cannot be met under any circumstances.*

Then, in parenthesis, and in a different type, there was the statement: *The editors of this paper agree that Elsevere cannot and will not jump to his whistle, come what may.*

Lamorak read it over three times. *His* attitude. *His* demands. *His* whistle.

Whose?

He slept uneasily that night.

III

(6)   He had no time for newspapers in the days that followed; but, spasmodically, the matter returned to his thoughts.

Blei, who remained his guide and companion for most of the tour, grew ever more withdrawn.

On the third day (quite artificially clock-set in an Earthlike twenty-four hour pattern), Blei stopped at one point, and said, 'Now this level is devoted entirely to chemical industries. That section is not important –'

But he turned away a shade too rapidly, and Lamorak seized his arm. 'What are the products of that section?'

'Fertilizers. Certain organics', said Blei stiffly.

Lamorak held him back, looking for what sight Blei might be evading. His gaze swept over the close-by horizons of lined rock and the buildings squeezed and layered between the levels.

Lamorak said, 'Isn't that a private residence there?'

Blei did not look in the indicated direction.

Lamorak said, 'I think that's the largest one I've seen yet. Why is it here on a factory level?' That alone made it noteworthy. He had already seen that the levels in Elsevere were divided rigidly among the residential, the agricultural and the industrial.

He looked back and called, 'Councillor Blei'.

The councillor was walking away and Lamorak pursued him with hasty steps. 'Is there something wrong, sir?'

Blei muttered, 'I am rude. I know. I am sorry. There are matters that prey on my mind'. He kept up his rapid pace.

'Concerning *his* demands?'

Blei came to a full halt. 'What do *you* know about that?'

'No more than I've read in the newspaper'.

Blei muttered something to himself.

Lamorak said, 'Ragusnik? What's that?'

Blei sighed heavily. 'I suppose you ought to be told. It's humiliating, deeply embarrassing. The Council thought that matters would certainly be arranged shortly and that your visit need not be interfered with, that you need not know or be concerned. But it is almost a week now. I don't know what will happen and, appearances notwithstanding, it might be the best for you to leave. No reason for an Outworlder to risk death'.

(7)   The Earthman smiled incredulously. 'Risk death? In this little world, so peaceful and busy. I can't believe it'.

The Elseverian councillor said, 'I can explain. I think it best I should'. He turned his head away. 'As I told you, everything on Elsevere must recirculate. You understand that?'

'Yes.'

'That includes – uh, human wastes.'

'I assumed so', said Lamorak.

'Water is reclaimed from it by distillation and absorption. What remains is converted into fertilizer for yeast use; some of it is used as a source of fine organics and other by-products. These factories you see are devoted to this'.

'Well?' Lamorak had experienced a certain difficulty in the drinking of water when he first landed on Elsevere, because he had been realistic enough to know what it must be reclaimed from; but he had conquered the feeling easily enough. Even on Earth, water was reclaimed by natural processes from all sorts of unpalatable substances.

Blei, with increasing difficulty, said, 'Igor Ragusnik is the man who is in charge of the industrial process immediately involving the wastes. The position has been in his family since Elsevere was first colonized. One of the original settlers was Mikhail Ragusnik and he –, he –'.

'Was in charge of waste reclamation.'

'Yes. Now that residence you singled out is the Ragusnik residence; it is the best and most elaborate on the asteroid. Ragusnik gets many privileges the rest of us do not have; but, after all – ,' Passion entered the Councillor's voice with great suddenness, 'we cannot *speak* to him'.

'What?'

'He demands full social equity. He wants his children to mingle with ours, and our wives to visit – Oh!' It was a groan of utter disgust.

Lamorak thought of the newspaper item that could not even bring itself to mention Ragusnik's name in print, or to say anything specific about his demands. He said, 'I take it he's an outcast because of his job'.

'Naturally. Human wastes and –', words failed Blei. After a pause, he said more quietly, 'As an Earthman, I suppose you don't understand'.

'As a sociologist, I think I do'. Lamorak thought of the Untouchables in ancient India, the ones who handled corpses. He thought of the position of swineherds in ancient Judea.

He went on, 'I gather Elsevere will not give in to those demands'.

'Never,' said Blei, energetically. 'Never.'

'And so?'

'Ragusnik has threatened to cease operations.'

'Go on strike, in other words.'

'Yes.'

'Would that be serious?'

'We have enough food and water to last quite a while; reclamation is not essential in that sense. But the wastes would accumulate, they would infect the asteroid. After generations of careful disease control, we have low natural resistance to germ diseases. Once an epidemic started – and one would – we would drop by the hundred.'

'Is Ragusnik aware of this?'

'Yes, of course.'

'Do you think he is likely to go through with his threat, then?'

'He is mad. He has already stopped working; there has been no waste reclamation since the day before you landed.' Blei's bulbous nose sniffed at the air as though it had already caught the whiff of excrement.

Lamorak sniffed mechanically at that, but smelled nothing.

Blei said, 'So you see why it might be wise for you to leave. We are humiliated, of course, to have to suggest it.'

But Lamorak said, 'Wait, not just yet. Good Lord, this is a matter of great interest to me professionally. May I speak to the Ragusnik?'

'On no account,' said Blei alarmed.

'But I would like to understand the situation. The sociological conditions here are unique and not to be duplicated elsewhere. In the name of science – '

'How do you mean, speak? Would image-reception do?'

'Yes.'

'I will ask the Council,' muttered Blei.

IV

(8)   They sat about Lamorak uneasily, their austere and dignified expressions badly marred with anxiety. Blei, seated in the midst of them, studiously avoided the Earthman's eyes.

The chief counsellor, grey-haired, his face harshly wrinkled, his neck scrawny, said in a soft voice, 'If in any way you can persuade him, sir, out of your own convictions, we will welcome that. In no case, however, are you to imply that we will, in any way yield'.

A gauzy curtain fell between the Council and Lamorak. He could make out the individual councillors still, but now he turned sharply towards the receiver before him. It glowed to life.

A head appeared in it, in natural colour and with great realism. A strong dark head, with massive chin faintly stubbled, and thick, red lips set into a firm horizontal line.

The image said, suspiciously, 'Who are you?'

Lamorak said, 'My name is Steve Lamorak; I am an Earthman.'

'An Outworlder?'

'That's right. I am visiting Elsevere. You are Ragusnik?'

'Igor Ragusnik, at your service,' said the image, mockingly. 'Except that there is no service, and there will be none until my family and I are treated like human beings.'

Lamorak said, 'Do you realize the danger that Elsevere is in? The possibility of epidemic disease?'

'In twenty-four hours the situation can be made normal, if they allow me humanity. The situation is theirs to correct.'

'You sound like an educated man, Ragusnik.'

'So?'

'I am told you're denied no material comforts. You are housed and clothed and fed better than anyone else on Elsevere. Your children are the best educated.'

'Granted. But all by servo-mechanism. And motherless girl-babies are sent us to care for until they grow up to be our wives. And they die young from loneliness. Why? There was a sudden passion in his voice. 'Why must we live in isolation as if we were all monsters, unfit for human beings to be near? Aren't we human beings like others, with the same needs, and desires and feelings. Don't we perform an honourable and useful function − ?'

(9)   There was a rustling of sighs from behind Lamorak. Ragusnik heard it, and raised his voice. 'I see you of the Council behind there. Answer me: Isn't it an honourable and useful function? It is *your* waste made into food for *you*. Is the man who purifies

corruption worse than the man who produces it? – Listen, Councillors, I will *not* give in. Let all of Elsevere die of disease – including myself and my son, if necessary – but I will not give in. My family will be better dead of disease, than living as now.'

Lamorak interrupted. 'You've led this life since birth, haven't you?'

'And if I have?'

'Surely you're used to it.'

'Never. Resigned, perhaps. My father was resigned, and I was resigned for a while; but I have watched my son, my only son, with no other little boy to play with. My brother and I had each other, but my son will never have anyone, and I am no longer resigned. I am through with Elsevere and through with talking.'

The receiver went dead.

The Chief Councillor's face had paled to an aged yellow. He and Blei were the only ones of the group left with Lamorak. The Chief Councillor said, 'The man is deranged; I don't know how to force him'.

He had a glass of wine at his side; as he lifted it to his lips, he spilled a few drops that stained his white trousers with purple splotches.

(10) Lamorak said, 'Are his demands so unreasonable? Why can't he be accepted into society?'

There was momentary rage in Blei's eyes. 'A dealer in excrement.'

Then he shrugged. 'You are from Earth.'

Incongruously, Lamorak thought of another unacceptable, one of the numerous classic creations of the medieval cartoonist, Al Capp. The variously-named, 'inside man at the skonk works'.

He said, 'Does Ragusnik really deal with excrement? I mean, is there physical contact? Surely, it is all handled by machinery'.

'Of course.' said the Chief Councillor.

'Then what exactly is Ragusnik's function?'

'He manually adjusts the various controls that assure the proper functioning of the machinery. He shifts units to allow repairs to be made; he alters functional rates with the time of day; he varies end production with demand.' He added sadly, 'If we had the space to make the machinery ten times as complex, all this could be done automatically; but that would be such needless waste'.

'But even so,' insisted Lamorak, 'all Ragusnik does, he does simply by pressing buttons or closing contacts or things like that'.

'Yes.'

'Then his work is no different from any Elseverian's.'

Blei said, stiffly, 'You don't understand'.

'And for that you will risk the death of your children?'

'We have no other choice', said Blei. There was enough agony in his voice to assure Lamorak that the situation was torture for him, but that he had no other choice indeed.

Lamorak shrugged in disgust. 'Then break the strike – force him.'

'How?' said the Chief Councillor. 'Who would touch him or go near him? And if we kill him by blasting from a distance, how will that help us?'

(11)   Lamorak said, thoughtfully, 'Would you know how to run his machinery?'

The Chief Councillor came to his feet. 'I?' he howled.

'I don't mean *you*', cried Lamorak at once. 'I used the pronoun in its indefinite sense. Could *someone* learn how to handle Ragusnik's machinery?'

Slowly, the passion drained out of the Chief Councillor. 'It is in the handbooks, I am certain – though I assure you I have never concerned myself with it.'

'Then couldn't someone learn the procedure and substitute for Ragusnik until the man gives in?'

Blei said, 'Who would agree to do such a thing? Not I, under any circumstances'.

Lamorak thought fleetingly of Earthly taboos that might be almost as strong. He thought of cannibalism, incest, a pious man cursing God. He said, 'But you must have made provision for vacancy in the Ragusnik job. Suppose he died'.

'Then his son would automatically succeed to his job, or his nearest other relative', said Blei.

'What if he had no adult relatives?' What if all his family died at once?'

'That has never happened; it will never happen.'

The Chief Councillor added, 'If there was a danger of it, we might, perhaps place a baby or two with the Ragusniks and have it raised to the profession'.

'Ah. And how would you choose that baby?'

'From among children of mothers who had died in childbirth, as we chose the future Ragusnik bride.'

'Then choose a substitute Ragusnik now, by lot,' said Lamorak.

The Chief Councillor said, 'No! Impossible! How can you suggest that? If we select a baby, that baby is brought up to the life, it knows no other. At this point, it would be necessary to choose an adult and subject him to Rugusnik-hood. No, Dr Lamorak, we are neither monsters nor abandoned brutes.'

No use, thought Lamorak, no use, unless –

V

(12)   That night, Lamorak slept scarcely at all. Ragusnik asked for only the basic elements of humanity. But opposing that were thirty thousand Elseverians who faced death.

The welfare of thirty thousand on one side; the just demands of one family on the other. Could one say that thirty thousand who would support such injustice deserved to die?

Injustice by what standards? Earth's? Elsevere's? And who was Lamorak that he could judge?

And Ragusnik? He was willing to let thirty thousand die, including men and women who merely accepted a situation they had been taught to accept and could not change if they wished to. And children who had nothing at all to do with it.

Thirty thousand on one side; a single family on the other.

Appendix A

VI

(13) Lamorak made his decision in something that was almost despair; in the morning he called the Chief Councillor.

He said, 'Sir, if you can find a substitute, Ragusnik will see that he has lost all chance to force a decision in his favour and will return to work'.

'There can be no substitute', sighed the Chief Councillor; 'I have explained that'.

'No substitute among the Elseverians, but I am not an Elseverien; it doesn't matter to me. *I* will substitute.'

VII

(14) They were excited, much more excited than Lamorak himself. A dozen times they asked him if he was serious.

Lamorak had not shaved, and he felt sick, 'Certainly, I'm serious. And any time Ragusnik acts like this, you can always import a substitute. No other world has the taboo and there will always be plenty of temporary substitutes available if you pay enough'.

(He was betraying a brutally exploited man, and he knew it. But he told himself desperately: *Except for ostracism, he's very well treated. Very well.*)

They gave him the handbooks and he spent six hours, reading and re-reading. There was no use asking questions. None of the Elseverians knew anything about the job, except for what was in the handbook; and all seemed uncomfortable if the details were as much as mentioned.

'Maintain zero reading of galvanometer A-2 at all times during red signal of the Lunge-howler', read Lamorak. 'Now what's a Lunge-howler?'

'There will be a sign', muttered Blei, and the Elseverians looked at each other hang-dog and bent their heads to stare at their fingerends.

VIII

(15) They left him long before he reached the small rooms that were the central headquarters of generations of working Ragusniks, serving their world. He had specific instructions concerning which turnings to take and what level to reach, but they hung back and let him proceed alone.

He went through the rooms painstakingly, identifying the instruments and controls, following the schematic diagrams in the handbook.

There's a Lunge-howler, he thought, with gloomy satisfaction. The sign did indeed say so. It had a semi-circular face bitten into holes that were obviously designed to glow in separate colours. Why a 'howler' then?

He didn't know.

Somewhere, thought Lamorak, *somewhere wastes are accumulating, pushing against gears and exits, pipelines and stills, waiting to be handled in half a hundred ways. Now they just accumulate.*

Not without a tremor, he pulled the first switch as indicated by the handbook in its directions for 'Initiation'. A gentle murmur of life made itself felt through the floors and walls. He turned a knob and lights went on.

At each step he consulted the handbook, though he knew it by heart; and with each step, the rooms brightened and the dial indicators sprang into motion and a humming grew louder.

Somewhere deep in the factories, the accumulated wastes were being drawn into the proper channels.

IX

(16) A high-pitched signal sounded and startled Lamorak out of his painful concentration. It was the communications signal and Lamorak fumbled his receiver into action.

Ragusnik's head showed, startled; then slowly, the incredulity and outright shock faded from his eyes. '*That's* how it is, then.'

'I'm not an Elseverian, Ragusnik; I don't mind doing this.'

'But what business is it of yours? Why do you interfere?'

'I'm on your side, Ragusnik, but I must do this.'

'Why, if you're on my side? Do they treat people on your world as they treat me here?'

'Not any longer. But even if you are right, there are thirty thousand people on Elsevere to be considered.'

'They would have given in; you've ruined my only chance.'

'They would *not* have given in. And in a way you've won; they know now that you're dissatisfied. Until now, they never dreamed a Ragusnik could be unhappy, that he could make trouble.'

'What if they know? Now all they have to do is hire an Outworlder anytime.'

Lamorak shook his head violently. He had thought this through in these last bitter hours. 'The fact that they know means that the Elseverians will begin to think about you; some will begin to wonder if it's right to treat a human so. And if Outworlders are hired, they'll spread the word that this goes on upon Elsevere and Galactic public opinion will be in your favour.'

'And?'

'Things will improve. In your son's time, things will be much better.'

'In my son's time', said Ragusnik, his cheeks sagging. 'I might have had it now. Well, I lose. I'll go back to the job.'

Lamorak felt an overwhelming relief. 'If you'll come down here now, sir, you may have your job and I'll consider it an honour to shake your hand.'

Ragusnik's head snapped up and filled with gloomy pride. 'You call me 'sir' and offer to shake my hand. Go about your business, Earthman, and leave me to my work, for I would not shake yours.'

X

(17) Lamorak returned the way he had come, relieved that the crisis was over, and profoundly depressed, too.

He stopped in surprise when he found a section of corridor cordoned off, so he could not pass. He looked around for alternate routes, then startled at a magnified voice above his head. 'Dr. Lamorak, do you hear me? This is Councillor Blei.'

Lamorak looked up. The voice came over some sort of public address system, but he saw no sign of an outlet.

He called out, 'Is anything wrong? Can you hear me?'

'I hear you.'

Instinctively, Lamorak was shouting, 'Is anything wrong?' There seems to be a block here. Are there complications with Ragusnik?'

'Ragusnik has gone to work', came Blei's voice. 'The crisis is over, and you must make ready to leave'.

'Leave?'

'Leave Elsevere; a ship is being made ready for you now.'

'But wait a bit.' Lamorak was confused by this sudden leap of events. 'I haven't completed my gathering of data.'

Blei's voice said, 'This cannot be helped. You will be directed to the ship and your belongings will be sent after you by servo-mechanisms. We trust – we trust – '

Something was becoming clear to Lamorak. 'You trust *what*?'

'We trust you will make no attempt to see or speak directly to any Elseverian. And of course we hope you will avoid embarrassment by not attempting to return to Elsevere at any time in the future. A colleague of yours would be welcome if further data concerning us is needed.'

'I understand', said Lamorak, tonelessly. Obviously, he had himself become a Ragusnik. He had handled the controls that in turn had handled the wastes; he was ostracized. He was a corpse-handler, a swineherd, an inside man at the skonk works.

He said, 'Goodbye'.

Blei's voice said, 'Before we direct you, Dr Lamorak – . On behalf of the Council of Elsevere, I thank you for your help in this crisis.'

'You're welcome', said Lamorak, bitterly.

21.4 REV: Crossword

Objective

- To develop the ability to distinguish the main concepts and author names from *ORBIT3*, Chapter 21, which deals with the management of conflict.

Introduction

Understanding a topic in organizational behaviour involves a familiarity with the research, authors, theories and concepts in that field. This activity gives you practice in correctly linking these together in the management of conflict with their definitions or descriptions.

Procedure

The crossword below already contains some of the letters in the answers. The shading indicates where a word starts and ends. Use the clues to identify the 25 answers, and position them correctly in the crossword grid. Each clue indicates the length of the answer word.

Crossword clues

1. Bargaining strategy which uses threats to force a submission (7).

2. He distinguished between the organizational theory and the industrial relations approaches to conflict (8).

3. A type of conflict which breeds discontent, destroys group cohesion, and threatens group security (13).

4. Conflict caused by ambiguity over 'who does what?' (14).

5. He felt that conflict was both endemic to organizations and beneficial for them (5).

6. Process in which a third party has the authority to impose a settlement on the other two (11).

7. A form of interdependence which requires the highest form of integration between the activities of the parties (10).

8. A type of bargaining which seeks to increase the total amount of resources available for distribution to the negotiating parties (11).

9. A perspective on conflict which holds that workers and organizations have fundamentally different interests (9).

10. A process in which a third party is invited to run this social process (9).

11. Adhering to these is a cheap way of aligning the activities of different parties (5).

12. The emphasizing of the differences between the parties reinforces these (11).

13. Distinguished the differentials and fragmentalist perspectives, in addition to the established integrationalist (6).

14. This role holder knits together the activities of different groups or departments (7).

15. Management's failure to _____ previously differentiated activities is a common cause of conflict (10).

16. Considered to be a factor present in nearly all organizational conflicts (8).

17. Originated the industrial relations conflict paradigm in the 1950s (11).

18. Opposite of avoiding (13).

19. Structurally-derived conflict excludes consideration of these types of clashes (11).

20. This process seeks to end a conflict between disagreeing parties (10).

21. The interactionist perspective spawns these types of conflict devices (11).

22. This can pass faster for some parties than others, thus causing conflict (4).

23. His model considers the co-operativeness and assertiveness of the conflicting parties (6).

24. This 'consultant-from-hell' can encourage new group thinking (6, 8).

25. The costs of litigation often encourage the use of such conflict resolving procedures (initials) (3).

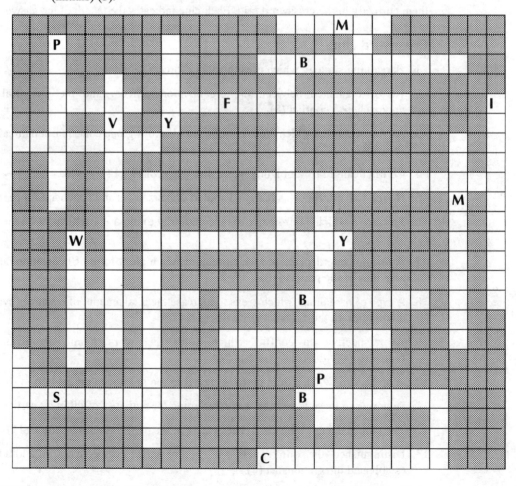

Chapter 22

Organizational power and politics

22.1 Large group activity: Assessing your politicking propensity
22.2 Small group activity: Exercising power
22.3 Prepared task: Political processes in organizations
22.4 Review: Quiz table

22.1 LGA: Assessing your politicking propensity

Objectives

- To assess the likelihood that you currently engage in political behaviour and use power within organizations.
- To assess the likelihood that you will engage in political behaviour and use power within organizations.

Introduction

The fact that politicking is a feature of all organizations does not mean that all employees engage in it to the same degree. These two short questionnaires are intended to allow self-diagnosis in relation to politicking. The first questionnaire allows you to determine how much power you exert in your group at present. The second questionnaire allows you to determine your locus of control, since this is a fundamental factor in influencing your propensity to engage in organizational activities.

Procedure

Step 1 Complete questionnaire 1 or 2, or both, as directed by your instructor.

Step 2 Calculate your visibility and influence scores, and locate your position on the Visibility–Influence matrix.

Questionnaire 1: How much power do you exert in your group?

Think of a group of which you are a member. It could be a work group or team, a committee, a group project at your university club or society. Respond to the statements below using the following scale:

Strongly Disagree	1	Slightly Agree	5
Disagree	2	Agree	6
Slightly Disagree	3	Strongly Agree	7
Neither Agree nor Disagree	4		

1. _____ I am one of the more vocal members of the group.
2. _____ People in the group listen to what I have to say.
3. _____ I often volunteer to lead the group.
4. _____ I am able to influence group decisions.
5. _____ I often find myself on 'centre stage' in group activities or discussions.
6. _____ Members of the group seek me out for advice.
7. _____ I take the initiative in the group and am often one of the first to speak out on important issues.
8. _____ I receive recognition in the group for my ideas and contributions.
9. _____ I would rather lead the group than be a participant.
10. _____ My opinion is held in high regard by group members.
11. _____ I volunteer my thoughts and ideas without hesitation.
12. _____ My ideas are often implemented.
13. _____ I ask questions in meetings just to have something to say.
14. _____ Group members often ask for my opinions and input.
15. _____ I often play the role of scribe, secretary, or note taker during meetings.
16. _____ Group members usually consult me about important matters before they make a decision.
17. _____ I clown around with other group members.
18. _____ I have noticed that other group members often look at me, even when not talking directly to me.
19. _____ I jump right into whatever conflict the group members are dealing with.
20. _____ I am very influential in the group.

Scoring

1. _____	2. _____
3. _____	4. _____
5. _____	6. _____
7. _____	8. _____
9. _____	10. _____
11. _____	12. _____
13. _____	14. _____
15. _____	16. _____
17. _____	18. _____
19. _____	20. _____

Total Visibility score _____   Total Influence score _____

1. *High visibility – high influence*: Group members in quadrant I exhibit behaviour that brings high visibility and allows them to exert influence on others. In organizations, these people may be upwardly mobile or 'fast trackers'.

Visibility/Influence Matrix

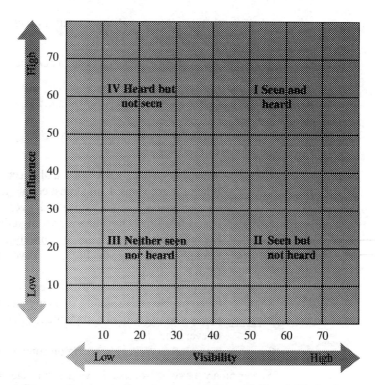

2. *High visibility – low influence*: Group members in quadrant II are highly visible but have little real influence. This condition could reflect their personal characteristics but could also indicate that formal power resides elsewhere in the organization. Often these people may hold staff, rather than line, positions that give them visibility but that lack 'clout' to get things done.

3. *Low visibility – low influence*: Group members in quadrant III, for whatever reason, are neither seen nor heard. Individuals in this category may have difficulty advancing in the organization.

4. *Low visibility – high influence:* group members in quadrant IV are 'behind the scenes' influencers. These individuals are often opinion leaders and 'sages' who wield influence but are content to stay out of the limelight.

Source: Adapted from Reddy, W.B., and Williams, G. 'The Visibility/Credibility Inventory: Measuring Power and Influence' In J. W. Pfeiffer (Ed.), *The 1988 Annual: Developing Human Resources*, San Diego: University Associates

Questionnaire 2: Measuring locus of control

The questionnaire below is designed to measure locus of control beliefs. Researchers using this questionnaire in a recent study of college students found a mean of 51.8 for men and 52.2 for women, with a standard deviation of 6 for each. The higher the score on this questionnaire, the more you tend to believe that you are generally responsible for what happens to you; in other words, higher scores are associated with internal locus of control. Low scores are associated with external locus of control. Scoring low indicates that you tend to believe that forces beyond your control, such as other people, fate, or chance, are responsible for what happens to you.

For each of these ten questions, indicate the extent to which you agree or disagree using the following scale:

Strongly Disagree	1	Slightly Agree	5
Disagree	2	Agree	6
Slightly Disagree	3	Strongly Agree	7
Neither Agree nor Disagree	4		

1. _____ When I get what I want, it's usually because I worked hard for it.
2. _____ When I make plans, I am almost certain to make them work.
3. _____ I prefer games involving some luck over games requiring pure skill.
4. _____ I can learn almost anything if I set my mind to it.
5. _____ My major accomplishments are entirely due to my hard work and ability.
6. _____ I usually don't set goals, because I have a hard time following through on them.
7. _____ Competition discourages excellence.
8. _____ Often people get ahead just by being lucky.
9. _____ In any sort of exam or competition, I like to know how well I do relative to everyone else.
10. _____ It's pointless to keep working on something that's too difficult for me.

To determine your score, reverse the values you selected for questions 3, 6, 7, 8 and 10 (1=7, 2=6, 3=5, 4=4, 5=3, 6=2, 7=1). For example, if you strongly disagreed with the statement in question 3, you would have given it a value of '1'. Change this value to '7'. Reverse the scores in a similar manner for questions 6, 7, 8 and 10. Now add the point values from all ten questions together.

Your score:_____

Source: Hellriegel, D. and Slocum, J.W. and Woodman, R.W. *Organizational Behaviour*, West Publishing Co, NY, 1992, 6/E p. 96.

22.2 SGA: Exercising power

Objectives

- To introduce students to the six bases of power described in *ORBIT3*, Chapter 22.
- To devise influencing strategies based on the different power bases.
- To provide practice in using each type of power.
- To assess the probable results of using each type of power base.

Introduction

It is one thing to know what the different types of power are, but quite another to apply them in practice. This activity gives you experience of using each type of power. In your groups, you will have the opportunity to implement and review them.

Procedure

Step 1   Divide the class into six groups of roughly equal size. The instructor will assign each group one of the six power bases – punishment, reward, referent, legitimate, expert and informational.

Step 2   Each group will read the case that follows and will prepare an actual influencing plan, using the power-base that it has been assigned. The group has to decide where the influencing attempt is to take place (classroom, instructor's office, students' bar, etc.). When the planning is over, each group selects one of their number to role-play the 'instructor', and another to be the 'student'. In the role-play that will follow, the student will be the recipient of the instructor's influencing attempt (5 minutes).

Step 3   The entire class reconvenes, and the pairs of 'students' and 'instructors' take it in turn to role-play their influencing plan in front of the entire class. The order of presentation is punishment, reward, referent, legitimate, expert and informational (each roleplay should not exceed 5 minutes).

During the roleplays, the members of the other groups think of themselves as the student being persuaded. At the end of each roleplay, all students fill out the *Reaction to influence questionnaire* sheet appropriate for the type of power used in that role play. Six role plays are performed, and six questionnaire sheets are completed. Members complete the questionnaire for the role play that they planned and/or presented themselves.

Step 4   Once the six role plays are completed, and the six sheets scored, these are cut by sheets and placed together according to their heading, and returned to the relevant team. For example, all the questionnaire sheets reporting students' reactions to the use of Punishment Power are collected, and returned to the Punishment Power group. The same is done with the other five groups. Each group calculates the average score for their four questions, inserts them in the relevant column in the *Reactions to influence questionnaire: Summary sheet*, and is ready to report their four numbers to the first point of decimal (e.g. 2.4).

Reactions to influence questionnaire: Summary sheet

Question	PUN	REW	REF	LEG	EXP	INFO
1. Compliance						
2. Change						
3. Reaction						
4. Relationship						

Step 5   Each of the six groups report their four numbers to the other members of the class who insert them in their summary sheets. The instructor provides comparative data, and the class engages in a plenary discussion of the activity.

Role play situation

You are an instructor in a university class, and have become aware that a potentially good student is repeatedly absent from class, and sometimes unprepared when they are present. The student concerned appears satisfied with the course work marks that they are receiving, but you would like them to attend regularly, be better prepared, and thus do better in class. You even feel that the student might become attracted to pursuing a career in this field, which is an exciting one for you. As an instructor, you are respected and liked by your students, and it irritates you somewhat to know that this person treats your dedicated teaching with such a cavalier attitude. You want to influence this student to attend your class regularly. You can choose one of the following six power strategies.

1. Punishment power Ability to influence because of capacity to coerce or punish (PUN).
2. Reward power   Ability to influence because of potential reward (REW).
3. Referent power   Comes from others' admiration of and liking for you (REF).
4. Legitimate power   Based on your formal position in organization (LEG).
5. Expert power   Comes from actual or perceived superior knowledge or ability (EXP).
6. Information power By having information others want (INFO).

For each of the 6 roleplays in turn, use the six *Reaction to influence questionnaires*, one for each power style, to circle the number on each of the scales below which best represents your view. That is, think of yourself to be *on the receiving end* of the influencing attempt described, and record your own reaction to it.

Reaction to influence questionnaire sheets

Punishment sheet

Questions		←		→	
As a result of the influencing attempt I will …	Definitely not comply 1	2	3	4	Definitely comply 5
Any change that does come about will be …	Temporary 1	2	3	4	Long lasting 5
My own personal reaction is…	Resistance 1	2	3	4	Acceptance 5
As a result of this influence attempt my relationship with the instructor will probably be …	Worse 1	2	3	4	Better 5

cut -

Reward sheet

Questions		←		→	
As a result of the influencing attempt I will …	Definitely not comply 1	2	3	4	Definitely comply 5
Any change that does come about will be …	Temporary 1	2	3	4	Long lasting 5
My own personal reaction is …	Resistance 1	2	3	4	Acceptance 5
As a result of this influence attempt my relationship with the instructor will probably be …	Worse 1	2	3	4	Better 5

cut -

Referent sheet

Questions		←		→	
As a result of the influencing attempt I will …	Definitely not comply 1	2	3	4	Definitely comply 5
Any change that does come about will be …	Temporary 1	2	3	4	Long lasting 5
My own personal reaction is …	Resistance 1	2	3	4	Acceptance 5
As a result of this influence attempt my relationship with the instructor will probably be …	Worse 1	2	3	4	Better 5

cut -

Legitimate sheet

Questions		←		→	
As a result of the influencing attempt I will …	Definitely not comply 1	2	3	4	Definitely comply 5
Any change that does come about will be …	Temporary 1	2	3	4	Long lasting 5
My own personal reaction is …	Resistance 1	2	3	4	Acceptance 5
As a result of this influence attempt my relationship with the instructor will probably be …	Worse 1	2	3	4	Better 5

cut -

Expert sheet

Questions		←		→	
As a result of the influencing attempt I will …	Definitely not comply 1	2	3	4	Definitely comply 5
Any change that does come about will be …	Temporary 1	2	3	4	Long lasting 5
My own personal reaction is …	Resistance 1	2	3	4	Acceptance 5
As a result of this influence attempt my relationship with the instructor will probably be …	Worse 1	2	3	4	Better 5

cut ---

Information sheet

Questions		←		→	
As a result of the influencing attempt I will …	Definitely not comply 1	2	3	4	Definitely comply 5
Any change that does come about will be …	Temporary 1	2	3	4	Long lasting 5
My own personal reaction is …	Resistance 1	2	3	4	Acceptance 5
As a result of this influence attempt my relationship with the instructor will probably be …	Worse 1	2	3	4	Better 5

cut ---

Source: Adapted from Gib Akin, *Exchange: Organizational Behaviour Teaching Review*, vol. 3, no. 4, 1978, pp. 38–39. Used with permission.

22.3 PREP: Political processes in organizations

Objectives

- To analyse and predict when political behaviour is likely to be used to influence decision-making in organizations.
- To compare students' ratings of politically-based decisions with the ratings of practising managers.

Introduction

Politics is the use of influence to make decisions and obtain preferred outcomes. Surveys of managers show that political behaviour is a fact of life in virtually all organizations. Every organization confronts situations which are characterised by uncertainty, and which engender disagreements among their members. This prevents their using standards rules and rational decision models. Political behaviour and rational decision processes often substitute for one another. The political behaviour that exists is revealed in informal discussions and unscheduled meetings with managers, in arguments, attempts at persuasion, and eventual agreement and acceptance of another's position.

In this activity, you are asked to consider the part that political behaviour plays in eleven types of decisions that are commonly made in all organizations.

Procedure

Pre-class

Step 1   Individual ranking
Members *individually* rank the eleven types of organizational decisions listed on the scoring sheet according to the extent to which they believe that politics plays a part in them. The most political decision would be ranked 1; the least political, 11. The rankings are entered on the first column of the scoring sheet.

Step 2   Manager survey
Before attending class, each student interviews three managers, working in medium or large organizations, about their experience of workplace politics. Ideally, the interviewees should be a first line supervisor, a middle manager (section or department head), and a senior manager (divisional or board member). In practice, any three would do, but indicate their level (supervisor, middle or senior) in your notes.

First, ask each to give you a specific, 'good example of workplace politics in action' from their experience. Note down the key features of the story that they tell you. Next, ask them to rank the 11 types of organizational decisions in terms of how 'politicized' they believe them to be. Enter each manager's ranking in the *Manager interview sheet*.

In the class

Step 3   Group analysis of managers' data
The class is divided into roughly equal sized groups of 5–6. Members now share the

interview data that they have collected about managers' views of politics. A group of 5 students will have 15 rankings.

First, all the rankings obtained are pooled and averaged to produce a single Manager's Score. These are inserted in Column 2.

Next, group members check if there is sufficient data to divide up their data by management level (supervisor, middle, senior). For example, the group collects 3–5 rankings from each level. If there is, average scores are produced for two or three levels, as appropriate. These are inserted in the *Manager interview sheet.*

Step 4   Discussion
Using their collected data and experience, students will try to arrive at some conclusions about the role of politics in real-world organizational decision-making. The instructor will direct them to consider some of the following questions.

1. Why did some individuals' ranking closely match those of the managers' more than others? Did they have more experience of organizational decision-making? Did they interpret the amount of uncertainty and disagreement associated with decisions more accurately?

2. If the 11 decisions were to be ranked in importance on a rational basis, how would the ranking compare to the one produced by the surveyed managers? To what extent does this mean that both rational and political approaches should be used in decision making?

3. What would happen if managers applied political processes to logical, well-understood issues? What would happen if they applied rational or quantitative techniques to issues about which there was great uncertainty and disagreement?

4. It is believed that political behaviour is more extensive in the higher levels of the organizational hierarchy. If you obtained data from different management levels (supervisor, middle, senior) does it support this belief? Why should politics feature more at the higher than the lower levels of management?

5. What would you say to managers or new recruits who feel that politics is bad for the organization and should be avoided at all costs?

Procedure

This exercise is designed for two very different groups of students. The first are undergraduates who have little experience of politics in the workplace, and typically none of that occurring at managerial level. The second group consists of young and middle managers on MBA programmes who will have observed the political process at first hand, and who may have engaged in it. The activities and debriefing need to be adjusted to suit the needs of these two student groups.

It is useful to introduce the concept of workplace politics before students embark on the data collection stage, and provide some specific examples of political behaviour in organizations (e.g. coalition building; creating obligations and calling in owed favours; blaming or attacking others; image-building and impression management; by-passing chain of command; whistle-blowing; duplicity; defecting; obstructionism and sabotaging). It is also useful to give examples of the ways in which such political behaviour might affect some of the eleven decisions described in the scoring sheet.

Manager interview Sheet

	Manager 1 ranking	Manager 2 ranking	Manager 3 ranking	Average All mgrs	Av Sup	Av Mid	Av Snr
Level (Sup, Mid, Snr) →							
Decisions							
1. Management promotions and transfers							
2. Hiring new employees							
3. Amount of pay							
4. Annual budget allocation							
5. Allocation of facilities, equipment, offices							
6. Delegation of authority among managers							
7. How activities between different departments are co-ordinated							
8. Specific personnel policies, e.g. no smoking							
9. Penalties for disciplinary infractions							
10. Performance appraisals							
11. Grievances and complaints							
TOTALS							

Scoring sheet

Decisions	1 Ranking Individual	2 Ranking (total average) Surveyed managers	3 Ranking (total average) Gandz and Murray's managers
1. Management promotions and transfers			
2. Hiring new employees			
3. Amount of pay			
4. Annual budget allocation			
5. Allocation of facilities, equipment, offices			
6. Delegation of authority among managers			
7. How activities and relationships between different departments are co-ordinated			
8. Specific personnel policies, e.g. no smoking			
9. Penalties for disciplinary infractions			
10. Performance appraisals			
11. Grievances and complaints			
TOTALS			

Note

This activity is a modified version of that developed by R.L. Daft and M.P. Sharfman, *Organization Theory: Cases and Applications*, West Publishing, 4/e, 1995. The scoring sheet and the survey data are taken from J. Gandz and V.V. Murray, 'The experience of workplace politics', *Academy of Management Journal*, vol. 23, pp. 237–51. An introductory treatment of organizational power, politics and impression management can be found in A.A. Huczynski, *Influencing Within Organizations*, Prentice Hall, Hemel Hempstead, 1996.

22.4 REV: Quiz table

Objectives

- To test students' memory of key ideas from Chapter 22 of *ORBIT3* concerning the definition and understanding of power and politics.
- To encourage the habit of remembering accurately the authorship of ideas, as a memory aid and also as good study practice.

Introduction

Understanding a topic in organizational behaviour involves a familiarity with the research, authors, theories and concepts in that field. This activity gives you practice in correctly linking these together in the areas of power and politics with their definitions or descriptions.

Procedure

Below are 26 clues. The first letter of each of the 26 answers is given, and together they spell out the phrase, *Parsimonious graphic implied.*

Clues

1. A statement of how things should be done.
2. The right to guide or direct the actions of others.
3. This model of organization emphasizes consistent goals, clear means of attaining them, and clear communications.
4. A form of power used for the common good, rather than one which is self-serving.
5. These strategies are based on a variety of different power bases.
6. A behaviour style which emphasizes guile, deceit, cynicism, and amorality.
7. Cohen and Bradford felt that these types of currencies could be used as rewards.
8. Those who rate highly on this dimension are likely to become company politicians (initials).
9. A form of power based on the possession of knowledge that others do not have.
10. Seeking the most favourable outcome for a particular end.
11. Reducing this can be one source of a department's power within a company.
12. A type of event or activity that has to occur inside or outside of an organization in order for it to achieve its goals.
13. Organizational dilemma believes that employees and organizations pursue different ones.
14. Propensity to gamble.

1.	P														
2.	A														
3.	R														
4.	S														
5.	I														
6.	M														
7.	O														
8.	N														
9.	I														
10.	O														
11.	U														
12.	S														
13.	G														
14.	R														
15.	A														
16.	P														
17.	H														
18.	I														
19.	C														
20.	I														
21.	M														
22.	P														
23.	L														
24.	I														
25.	E														
26.	D														

15. A persuasion strategy that uses insistent, forceful communication.

16. The act of acquiring, developing and using power to obtain one's own preferred outcomes.

17. She considered simplicity and complexity in the history and development of the concept of power.

18. Perspective which holds that all members of an organization share common interests.

19. The notion that a person acts in the same way in similar circumstances.

20. A situation in which the actions of one party affect those of another.

21. A writers from the 1960s who challenged the rationalist view, and who saw organizations as political coalitions.

22. He described the conditions which led to the use of power and politics in organizations.

23. Belief as to whether or not your circumstances are determined by yourself.

24. An evaluative prescription which affects organizational members' decisions as to whether they will engage in political behaviour.

25. A type of power, often used by consultants, which is based on the reality or perception that an individual knows the best course of action in a given situation.

26. A type of statement claiming to outline how things are actually done.

Chapter 23
Management control

23.1 LGA: The need to control

Objectives

- To introduce the behaviour pattern known as *Machiavellianism*.
- To assess individual differences in *Machiavellianism*.
- To develop an understanding of how such behaviours are related to job performance.

Introduction

Chapter 23 of *ORBIT3* introduces the concept of the *authoritarian* personality. This collection of traits implies intellectual rigidity, resistance to change, deference to authority, and a preoccupation with power and status. Authoritarians can thus be expected to perform badly in jobs that require sensitivity, tact, flexibility and the ability to deal with complexity and change. However, where the task is stable and performance requires strict adherence to rules and procedures, an authoritarian may perform well.

In this exercise we wish to introduce the related personality construct of *Machiavellianism*, and give you an opportunity to find out how Machiavellian you are yourself. The authoritarian respects authority and shows deference to those who possess it. The Machiavellian, in contrast, seeks power with which to manipulate and control others. This personality construct is named after the sixteenth-century writer Niccolo Machiavelli from whose book *The Prince* some of the initial thinking around this idea was drawn. What traits does someone with a strong Machiavellian personality possess? What behaviours do these traits imply? In what ways can the desire to manipulate and control others affect job performance? What moral or ethical issues are raised by Machiavellian behaviour? Here is an opportunity to relate these questions to your own personality, by first assessing your Machiavellianism score.

Procedure

Step 1 Working on your own and without discussion with colleagues, complete the *Control orientation test* on the following page.

Step 2   In buzz groups of about three members, compare your answers to the test. Note and discuss differences.

Step 3   Turn to the scoring instructions and work out your score.

Step 4   In buzz groups of about three members, share and compare your thinking in response to the two sets of analysis questions.

Step 5   Feedback is optional, according to the instructor's wishes.

Control orientation test

This is a test of your orientation towards the manipulation and control of others. In response to each statement, circle the number that most closely represents your attitude.

Statement:	Disagree a lot	Disagree a little	neutral	Agree a little	Agree a lot
1. The best way to handle people is to tell them what they want to hear.	1	2	3	4	5
2. When you ask someone to do something for you, it is best to give the real reason for wanting it rather than giving reasons that might carry more weight.	1	2	3	4	5
3. Anyone who completely trusts anyone else is asking for trouble.	1	2	3	4	5
4. It is hard to get ahead without cutting corners here and there.	1	2	3	4	5
5. It is safest to assume that all people have a vicious streak, and it will come out when they are given a chance.	1	2	3	4	5
6. One should take action only when it is morally right.	1	2	3	4	5
7. Most people are basically good and kind.	1	2	3	4	5
8. There is no excuse for lying to someone else.	1	2	3	4	5
9. Most people forget more easily the death of their father than the loss of their property.	1	2	3	4	5
10. Generally speaking, people won't work hard unless they're forced to do so.	1	2	3	4	5

Source: R. Christie and F.L. Geis (Eds), *Studies in Machiavellianism*, Academic Press, New York, 1970.

Control orientation test: scoring instructions

This test is designed to assess your Machiavellianism score. To score your answers, first add the numbers that you have checked on these items:

Item: Score:

1   _____
3   _____
4   _____
5   _____
9   _____
10   _____

             Sub total: _____

Then for the other four items, add the *reverse* scores, giving yourself a 5 if you checked 1, a 4 if you checked 2, and vice versa; a 3 stays a 3.

Item: Score:

2   _____
6   _____
7   _____
8   _____

             Sub total: _____

                         Final score:_____
The average score is 25.

Analysis

First, some personal issues. Is your score much as you expected – consistent with your own self assessment? Would you like your score to be lower or higher, given what this would mean about your behaviour with respect to other people? Why? Share and compare your thinking on these points with your immediate colleagues.

Second, some organizational issues. Should we dismiss Machiavellianism out of hand as unethical and therefore inappropriate? Or should we take a more balanced stance: in what organizational settings would Machiavellian behaviour be appropriate and effective? Once again, share and compare your thinking on these issues with your immediate colleagues.

23.2 SGA: Design your control system

Objectives

- To identify the procedures and problems of designing an effective organizational control system.
- To explore the nature and characteristics of *dysfunctional* controls.

Introduction

The STOP! exercise on page 709 of Chapter 23 of *ORBIT3* invites you to consider how your behaviour and performance on your organizational behaviour course are controlled. Here is an opportunity to turn the spotlight on your instructors, to consider their performance, and to consider how it in turn is controlled. However, we can take this analysis at least one step further; let us consider the design and implementation of controls on organizational behaviour instructors in order to *improve* performance on specific, predefined, criteria.

In approaching this exercise, and in tackling any similar control problem in an organizational setting, there is one fundamental aspect of controls on people that must be remembered. *We respond as individuals to the measures on which we will be appraised.* The corollary of this observation is that we are unlikely to attend to aspects of behaviour and performance that are *not* measured. Consider the apparently straightforward example of a machine operator. We want the operator to produce as many items as possible during an eight hour working shift, or to produce to and exceed a quota. It is easy to count the number of items produced, and also easy to tie financial reward through a 'piece rate' to the output. However, this situation is *not* straightforward if there is a negative correlation between output and quality (in other words, if quality is likely to suffer as the volume of items produced increases, as the operator gets careless in an attempt to boost earnings). The control on volume of output in this case is *dysfunctional*, because it can lead to behaviours opposite to those actually required (i.e., it can lead to the production of defective items).

The 'simple' solution, of course, is to introduce a quality control; only count the good items. However, somebody now has to check quality. Can you trust the machine operator to do that? Will you employ specialist inspectors to do this, with the extra costs this will involve? What controls on the performance of the inspectors will be required? What began as a simple control problem turns out to have other costs and organizational complexities. Effective control system design must therefore take into account the likely responses of those to be controlled, the dysfunctional nature of some controls, and the need to look beyond what may be 'ideal' in any given setting and to design a *cost effective* control system.

Academic promotion in many universities is dependent on volume (and perhaps quality) of published output from scholarship and research. To the extent that this control diverts attention away from other aspects of the academic task, that control may also be seen as dysfunctional. An educational institution that links academic salary progression to the educational level of its staff's teaching activities may find that 'low level' and vocational course innovation slows or stops, while staff creatively introduce innovative new 'high level' courses at degree and postgraduate level. To the extent that the mission of such an institution is to offer a broad range of vocational and academic courses, such a control on staff earnings is dysfunctional in that through time the portfolio of courses will be biased towards those which contribute most effectively to staff salaries. In some payment systems, a component of management salary is linked to the number of staff for whom that manager is responsible. This too can be a dysfunctional control, encouraging and rewarding behaviour inconsistent with the interests of the organization. Why? Because a manager in this situation is rewarded for recruiting more staff, regardless of the actual workload of the section concerned.

With these considerations in mind, we would like to invite you to consider the design of a cost effective control system to maintain and perhaps improve your instructor's teaching performance.

Procedure

Step 1 Working on your own, read the following *Control system design* brief and make preliminary notes on how you plan to tackle this assignment.

Step 2 Working in syndicate groups of three to five members, design a control system that meets the specified criteria.

Step 3 Produce a realistic assessment of your control system, concentrating in particular on how cost effective it is, identifying any dysfunctional aspects.

Step 4 Nominate a spokesperson to present your design and its assessment to the class as a whole.

Control system design

The problem facing you is how to control the teaching performance of your organizational behaviour instructor. Your institution may already have some mechanisms in place that seek to achieve this – student feedback questionnaires, or a staff development unit that carries out classroom observation, perhaps. However, surely you can improve on what is already there, and you can always build existing controls into your new design.

You will recall that control is a process that involves setting standards, measuring performance, comparing actual with standard, and determining as necessary any corrective action. Applied to the control of teaching performance, you will need to consider the following issues:

1. How are you going to define the standard of teaching performance expected of your instructor? Will you use one measure or several? Can you define these measures clearly and unambiguously? In setting this standard, or these standards, do you wish to stay with current levels of performance, or to set 'stretch goals' that will improve standards of performance?

2. How are you going to measure your instructor's actual performance against your standard or standards? You need to specify not only how this will be done, but also who will do it, and how often.

3. How are you going to compare the actual performance measures with your standards? Once again, you need to specify how this will be done, by whom, and when.

4. What will happen if performance is not up to the standard or standards required? Specify the actions that will unfold in this instance.

5. Now that you have designed your control system, give some thought as to how cost effective it will be in operation. What would be ideal, and what will work as intended,

may not be the same, and could have significantly different cost implications.

6. Now consider whether any of the controls you have introduced are dysfunctional – and will lead to behaviours opposite to or different from those you desire. Will your system encourage rigid bureaucratic behaviour or information distortion, and will any aspect of your system threaten need satisfaction and create hostility and lack of co-operation?

7. Prepare a presentation of your design and assessment to your Instructor and the assembled class in plenary session.

23.3 PREP: Control to commitment

Objectives

- To develop understanding of the practical implications of Richard Walton's argument for a shift from cultures of control to cultures of commitment.
- To apply this argument to a specific organization.

Introduction

Richard Walton (*ORBIT3,* p. 729) argued in 1985 that managers have to choose between a strategy based on imposing control and a strategy based on eliciting commitment. If you are not already familiar with this argument, turn to it now and read it through. The summary provided in the textbook is comprehensive but, of course, can never be as good as the real thing. If you have the time and opportunity, you could find it helpful and interesting to track down the original in *Harvard Business Review* which should not be a difficult journal to trace. The argument revolves around notions of high involvement management, participation and empowerment, and it offers an account of a desirable organizational culture that can be difficult to criticize. It is a relatively simple matter to specify a desirable organizational culture on a sheet of paper. However, it may not be so easy to take an existing organization and introduce the changes required to move the culture in that direction. In addition, the existing culture may already contain elements of the 'ideal'. There may be aspects of the organization's environment or of its business which discourage the full implementation of a commitment culture. To establish the problems of taking advice such as Walton's and putting it into practice, it is necessary to try and do just that – with respect to a particular organization. That is what we would like to invite you to do in this prepared assignment.

Procedure

Step 1   Make sure that you are familiar with the arguments in the Assessment section of Chapter 23 of *ORBIT3*, beginning on page 728. Pay particular attention to the work of Richard Walton, and note that similar arguments have appeared earlier in the book.

Step 2   Read the *Task briefing* which follows.

Step 3   Carry out whatever field research you feel is necessary to complete this assignment.

Step 4   Write a report which describes the current organization culture with respect to Walton's framework. Indicate the nature and extent of the gap between current practice and what Walton identifies as ideal.

Step 5   Formulate recommendations for the organization with respect to the management action required to move the organization closer to the ideal. Be as specific and detailed in your recommendations as you feel it necessary.

Step 6   Feedback according to your instructor's wishes.

Task briefing

You have two tasks in this assignment.

Your first task is to establish the extent to which your educational institution has a commitment culture as opposed to a control culture. Having identified any 'gap' between current reality and Richard Walton's ideal, your second task is to develop a set of recommendations for the development of a commitment culture in your institution.

To carry out this analysis, you will need to speak to at least a small number of people who work for the organization. You will need to decide what questions you want to ask them. You could, for example, show them Walton's two specifications and ask them to comment under each heading (job design, performance expectations, and so on) where they feel their organization lies at present. It might take you some time to explain Walton's material in enough detail to enable your respondents to give you ready answers, so you could instead work out an interview schedule to get the information you need. You must decide what approach to use; there are practical research method problems to resolve here, and you may find the content of Chapter 2 of use in that respect. However, when writing up the report of what you have found, indicate clearly how you gathered the information on which your analysis and recommendations are based. Remember that one particularly valuable source of practical recommendations lies in your informants; after all, they work here.

When planning the fieldwork for this assignment, note that your educational institution employs people in capacities other than lecturers. You may find it instructive for the purposes of this assignment to speak to secretaries and to administrative and library staff as well as to academic personnel. Don't expect their perspectives on the culture of the organization to be consistent. If there are significant differences in perceptions, what does this tell you about the culture of the organization?

Your final report should have the following broad structure:

1. *Executive summary:* a single page outline of the main findings and recommendations;

2. *Introduction:* a short statement of the aims of your report, explaining also the background to your analysis of the work of Richard Walton;

3. *Methodology:* a summary of how you gathered the data for this assignment, with a candid assessment of the strengths and limitations of your approach;

4. *Gap analysis:* the heart of the report in which you present a structured assessment of the extent to which the organization matches the 'ideal' commitment culture;

5. *Recommendations:* where you set out proposals, based on your gap analysis, for changing the culture or aspects of it from a control orientation to a commitment orientation.

23.4: REV: Sentence completion

Objective

- To encourage students to pay attention to detail in their reading.

Introduction

This test is based on Chapter 23 of *ORBIT3* on management control. If you have read and remembered this chapter, this test will present few difficulties. However, if you have not absorbed it, there may be little point in proceeding with this review.

Some students may be able to guess some of the correct responses, but most of these require a close reading of the material first. If somebody wants to claim that this is a test of memory and not of understanding – then they are correct. We simply wish to reinforce the point that attention to detail is one desirable learning discipline. Ask students to score out of 20 the answers of someone else in the class, by reading them the correct responses. Or, have them find all the correct answers for themselves in the text.

Procedure

Complete the following twenty sentences by inserting the appropriate letters. The word spaces, including the vowels, have been included to help you along. A gap indicates the existence of a separate second or third word.

1. ___ A ___ O ___ considered control to be one of the main five management activities.

2. ___ ___ A ___ ___ A ___ ___ S are used to guide performance direction and norms.

3. The cost for employees of working in an organismic organization are I ___ ___ E ___ U ___ I ___ ___ and A ___ ___ I E ___ ___ .

4. When controls create behaviours that are in direct opposition to those wanting to be encouraged, they are termed ___ ___ ___ ___ U ___ ___ ___ I O ___ A ___ .

5. Unobtrusive and seemingly neutral controls have been termed I ___ ___ I ___ I O U ___ .

6. People who like tight, organizational control processes often possess an A U ___ ___ O ___ I ___ A ___ I A ___ ___ E ___ ___ O ___ A ___ I ___ ___ .

7. Since managers are both 'agents of capitalism' and highly paid, but still company employees, they are concerned about the ___ E ___ I ___ I ___ A ___ ___ of their controlling role.

8. Numerical targets which are used by companies to direct the behaviour of employees are often in the form of ___ U ___ ___ E ___ ___.

9. According to Braverman, management's use of control to deal with uncommitted workers leads to the ___ E ___ ___ A ___ A ___ I O ___ of work skills and workers.

10. An important aspect of control is that it provides employees with ___ E E ___ ___ A ___ ___ on their own performance.

11. Ensuring that company standards become part of every individual employee's value system can be achieved through ___ ___ A I ___ I ___ ___.

12. Using interpersonal and social processes to impose predetermined standards of behavioural obedience and compliance is called ___ O ___ I A ___ ___ O ___ ___ ___ O ___.

13. Controls can encourage ___ E ___ E ___ ___ E ___ ___ ___.

14. What primarily distinguishes organizations from other social arrangements is their emphasis on ___ O ___ ___ ___ O ___ ___ E ___ ___ E ___ ___ O ___ ___ A ___ ___ E.

15. Employees' behaviour can be controlled through the use of a ___ O ___ ___ E ___ ___ ___ I ___ ___ I O ___ which tells them what they can and cannot do.

16. A control process can encourage ___ I ___ I ___ ___ U ___ E A U ___ ___ A ___ I ___ ___ E ___ A ___ I O U ___ which can be counterproductive for the organization as a whole.

17. The primary aim of company rules and policies is to establish ___ O ___ ___ I ___ ___ E ___ ___ ___ of action between different employees.

18. The third stage in the feedback control system is the ___ O ___ ___ A ___ A ___ O ___.

19. An assembly line is an example of control through ___ A ___ ___ ___ I ___ E ___ ___.

20. Control tends to encourage the ___ I ___ ___ ___ O ___ ___ ___ I O ___ of information so that individuals can 'look good'.